TONY

TONY

by Patrick Dennis

E. P. DUTTON AND COMPANY, INC.

NEW YORK

To G. M. K.

Contents

I   T O N Y *at* school   3

II   T O N Y *at* home   45

III   T O N Y *at* play   61

IV   T O N Y *at* arms   81

V   T O N Y *in* Sodom   108

VI   T O N Y *in* love   142

VII   T O N Y *in* suburbia   168

VIII   T O N Y *in* town   190

IX   T O N Y *at* large   213

X   T O N Y *at* present   239

TONY

T O N Y

at school

"You'll be sharing a room with Winthrop and Perry," the house-master said. "Of course you know who they are."

Of course I didn't, so I said nothing.

"And also with another boy from out west. From Chicago."

Out *west?* To a sixteen-year-old who had never before been away from Santa Fe, New Mexico, Chicago seemed as Eastern as Cathay and as exotic. I had changed trains there the day before and had dutifully done all the things my mother told me to do: Go to the Art Institute; Visit Marshall Field's but don't buy anything; Eat lunch in the Victorian Room at the Palmer House—but from the regular luncheon and not à la carte; Leave the waiter fifteen cents; Get to the station at least an hour before

3

train time; Don't speak to strangers. It had been my first brush with the high life and here was this man, with his strange Eastern accent, speaking of Chicago as though it might be Bernalillo or Mexican Springs.

"I was in Chicago yesterday," I said, trying to cloak myself in an aura of worldliness.

"That so? Never been there myself although we've had a few boys from out that way during my time—two Armours, a Swift, . . ." He rattled off a list of names smacking impressively of tractors and toilets and meat and money. "Most of our boys come from around this area—New York, Boston, Philadelphia."

"I see," I said. Then I remembered to add "sir," as my father had instructed.

"It's a very old school."

"It must be," I said, again conscious of the grimness of the long corridor. Old it was and old it looked; not the kind of really old I'd grown up with in Santa Fe, where everything—whether it did or not—was said to date from 1610, but a terrible institutional old. The yellow shellacked floorboards clanging beneath our heels, the dun-colored walls hung with dun-colored group photographs of bygone football and hockey and tennis teams or, in an inexplicable burst of frivolity, the all-boy casts of a couple of dozen Gilbert and Sullivan operettas, the dank, sour smell of the shower room combined to give the impression of a substandard orphanage rather than the "best" preparatory school in the United States where, in 1936, a year's tuition was more than enough to support an average family.

"I believe your father is an old boy," the housemaster said in a last-ditch attempt at conversation.

"Only about forty-five, sir. But he hasn't been well."

"I mean that he came here to school."

"Oh, yes, sir. He was in the class of 1909. He talks about it all the time."

Talked about it? I don't think any experience of my father's life—not college, not medical school, not the war, not marriage—

4

ever meant as much to him as his career in that spartan boarding school. Although it seemed impossible to me, walking down that dismal corridor, those four years had probably been the only sustained period in my father's life when the poor man ever had any fun.

Austere as it was, the place was famous—notorious—as a school for the sons of the very rich. My father had been the son of one of the very richest, or so he had assumed until the afternoon in 1910 when he was summoned from college to identify the body of his own father who turned out to be not only a suicide, but a bankrupt embezzler, a perpetrator of frauds, and a swindler of widows and orphans in the grandest turn-of-the-century tradition.

From that day forward my father's joyless life was dedicated to expiating the family sins. Having once dreamed of being a sort of Anglo-Saxon Bernard Berenson and assembling an unrivaled collection of English furniture, with porcelain, pictures, and silver to match, he became a doctor instead—but not a very good one, I'm afraid. When President Wilson declared war on the Hun, my father was one of the first in uniform. Sent to the front, he was gassed almost immediately and spent the rest of the war convalescing in England. However, something did come of it. He married my mother and, with her, a lot of English furniture.

After the armistice my father moved my mother and the English furniture to Santa Fe where the air and the altitude were expected to be beneficial to his ravaged lungs and where the living was very, very cheap. There he set up his practice—treating mostly Indians who couldn't pay and Spanish who wouldn't—with my mother helping out by giving lessons on her enormous Blüthner piano, which looked as strange in the adobe architecture of our house as the highboys and lowboys and Chippendale chairs and Waterford chandeliers that had crossed the Atlantic and most of the continent with her.

It was into that little corner of Sussex set six thousand feet high in the Sangre de Cristo mountains that I was born—a blessed event that, with my father in attendance, very nearly cost my mother her life. And it was in their world of impossibly high standards on an impossibly low income that I spent the first sixteen years of my life.

In New Mexico the people who are not of Spanish or Indian descent are known as Anglos—hardly a term of endearment—and there was no one more Anglo than our family. My father, whose meager living came from people just barely poorer than himself, was no more able to forget that he had been reared in the depths of luxury than he could forget the shame and ruination brought about by his father. His days were passed in squalid pueblos and miserable Spanish hovels among the wretched of the earth in a bumbling attempt to better his father's world. His nights were spent in a threadbare dinner jacket and cracked pumps at a Sheraton table covered with a great deal of Georgian silver and only a little food, in an even more bumbling attempt to reproduce that very world. My mother, though less vivid, was the daughter of a colonel in the Guards and she never overcame it. She grew more English every day away from Britain. In a land of piñon and yucca she spoke of the "drawing room," the "morning room," and the "domestic offices." As for the domestics themselves—a series of Indian girls who worked sporadically for room and board and a couple of dollars a week—my mother did her damnedest to turn them into proper English parlormaids. With her copy of Mrs. Beeton's *Book of Household Management* at the ready, she stood over them like some benevolent sergeant-major trying without any marked degree of success to indoctrinate them into the mysteries of trifles and savories, the dessert spoon, the finger bowl, the tea service.

Except for their incessant, grinding poverty, I suppose that my parents were as happy as most people. They had each other, their furniture, their overseas subscriptions to *Punch, The Tatler,* and *Country Life,* their semiannual shipments of tea and jam and biscuits from Fortnum & Mason, and their pretensions. About the only thing they shouldn't have had was a child. But there I

6

was—a son to be "educated as a gentleman" and a constant reminder that the Santa Fe public school system was as much as they'd ever be able to swing.

It made very little difference to me. Never having experienced yachts, seasons in London, Newport, cricket on the green, Fifth Avenue, a royal garden party, a footman behind each chair—or any of the things which my parents spoke of with a familiarity and tenderness usually reserved for a long dead younger brother —they seemed as foreign and remote to me as the Punic Wars. I was content with my lot and a fairly good lot it seemed—horse of my own, the movies on Saturday, and the companionship of kids my parents tacitly felt were my social inferiors. Considering the widespread unpopularity of my mother and father, I was lucky to have any friends at all.

But then it happened—the ways and means of finally educating me as a gentleman appeared in a very short squib on the obituary pages of the New York Times, followed, some days later, by more tangible evidence from the Metropolitan Life Insurance Company. A distant cousin of my father's, a former poor relation who had been transformed into a comparatively rich relation after my grandfather's bankruptcy and suicide, died as obscurely as he had lived in an unheard-of New York hotel. By means of an eccentric but watertight holographic will, all that he possessed—a watch, a miniature radio, an alarm clock, a hideous oil painting of some cows udder-deep in the mud, a closet full of rusty old suits and coats, a few hundred dollars in a savings bank, and a ten-thousand-dollar insurance policy—were left to my father "because," as the deceased stated in his shaky hand, "of his grit and intestinal fortitude in the face of adversity and public disgrace," and also because there was no one else in the family to leave the money to except my father's Aunt Harriet, a parsimonious old lady suffering the pangs of poverty in a suite at the Plaza, who was heard from every Christmas when she wrote to ask for free medical advice and to announce that she was too poor to send so much as a nickel greeting card.

In the long run I became the principal beneficiary. The suits, with minor alterations, were found to be quite good enough for a boy of sixteen. "They don't make material like that nowadays," my mother kept saying, "at least not in *this* country they don't." They didn't and they hadn't for at least a quarter of a century. The watch had almost my initials on it and it came from Tiffany's. The alarm clock and the Peter Pan radio were discovered to be nice-enough adjuncts to the eclectic decor of my bedroom. The terrible cows were, according to an art dealer in Taos, "almost certainly painted by J. F. Tenant, R.A." (1796–1872) and, according to my mother, would be "very valuable some day when this la-di-da modern art craze runs its course." The painting was hung in a dark corridor over a dubious Thomas Hope chiffonier—in escrow, so to speak, until the day when all the English furniture would be mine. As for the money, that was to be mine, too. With careful budgeting and a partial scholarship, it would be almost enough to send me to my father's college and to one year—the last—of his school. God and the poor relation were in their heaven. No sacrifice, my father said, would be too much to have me educated as he had been. "The boys you meet there—boys from the finest families in the country—will be your friends for life." It occurred to me to ask why none of his former schoolmates had ever been heard from, but then my mother murmured something wistful about Eton and the Indian maid of the moment shuffled into the room and shouted "Come eat!" instead of "Dinner is served."

"This is your room," the housemaster said. "Winthrop and Perry have beds near the window. They've been here the longest. You and the other one—uh—Vandenberg," he said reading from the index card thumbtacked to the wall above the iron bed opposite mine, "will have this end of the room. No frills you notice." I noticed. "We take boys from the richest families in America here—a lot of them rotten spoiled—and we turn them into men. I guess your father must have told you. Lunch is at twelve. You'll hear the bell."

"Thank you," I said, adding, "sir." Then I was alone. My father had told me about his school even before the days when I knew exactly what a boarding school was. His accounts of jolly romps, the firm friendships, the thrilling athletic contests, the saintliness of the headmaster, had led me to expect . . . well, I don't know exactly what I had expected, but certainly not this. The room was large, but not quite large enough to be shared by four. The brown linoleum floor, waxily mottled from its summertime machine buffing, was divided into four quarters by painted white lines as though it had been marked off for some indoor court game. Each quarter contained four pieces of furniture: a narrow iron bed; a wooden chair; a combination desk and chest of drawers, inadequate for either clothing or writing; and a fiberboard portable closet. Each boy's section was fitted out with a goose-necked lamp and a small pockmarked green baize bulletin board. A notice, thumbtacked to the wall, proclaimed that anyone thumbtacking anything to the wall would be severely punished.

Except for the lack of bars at the window—either through oversight or in the interests of economy—the room reminded me of a rehabilitation center for delinquent boys in some very unprogressive southern state. I again wondered what my father had ever seen in the place.

It was as still as death, the only evidence of habitation being the section reserved for Vandenberg. A maroon shirt, a soiled white necktie, and a copy of *Esquire* were strewn over the somber olive drab of his bed. Some brown and white saddle shoes and a pair of shorts with an arresting red and blue pattern made up of the expression "Hiya Toots!" were on the floor. Vandenberg's bulletin board was the only one in the room with anything on it and, for the day before the first day of the school year, it was quite a collection. Occupying the center of the bulletin board was a large photograph of a dark imposing woman who somehow

9

made me think of a diva—Mary Garden? Frances Alda? Geraldine Farrar? She wore a tiara in her slick, dark hair and a full-length ermine cape. (I could tell it was ermine because of the little black tails bobbing from the collar.) Sharing honors with the lady in ermine were pictures of four automobiles, a Dusenberg roadster, a sixteen-cylinder Cadillac phaeton, a Cord coupé, and one of those never-never machines done entirely with the airbrush and imagination of Alexis de Sakhnoffsky and clipped from the pages of *Esquire*. This particular fantasy was a brougham or town car, its carriage lamps and canework strange anachronisms with its chrome and streamlining. I remembered having once shown the same picture to my mother. Her comment had been "Too vulgar for words! Why do you waste your pocket money on some tatty magazine that's printed for shipping clerks?" Naturally she had pronounced the word "clarks." There was another photograph of four assorted kids of about my own age sitting around a table at a place called the Marine Room. That rather impressed me. I had never been to a night club. Indeed, Santa Fe had none, although Albuquerque, seventy miles away, boasted three.

But what really caught my eye was a photograph of a splendid long, low building of the purest Georgian architecture. It was Flemish bond brick with a regal placement of stone quoins, gracious bows, tall windows, black iron balconies, shapely balustrades and urn finials, and all of it smothered in ivy. It stood three stories above its ground floor. A large, low, rakish car—its exact lines obscured by small trees and ornamental shrubbery—paused in the shallow horseshoe driveway. An iron fence surrounded the whole structure, pierced by two pairs of imposing gate posts, also bristling brick, quoins, and urn finials. At one of them stood a man in splendid black boots, white breeches, a frogged coat, and a towering beaver hat. Next to him was a rather nondescript kid.

"Hi," a voice said. I turned around and there was the kid. Nondescript is hardly a fair word. Difficult to describe is probably a more accurate term. He was compactly put together—slim and of medium height—and gave the impression that his sinews and muscles were never still, that he might at any moment pounce like a tiger. His features, taken one by one, were all wrong—some of them being too large, others too small—but the combination was so striking and unusual that people generally thought of him as handsome. His hair varied in different lights from a rusty ocher to carrot to mahogany to almost black. Like his body, his face seemed to be very busy. Actually it was not. But his eyes were never at rest. "Merry eyes" and "dancing eyes" are popular terms. They were not that, nor were they ferretlike. They were simply hard-working eyes, constantly seeing, recording, registering. I always imagined that even in sleep they were on duty behind their closed lids. His eyes were the first thing anyone ever noticed about him, yet to this day I cannot tell you their color.

"My name's Vandenberg," he said. "J. Anthony Vandenberg. Tony. Tony Vandenberg. By the way, we're not Jewish."

"I—I never said you were," I said—almost gasped. Even back in the thirties there were probably a few Jews in Santa Fe. But if there were, I had never been conscious of who was and who was not. There were simply not enough of them to make any sort of prejudice locally fashionable. The warfare among the Anglos, Spanish, and Indians had been quite enough to keep the citizenry of Santa Fe on its ethnic toes. Yet from some musty pigeonhole of my unconscious it occurred to me that if Vandenberg were Jewish he would probably not be enrolled in this particular school. In 1936 the "top" boarding schools were kept sacrosanct from any democratizing influence. There were still two decades to wait before Groton, our arch rival, would daringly accept its first Negro. While poverty, such as mine, was condoned, it had to be very genteel poverty—preferably the penniless son of an old boy who hadn't quite become the leader of men the school prided itself on turning out. Catholics were on a quota basis and that quota very rarely included *Irish* Catholics. While Harvard—and sometimes Yale and even occasionally Princeton—took Jewish students of exceptional promise, the most fertile spawning grounds for those institutions maintained a tacit and mystifying policy of discrimination against almost all, save a handful of Warburgs or Strauses or *real* Rothschilds.

"It's an old Dutch name," Tony said, "like Vanderbilt."

"I—I see," I said. Then I managed to blurt out my own name and, as an afterthought, held out my hand to be shaken as my father had taught me to do. We exchanged a limp and rather foolish handclasp.

"But just call me Tony," he said. "Been here long?"

Did he mean, I wondered, whether I had been in his quarter of the room for very long—and obviously prying into his personal effects—or had I been at the school for any length of time?

"I got here about half an hour, forty minutes ago."

"Not that." Tony laughed. "I mean how many years?"

"This is my first. I mean it's also my last, but it's still my first. I mean I'm in the last year, but I've never gone here before. That's why I got here a day early."

"Me, too. Get kicked out of St. Mark's or something like that?"

"Yeah, something like that." I sensed that the Santa Fe public high school was not a sufficiently lustrous alma mater to come right out and flaunt. I was correct.

"I've always been tutored. You know, kicking around Paris, Palm Beach, Monte Carlo, Capri . . ." He pronounced it Cuppree, but so did I, then. "Well, it just seemed a good idea to hire some smart cookie from Oxford or—or someplace like that— who'd fit in with my mother's crowd. You know."

I *didn't* know. Except for the movies or in the funny papers on those sporadic occasions when Daddy Warbucks was back home with Orphan Annie, I had never had any experience with wealth. Yet here it was, so close that I could reach out and touch the hem of its robe. And what a robe! Tony's was red. Not the dull, mulled maroon of my father's old dressing gown. But *really* red! As red as a fire engine and twice as shiny, with what I took to be the double-headed eagle of Imperial Russia emblazoned on the breast pocket. I was almost too overcome with the glamour of it all to speak. Finally I blurted out, "That's some bathrobe!"

"Oh, this?" Tony said. Even at sixteen he could toss aside a heartfelt compliment as casually as a hardened siren her suitors. He unknotted what I thought was just an old white silk muffler but later learned was called an ascot, and stepped out of the robe. His shorts were salmon pink with "Oh you nasty man!" printed on them in brown and red. (Other eye-catching items in Tony's trousseau for school included underpants printed with "Pul-leeze, Mr. Zilch!" "Wanna buy a duck?" and "Nertz to you!" Gans's department store in Santa Fe had carried a limited selection of these, in what I assumed were but cheap copies of Tony's originals, but my mother, seconded strongly by my father, had been very firm in the matter of underwear and I had settled grudgingly for plain white.)

Tony must have mistaken my envy of his underwear for admiration of his body because he said, "I have the perfect physique for wearing clothes well. That's what my mother says," he continued, bobbing his head in the direction of the lady in ermine, "and she ought to know."

"Is that your mother?"

"Yeah. That picture was taken at the opera. In Mrs. Insull's box." I was relieved to know that the vague operatic connection I had formed with the photograph had at least a germ of accuracy. I was also impressed by the connection with Samuel Insull, whose speculations made my own grandfather's look like petty larceny. I was even on the verge of confessing that, poor and colorless as I might seem, I was the grandson of the Samuel Insull of a quarter century ago, but my father had always warned me never to mention the old crook and to be thankful that our family name was a usual enough one, unlike, say, Tweed or Sinclair or Doheny, so as not to pique the curiosity of strangers. "You may have seen her picture in *Town & Country*," he said. I had not. No one in Santa Fe subscribed to *Town & Country*.

There was a soft jangling sound and Tony pulled a key chain from the pocket of his dressing gown. Attached to the key chain was a hank of black and white fur. "See this? It's my rabbit's foot—my good luck charm—only it happens to be ermine."

"That should bring you even better luck," I said.

"It came off that cape of my mom's. I always carry it."

"Oh."

As far as I was concerned, the conversation was at an end. From the moment my father had triumphantly announced that I was to be among the very, very rich at his old school—while reminding me that I would be poorer than ever before on account of the sacrifices the family would be making to send me there—I had expected to feel hopelessly outré among my peers. I had long ago decided to be attentive, polite, silent, and then to retire into my own shabby shell in the presence of the Eastern Seaboard's gilded youth, grateful for having been tossed a crumb. ("Just remember, dear, that you're a very good student and, I hope, a gentleman," my mother had said without much certainty.) But Tony seemed almost too much of a good thing for my very first encounter with Mammon. Thoroughly defeated, I prepared my retreat.

Tony, however, was filled to overflowing with small talk. It was part of his great charm. "I suppose you're wondering why I took a shower so early in the day," he said. Actually I hadn't wondered about it at all and rather wanted to wash off the dust of the railroad myself. "You see, I didn't come the usual way." A private railway car? His own plane? A dirigible? While I speculated, Tony babbled on. "No, you see I came by road. The Caddy."

"Caddy?" Golf was the only connotation I could work up.

"The V-16," he said, gesticulating toward his bulletin board. It was becoming almost an illustrated lecture. "It's the biggest Cadillac they make. It's the oldest car we've got, but I sure am nuts about it. And, boy, do you ever get dirty driving with the top down!"

"You drove? *Yourself?*"

"Oh no. The chauffeur drove. I wanted to bring the Cord—that's my little car—but the school said ix-nay."

I was not surprised. The school said no to practically everything—radios, phonographs, alarm clocks, medicines (except with doctor's prescription), pets, electrical appliances, liquor, and cigarettes.

Tony launched into a discourse on the fleet of automobiles belonging to the Vandenberg family. The car sketched by Alexis de Sakhnoffsky was, I discovered, being specially built to facilitate his mother's rich, full social life. My own family owned a Ford of only recent enough make to have a V front. Again I felt decidedly out of things.

However, the Georgian building interested me and here at least I was on fairly firm ground. My mother, in order to preserve as much of England as possible in what she almost referred to as "the colonies," had brought with her a large scrapbook containing exhaustive memorabilia of her Sussex girlhood. In it were school reports, dance programs, invitations, menus, press cuttings, and the photographs of dozens of houses belonging to her better-heeled friends and relatives. They ranged from Queen Anne to Regency. They were all called Something Manor or Hall or Park or Place, and they had been described to me so often and so thoroughly that I knew every cornice and molding, every leak and draft, every stick of furniture—even the names of the servants. In fact one of my earliest childhood dreams was to make a lot of money in some unspecified way so that I could someday surprise my parents with a glorious Palladian pavilion more suitable to their possessions and aspirations than the rambling adobe house where we lived, although it often occurred to me that it would look just as out of place in the hills of New Mexico as my mother's English garden. I mentioned the Georgian building.

"Oh, that's Lochby Court. It's where I live in Chicago."

"*In* Chicago?" To me Chicago was a city of skyscrapers and all of the country seats of my mother's connections were hidden away in the counties of England.

"Yes," Tony said in an offhanded way. "Know where the yacht club is?" I didn't, but I said I did. "It's right across from that— 3200 Lake Shore Drive. Swell view." For sheer size, it put the Manors and Halls and Parks and Places of my mother's youth— some of which contained upwards of twenty principal bedrooms—to shame. A house of this size would have had to be larger than two hundred rooms. "Do you come from a big family?" I asked.

"Nope. Just my folks and me."

"Is—is that your father?" I said, pointing to the distinguished older man in the boots and breeches.

"Henry? Gosh no. He's just . . . he's just one of the grooms."

"Lochby Court," I said in wonderment. "Lochby Court."

"The—the Duke of Lochby was one of Mom's ancestors."

"My mother is English, too," I said, feeling for the first time as though she were some sort of plucky little Cockney charwoman.

The housemaster stuck his head into the room. "Finished unpacking yet?" he said cheerfully.

"No, sir," I said. I hadn't even begun and I wasn't sure that I wanted to. If the other four hundred boys were going to be as filthy rich as this one, it might be easier simply to go back to the Santa Fe high school where, even though my parents' eccentricities had made me a marked man, I was not considered a charity case.

Then the housemaster caught a glimpse of Tony's cluttered bed. "Vandenberg! What's that stuff doing all over your bed? And on the floor? Stow it away and make it snappy. And get dressed!"

"Okay, okay," Tony said.

"Say 'Yes, sir,' when you address a master in this school."

"Shmuck," Tony muttered at the master's retreating form. Then he grinned at me and said, "Here, you help me and then I'll help you." The little cardboardy cupboard supplied for each boy's clothing was hopelessly inadequate to house Tony's finery. It already bulged with robes and sports jackets, slacks and suits.

Nor were there enough hangers, so that things were hung on top of one another.

"Let me unpack," I said. "Then I can lend you some hangers. I—I didn't bring many things." I'd brought every stitch I possessed.

"Okey-doke," he said.

My luggage—actually not mine, but one piece of my father's and one of my mother's, plus the small camp trunk that had arrived before me—was very old, but at least it was very good. There was a Vuitton bag with a marvelously complicated lock which I had mastered after a great deal of practice and a small suitcase from Asprey. Each bore a modest array of stickers from various Ritz Hotels of more prosperous days. Tony seemed to be actually impressed. "Quite the traveler, aren't you?"

"Mm-hmm."

"I've got a lot of View-tone luggage back in the Windy City. I didn't feel like bringing it along."

Tony was the most label-conscious person I've ever met in my life. Naturally the labels in my clothes, all coming from unheard-of shops in Santa Fe or, at the utmost, Kistler-Collister's in Albuquerque, could mean very little to one who prattled away about Brooks Brothers, Knize, Peale, and Abercrombie & Fitch. And when it came to labels Tony also had the curiosity of a monkey, asking why I had chosen underwear by BVD instead of Cluett & Peabody, why my jock straps were from Bauer & Black rather than Spaulding or Johnson & Johnson. When it came to unpacking my hand-me-down suits, Tony delved right into the inside breast pockets and came back up into the daylight with an almost beatific expression on his face. " 'Davies & Son,' " he quoted. " 'By appointment to King George V and H.R.H. The Prince of Wales.' " Sartorially, at least, I had scored. Thank God the suits were so old that the dates when they were made—all preceding my birth—had faded away.

"I can see you're a very conservative dresser," Tony said, hanging up an ancient altered Burberry.

Tony was anything but conservative. I was stunned by the amount of stuff he had brought with him and by the jazziness of it. I realized later that Tony's clothes were horrible. (He realized it even sooner and gradually his dark shirts and pale suits, his horse-blanket jackets and suède shoes gave way to a quieter taste.) But on that September afternoon in 1936 I thought that Tony Vandenberg was glamour on the hoof.

"Gosh but you've got a lot of duds," I said, cramming a bush jacket into his closet.

"Oh, my val-lay just packed a few things," he said. I was startled: not because Tony had a valet. I would have expected nothing less. But the pronunciation jarred me. My parents had always said "val-et" and of course the word was originally French. For the first time I suspected them of having feet of clay and felt miserable and provincial because of it.

Tony got into a pair of navy blue pants with shirt and suède oxfords to match. He put on a pale yellow necktie and tucked a matching handkerchief into the pocket of his fuzzy baby blue jacket. As a final fillip, he put a yellow feather carnation into his buttonhole. I found the ensemble too George Raft to be true, and, somehow, desirable. He reached into the coat pocket and withdrew a large red, white, and blue Roosevelt-Garner button. This he put on his bulletin board. Then from under his pillow he took out a silver cigarette case decorated with a black enamel Scotty. "Tiffany's," he said. "I left my gold one back in Chi." He flipped the case open to reveal three rather crumpled Camels held in place by an elastic band. I shook my head. "I don't smoke," I said, feeling about four years old instead of sixteen. "We're not allowed to anyway."

"What they don't know won't hurt 'em. Want to take a little toddle and get the lay of the land?"

The day before the first day of school was set aside to indoctrinate the new boys into the mysteries and intricacies of that ancient institution. Since Tony Vandenberg and I were the only two new boys in the fourth year, we were thrust together whether we wished to be or not, taking our meals alone in the senior dining room, sitting high above the youngsters in the gallery of the chapel, strolling side by side in Senior Yard, lounging in the lonely grandeur of the Senior Common Room, and being called "sir" by the other new boys who had the misfortune of being younger. In between learning from the headmaster and his disciples the fine old traditions of the school, which were as tiresome as they were abundant; the locations of rest rooms, fire exits, infirmary, and chaplain, to meet with any unforeseen emergency; and the hundreds of rules and regulations governing our conduct, I heard a great deal more about the fabulous Tony Vandenberg from the fabulous Tony himself.

His father, he told me, was a world-renowned surgeon—but only as a sort of hobby—who had just recently snatched none other than John Barrymore from the very jaws of death. His mother was the unquestioned social leader of Chicago and points north, south, and east. The Vandenbergs owned a yacht—several, as a matter of fact. In addition to Lochby Court on Chicago's Lake Shore Drive, the Vandenbergs kept a penthouse in New York, a villa at Palm Beach, a pied à terre in Paris, a townhouse in London, a château in France, a schloss in Austria, a palazzo in Venice, and, anticlimactically, a fishing shack in northern Wisconsin, all fully staffed. A social secretary or two, the private plane and railway car I had earlier expected, a string of unspecified race horses, polo ponies, and quite a lot of famous names—some of which I had even heard before—were also mentioned.

Reticent for fear of being found wanting, I volunteered only the sketchy information that I, too, was an only child; that I lived in New Mexico because of my father's lungs; that my father had gone to the school before me (oddly enough, this seemed to impress Tony); and that he was a doctor, although hardly of international eminence. It seemed a wan list of qualifications to spread before so dazzling a classmate, but Tony gave every appearance of not minding in the least. He was perfectly content to talk about himself all day and into the night, and I was flattered to think that I was not absolutely beneath his contempt. However, I felt certain that our brief intimacy would end on the following day when hundreds of his own sort poured into the school. Even among the little boys in the first class he had spotted a Du Pont and a Hearst; a Ford, a Whitney, and a Morgan who might or might not be scions of the Ford, Whitney, and Morgan families; and the son of an exiled Spanish count, whose many names, each connected to the next with the letter Y, I never fully mastered. Surely my hours as confidant were numbered. It had been a fascinating encounter but nothing more. Tony was telling me about a fabulous coming-out party he had recently attended in Lake Forest when the housemaster stuck his head into the room and shouted "Lights out."

After my baptism of fire with Tony Vandenberg, I faced the next day with a heart of pure lead. It was fashionable to be sympathetic to the Communist cause in the thirties, and even though I had never shown any political awareness, I sensed that a school full of boys as rich as Tony might easily drive me to what my father called "the Red Menace."

We were awakened at six, just as though the whole school were in session, and put through setting-up exercises in our pajamas by the housemaster. Tony, an incongruous picture in a black Chinese robe embroidered with a huge, snorting dragon, was not very good at them and evinced little interest in improving. The housemaster was especially hard on Tony, pointing out his bent knees, bad breathing, and lack of coordination, as he was especially kind to me. If his attitude was meant to make me feel better, it fell far short of the mark. I remembered what he said about rich boys being spoiled and hated him for his patronage of the poor. Over breakfast Tony described to me far grander meals brought to him at a much later hour (Chicago time) by Newton, the Vandenbergs' butler, in his ultramodern bedroom with black silk sheets. It sounded to me like the sort of chamber generally occupied by Carole Lombard and William Powell. The housemaster came into the senior dining room and cut short Tony's recollections of the breakfast tray with a curt, "Clean your plate, Vandenberg, and don't dawdle."

From the vantage point of our window we watched the rest of the school piling in. The railroad station was, as the crow flies, not too many miles away, but so inconvenient as far as transportation was concerned that most of the kids came by car. I was relieved, but at the same time almost disappointed, to see how many of them came in just ordinary automobiles with neither chauffeur nor footman sitting up front. True, there was a small array of Packard, Pierce-Arrow, Lincoln, and Cadillac limousines and even one very old Rolls-Royce, but most of the student body arrived with a tweedy father at the wheel and a generally tearful mother in a good little dress and hat from Sally Milgrim or Jay Thorpe. There were even a few splintery old Ford station wagons like ours and one even older. I drew a certain amount of comfort from that old wreck until I recalled my mother saying that the very richest rich often played it down by affecting the utmost simplicity. As a prime example she recalled the belted earl whose property surrounded her father's place in Sussex and who wore only his gamekeeper's cast-off clothing. She usually neglected to add that he died in a madhouse.

Tony recognized a Drexel, a Cadwalader, and a Mellon in the incoming crowd but instead of going out to greet them, he remained at the window watching the luggage being unloaded and the boys being kissed good-by. Once he remarked, "Not very snappy dressers, are they?" They looked all right to me. Another time he said, "Don't their mothers own so much as a mink coat?" As the temperature hovered in the high seventies that day, even the women in suits looked as though they were about to die of sunstroke. But Tony knew the make, model, and price of every car—especially the fancy ones—that rolled up the drive.

About my only contribution to the conversation was "Look at

21

all the sunflowers," for practically every boy, father, and mother who arrived that day was wearing a yellow and brown felt Republican campaign badge with "Off the Rocks with Landon-Knox" emblazoned on it.

"Excuse me," Tony said as he wandered back into the dimness of the room. The next time I looked at his bulletin board, the Roosevelt pin was gone.

Shortly before noon we were joined by our other two roommates, Seth Winthrop and Greer Perry. Today, thirty years later, I can sum them up in a sentence. Winthrop was rich Boston at its best; Perry, rich New York at its worst. Seth Winthrop could, but wouldn't, trace his lineage back to dozens of Bay Colony governors, Harvard presidents, Revolutionary generals, and Cabinet members. Greer Perry could and would hark back to a Civil War profiteer more recently deified as a Captain of Industry, to a well-known typewriter company, to a Wall Street brokerage house, to the New York Social Register (a recent listing), to the River, Racquet, and Piping Rock Clubs, to El Morocco, the Stork, and LaRue.

Although he had never laid eyes on Tony or me before and had a whole summer to catch up on with Greer, Seth took the trouble to make introductions and volunteer his services at showing us the ropes. Greer said, "How do you do?" and without waiting for an answer, launched into a long and apparently hilarious anecdote concerning Good Old Bunny and a girl named Muriel—"both perfect riots"—who had set Southampton on its ear for the whole season. I felt that Greer Perry and Tony Vandenberg were probably made for each other, but they were not. Their relationship got off to a bad start when Tony put on a dove gray suit with a black shirt and an orange tie. He thought it very Princeton until Greer Perry said, "Is that what they're wearing in the Middle West this year? Who's your tailor, Al Capone?" When Tony, stunned, said that it was the latest thing on the West Coast, Greer said, "With Edward G. Robinson?"

Seth said that he thought it was very colorful. Seth Winthrop, by the way, personified one of my mother's most tiresome homilies: "Politeness is to do and say the kindest thing the kindest way." That makes him sound deadly, I know, but he was genuinely nice. Tall and rather lanky, good looking but by no means handsome, Seth had a natural, unaffected pleasantness that made people of all walks of life like him. Never once in the years that we knew each other did I hear him knowingly hurt anyone. Even when it came to people he obviously disliked—and he was not so saintly as to be beyond all human feeling—he kept his distance rather than indulge in open warfare, backbiting, or snide comments. He was a better than average student, but far from the head of the class. He played decent enough football and hockey to be on the first team. His golf and tennis were good but not world-shaking. He was captain of the school's swimming team not because he was anything like the best swimmer, but because the rest of his water-logged crew had demanded that he be put in charge. He was scrupulously neat, always considerate, and so generous that whenever a parcel was sent to him the whole floor received a blanket invitation to come into our room and load up. It was no surprise to anyone except to Seth Winthrop himself when, later on in the year, he was elected president of the whole damned school.

Of Greer Perry I can say very little except that he had a certain mordant wit and that we got along together mostly because, after I had lost some of my shyness, we made each other laugh. Laughter is supposed to be a great bond and Greer was amusing, but his witticisms were cruel and always at the expense of someone weaker than he was. He was rich and didn't care who knew it. Although he could hardly buy his way through school, the Perry Faculty Lounge was dangled before the board of trustees like a carrot before a donkey. It was scheduled to start building in July. Greer was scheduled to graduate in June. And in a way he did buy his way out of doing any real work. At a penny a word I wrote most of his English compositions for him and for a flat ten dollars a semester saw to it that his Spanish translations were letter perfect. He was a whiz at math, just as he was one of the sharpest traders in the whole school—always getting the best of any bargain and always crowing about it later.

In line with the school's tradition of austerity, parents were urged to keep our pocket money down to less than two dollars a week—a request my family was only too happy to comply with. Greer not only arrived at school with a wallet bulging with tens and twenties, but his allowance was at least five times the prescribed maximum. Still he was always short of ready cash. His method was simple. He would sell an expensive sweater, a jacket, a whole suit for a fraction of its cost and then write home to report that the item had been lost or stolen. It was invariably replaced—and sometimes in duplicate—by return mail.

He was almost criminally indulged by a doting mother and an easygoing stepfather. At least twice a week a velvety blue letter deeply engraved with 888 FIFTH AVENUE would announce the impending arrival of yet another package and Greer would lick his rather thick lips in anticipation. Nor were the Perry packages the usual run of boarding school treats such as fudge, brownies, cookies, and sourballs. Greer's goodies came from places like Charles & Company, the Vendôme, and Maison Glass. If the rest of us happened to be in the room, he would offer us one each of whatever he liked least and then disappear with the package to wolf down its contents alone in the toilet.

Perhaps generosity would have been the wiser policy as Greer's gormandizing did little for his face or figure and he was very, very vain. Not bad looking in a big-boned, soft sort of way, Greer had a terror of baldness and blemishes. No week passed without his clipping an ad from *Film Fun* or *Spicy Adventure* (his taste in literature lagged far behind his taste in groceries) and sending away for a new scalp or acne cure in the name of a first-year boy—a sort of halfhearted fagging system was still condoned by the school and, as Greer explained, the Perry name was too distinguished to fall into the hands of some disreputable patent medicine company. Reputable or not, their stinking products made our room almost uninhabitable as Greer stood naked before our only mirror rubbing black muck into his skull and dabbing white goo onto his flesh. Even Winthrop complained and Tony spoke of Greer as "Narcissus" and, finally, simply "Sis." Like many witty people, Greer Perry was far less amused by a barb aimed at him than by the hundreds he sent out in every other direction. It did nothing to strengthen the bond between him and Tony Vandenberg.

The first couple of weeks were filled with surprises. First of all, I discovered that the curriculum was neither as difficult nor the standards of the Santa Fe school system as low as my father had led me to believe. I also learned that I was not quite the outcast I had expected to be. I came from a part of the country that spelled mystery, adventure, glamour, and romance to the rest of the student body, not unlike little Don Jaime Luis Maria Jesus Something y Something y Something in the first class or those French-talking brothers in the third class who'd done two years at Le Rosey in Switzerland while their father was ambassador to someplace. I lived on a ranch of sorts, rode my own Palomino pony, and spoke Spanish and Tewa, which cut a lot more ice than hailing from the North Shore, the Main Line, or West-chester County, although I was too shy and unsure of myself to make any capital of it. But to my surprise and delight, general acceptance—if not devastating popularity—was mine.

I also learned that as poor as we were, my family was not the only one making sacrifices to send me to an expensive school. With the convenient way human beings have of forgetting unpleasant things like illness, hardship, or labor pains, a lot of people look back upon the depression as something that lasted for a week during 1932. Not true. The depression had a healthy life span of more than ten years with the rolls of the unemployed reaching as high as fourteen million people and the minimum hourly wage as low as twenty-five cents. A letter I found in the locker room finally made it clear to me that even among the idle rich I was not alone. It read in part:

Darling—

Don't be surprised by the new address. Daddy and I have given up the house in Rye. Just too big and expensive. It broke my heart to let Hans and Frieda go. Hope they have something laid away. But it was a question of keeping them in the kitchen or you in school—*and you come first!!!*

This little apartment isn't half bad, although with all of our furniture crammed in, it looks like the Year End Clearance Sale at Sloane's. Daddy and I feel like newlyweds again and your old mother is turning into some cook!

Having so much time on my hands I've taken a job selling dresses at Jane Engel's. It would be fun if we only had some customers. Daddy says the market is absolutely dead but at least we're not starving and by cutting a few corners we can manage nicely until Landon gets that old Roosevelt and his wife out of the White House. . . .

Hot with shame, I tore the letter into thousands of pieces and flushed it in three installments down three different toilets. Not knowing who, of four hundred boys, "Darling" was, I couldn't return it and, having read it, I would have been too embarrassed anyhow. But I was beginning to get the breezes. Not everybody was as rich as Tony Vandenberg, and his endless talk of houses and cars and servants, of such fashionable resorts as Palm Beach and Bar Harbor, of such soignée supper-club chanteuses as Eve Symington and Lucienne Boyer was winning him few friends. On the contrary, there was a sizable anti-Tony group led by Greer Perry, naturally. One of the guys had an older brother who had a roommate who was said to have dated Patty Ann Vandenberg, daughter of that august Republican Senator, and he was going to write immediately to find out if Tony actually was related to *those* Vandenbergs, as Tony had claimed. If he ever did write the letter, the question went unanswered and it was assumed among the Perry Set that Tony was lying and therefore, inexplicably, Jewish as well. Someone else said that Lochby

Court looked like an apartment building and that he was going to write to an aunt who lived in Winnetka and ask her. He needn't have bothered, if he ever did. From that moment Tony's home became a tenement with Greer's clique. They made fun of his clothes, his accent, his table manners, his French—he could do nothing right.

"Why do you want to mess around with a meatball like Vandenberg?" Greer asked. "His only friends are second-raters."

"Thanks," I said. "I happen to be one of them." I put Greer's intense dislike of Tony down to jealousy. Everyone knew that Greer's family was rich, but everyone also knew that the Vandenbergs were even richer. Tony had told them so. It was easy to understand Greer's position. He had, at least, some basis for comparison. But for someone as poor as I was to be jealous of Tony's wealth would have been as silly and stupid a waste of emotion as to envy the fortune of John D. Rockefeller. I was so far removed from it as to qualify only as an interested—fascinated—spectator. Tony could irritate me more than any other kid in the whole school and he often did. But even when I found him being obnoxious, even when his behavior struck me as what my mother would call "vulgar," I always admired him for his vitality. It was something that Greer Perry would never have.

On the other hand, Tony's circle of friends—or, rather, syco-phants—were *decidedly* second-rate. They were, for the most part, rather blah kids, corny, immature, easily and loudly im-pressed. In and out of Tony's presence they gabbled about his wealth, his clothes, his wit (Greer Perry did not, as I have said, like other people to be amusing unless Greer happened to be leading the discussion), his amazing success with a score of Chicago heiresses (Greer also preferred to feel that he had a corner on sex); they toadied for his favor and angled blatantly for invitations aboard the largest of the Vandenberg yachts (it slept twenty) on its Mediterranean cruise scheduled for the following June.

As for myself, I confess to being impressed and helplessly

27

flattered not only because I was Tony's first friend—there had been no one else for him to talk to on the day we met—but because I had not been dropped in favor of grander society when it became available. I can honestly say that, awed as I was, I never asked Tony for a favor, never tried to wangle an invitation to any of the various outings he spoke of for the holidays. I knew at the time that my father expected me to get any kind of job—helping out in a store for the Christmas rush, wrangling on a dude ranch during spring and summer vacations—that might, with luck and a certain amount of wheedling, come my way. Even if my time had been free, I would never have presumed to be included in such lavish doings. I hadn't then, and never expected to have, the basic essentials—wardrobe, pin money, and polish—to fit into any life quite so highfalutin.

Tony's vitality appealed to me a good deal more than to the headmaster, the housemaster, the chaplain, the athletics coach, and practically every other man on the faculty. With unerring instinct Tony could run afoul of the authorities faster than any other kid in the school. I felt then—and feel even more strongly now—that there was a prejudice against Tony. The housemaster had been against him from the very first day and he never let up. As I have said, the school set great store by the Spartan tradition and on things that were capital M: manly. It was an adjective that could never be applied to the senior housemaster. He was small, wizened, pale, ascetic, and spinsterish. Therefore he laid special emphasis on things masculine, at least verbally. Dressed in gray flannel pajamas and a dun-colored woolen robe to match the walls and what sparse hair he had, he was especially sadistic every morning when a hundred of us with cold bare feet on the cold bare floorboards of the corridor were put through our nip-ups.

Tony, cheerier than anyone ought to be at so early an hour, invariably chose the last row where he hoped he could get away with as little exertion as possible. He always set the kids on either side of him to laughing. During the squats he could break wind at will and with a volume that bordered on sheer artistry. The day he stood behind Perry who, conscious of his broadening beam, went at his stretching and bending with a violent gusto, Tony managed to deliver a goose that sent Perry catapulting square into the housemaster's stomach. It broke up the whole senior hall, but Perry and the housemaster were not amused. One day when Tony was really loafing through his calisthenics, the housemaster said, "I notice you don't do your exercises with very much enthusiasm, Vandenberg."

"I notice you don't do them at all, sir," Tony said. After that there was marked hostility on both sides.

Knowing how the housemaster loathed all that smacked of "lounge lizard," Tony went out of his way to flaunt a more annoying get-up each day. The mandarin robe, the Russian Imperial dressing gown, the reds and greens and purples and golds of Tony's pajamas were augmented by garish cardigans and blazing ascots which the housemaster, powerless to find sufficiently withering comment, endured in furious silence. Among the rest of us in our rumpled whites and blues and yellows, our sober stripes and timid patterns, Tony was literally a red flag before an enraged bull.

We underwent a rigid inspection of our quarters every morning after breakfast. Rooms were to be aired, floors dry-mopped, personal effects concealed, and beds made in the West Point fashion with blankets so taut that the housemaster could bounce a half-dollar on each. Superficially Tony's quarter of the room was always fairly neat, although his cupboard would never bear looking into. But the housemaster always seemed to take twice as long inspecting Tony's section as Winthrop's and Perry's and mine put together. Once or twice I even timed him and it was true.

The real trouble started at the end of October. During inspection we were permitted to have our books exposed on our dresserdesks, but nothing else. Tony's first class that day was French. In order to make the language "come alive," the French master had asked each of his students to choose a subject—any subject—that dealt with day-to-day living in France and write a theme of not less than five hundred of the best French words. Tony had chosen French furniture, probably because it was so easy, words like *bergère, chaise longue, secrétaire, bureau,* and *commode* being much the same in both languages, and also, as Tony explained, because Lochby Court housed the Vandenberg collection of fine French furniture, every stick of which had come from Versailles. As luck would have it, he had happened on two issues of *House Beautiful* containing a long and easily translated two-part article on that very subject. He had done his work well and thoroughly, letter perfect to the last *circonflexe.* It was tucked into one of the copies of *House Beautiful* all set to be taken to French class as soon as inspection was finished.

Tony had irritated the housemaster more than usual by appearing at calisthenics that morning wearing an especially outlandish costume and by convulsing the whole senior hall with his moans and groans during push-ups. It was raining, the breakfast had been worse than ever, and everyone—especially the housemaster —was in a lousy mood. Finding nothing to complain about, the housemaster was about to move on to the next room when he spotted Tony's copies of *House Beautiful.* "Vandenberg," he shouted, snatching them up, "this is a school that turns out men—not interior decorators. You know the rules. At least you ought to. You've broken enough of them. Now if you want to find your ruffles and chintz you can look for them in the fireplace in my study."

"But, Mr. Bl—"

"As you were!" With that he marched across the hall and slammed his door. Tony raced right after him.

"Vandenberg!" we heard the housemaster scream—and that is the word, for his voice was suitably deep and manly only when he happened to be thinking about making it so—"how dare you enter my study without . . ."

"You goddamned son of a bitch," Tony shouted, "you're burning up my French assignment!"

"Van-den-berg!"

It was quite a day. The whole senior class was confined to the dormitory while Tony was dragged off to the headmaster. The consensus was that even though the housemaster was a prick and entirely in the wrong, Tony was as good as on the next train for Chicago. Since no one in the school happened to be sick at the time, Tony was put in solitary confinement in the infirmary. Late that afternoon Winthrop and Perry and I were each called into the headmaster's study to give our versions of the story. Even Greer Perry, who would have been delighted to have Tony expelled from the school forever, had to confess that Tony had been blameless.

I was the last witness. Since parents sometimes saw it, a halfhearted attempt had been made at decorating the headmaster's study. That is to say, it had curtains at the windows, a rug on the floor, and cushions on the chairs.

"You heard what Vandenberg said this morning?" the headmaster said.

"Yes, sir. I guess everybody did."

"Not very nice language, do you think?"

"Tony didn't realize what he was saying. He'd worked very hard on his French theme and he . . ."

The headmaster held up his hand. It was like the hand of God. "Just answer my question, please. You were in the room when the—uh—the contretemps took place?"

"Yes, sir. I had to be. It was inspection."

"Tell me, then, very briefly, what happened."

I told the story—the same one Winthrop and Perry had told. When I had finished the headmaster said, "Then you think that Vandenberg was provoked?"

"Yes, sir."

"I see. Vandenberg is your best friend, is he not?"

"I don't know that you could say *best* friend, sir. We are friends. I like him a lot."

"I suppose you realize that you and Vandenberg come from entirely different backgrounds."

I couldn't help blushing. It seemed unfair—unmanly—to point out to me how hard up my family was. "I know that, sir."

"Very well. I think that for once your housemaster was not entirely—that is to say, I think that he acted hastily. Your father is an old boy, is he not?"

"Yes, sir. Class of 1909."

"Yes. Yes, of course. He was a year behind me. I remember him. Very rambunctious." Rambunctious. *My* father? "You seem to have settled in here very nicely. Doing good work, I understand. Just one more thing and what I'm going to tell you is in the strictest confidence. Is that understood?"

"Yes, sir."

"As you undoubtedly know, we don't usually take boys in for only the final year. If we did, we'd have a graduating class of more than a thousand every June. The name of this school means something all over the world. You, of course, were an exception, and one we were happy to make. Your father is an old boy and if his financial circumstances had—well, what I mean to say is that you have not been a disappointment to us. Not so far."

"Thank you, sir."

"As for Vandenberg, he was very highly recommended by another old boy who is, um, extraordinarily active in alumni circles and . . ."

"Oh, yes. You must mean old Mr. Willingham, that railroad president in Chicago who gave all that money to the scholarship fund. Tony says he . . ."

"That will be enough." Again the hand of God was raised. "Yes, I believe Mr. Willingham did recommend Vandenberg very highly. But then so did a number of other old Chicago boys."

"Oh yeah, they all work for Mr. Willingham. Tony says . . ."

"Silence!"

"Sorry, sir."

"From such important and, um, importunate sources of reference all of us here had rather expected Vandenberg to be a good deal more than he has turned out to be. We had been led to believe that he was an excellent scholar, a superb athlete, a leader in extracurricular activities—the sort of boy that has made this school the place it is and always has been. I am not loath to say that we have been disappointed—sorely disappointed. Vandenberg is simply not quite our sort." I saw then that what made Tony so attractive was that he wasn't their sort. "We took Vandenberg in as a sort of experiment and we realize, too late, our serious mistake. I say to you now: Don't let him drag you down with him. I don't mean to tell you how to conduct your personal life or whom to choose as your friends. I simply wish to remind you that you and Vandenberg come from very different environments. Be as friendly as you like, but don't become too close."

"Yes, sir."

"One more thing—and you needn't answer my question if you don't wish to. I have no intention of prying. Does Vandenberg owe you any money?"

"Tony owe me money? Oh, no, sir."

"Very well. You may go. Just bear in mind what I have said. A word to the wise."

Tony was put on probation, forced to apologize to the housemaster, and confined to campus until the Christmas holidays. I suspect that the housemaster also got a bit of hell, as the atmosphere was more charged than ever. Tony flunked French. But Tony became something of a hero around the school. His coterie of hangers-on were bug-eyed at his bravado. "Hot damn," they kept saying, "ya gotta admire old Tony. He just stood there and let the old bastard have it. No bullshit about Van!"

33

Tony, who was having hamburgers and malteds smuggled in from the village by sympathetic and admiring friends, took their adulation lightly. "It wasn't much," he said casually, "I simply said, 'Take your choice. Do you want to send me home or do you want the Vandenberg Auditorium?'" For the time being, at least, it put the Perry Faculty Lounge in the shade.

Around Thanksgiving time—once the school had overcome the defeat of Alfred M. Landon by that "traitor to his class," F.D.R.—another relative of mine was heard from. This time my father's elderly aunt—the one who lived on a comfortable trust fund in New York—wrote to say that she had heard that I was tall, dashing, and not too inaccessible and added that she admired my father's courage in the face of scandal and disgrace. The real point of her letter was an invitation to spend Thanksgiving weekend with her at the Plaza. It occurred to me that my father had spoken of her as "bone selfish," that she had never admired anything about him enough in the past to help out with so much as a penny, and that she had never acknowledged my existence until such time as I was attending a fashionable and convenient school and shaving two or three times a week. However, my mother instructed me by airmail to accept Aunt Harriet's invitation by all means, to buy a hat—"but not one of those frightful collegiate ones"—not to pay more than ten cents to check it anyplace, and to be a little gentleman. "How kind and generous of your Aunt Harriet to give you this treat."

Most of the kids at school lived close enough to home to take off the long Thanksgiving weekend. Owing to his period of probation, Tony couldn't have left school anyhow. But he perked up a bit when he heard that I was going to New York. "Gee, that's tough. If I hadn't got myself stuck here my folks were going to go to New York and open up the penthouse so we could be there together. Of course if you want to use the place . . ."

"No thanks, Tony. I'll be staying with my aunt. But thanks, anyway."

"Just where is your penthouse?" Greer Perry asked.

"Uh, on Park Avenue."

"Where on Park?"

"Uh, 200 Park Avenue. Why?"

"I just wondered."

When Greer heard where I would be staying, he offered me a lift. It was quite a day, marking not only my first visit to New York, but also my first ride in a limousine (with a chauffeur separated from us by glass but in constant telephonic communication), and my first drink. The car—the very biggest Packard made—had a bar in the back, and no sooner had we swept out of the gates of the school than Greer poured out two neat whiskies and settled back to run down all the people we knew in common.

One drink was more than enough for me. It hadn't tasted very good. Greer went right on, his rather wet mouth becoming wetter and looser with every sip. "And as for your great and good friend Phony . . ." He hiccuped and spilled a bit of Scotch on his new polo coat. "Shit!"

"Tony?" I asked, conscious that Greer was getting a little drunk and not quite knowing what to do about it.

"No, Phony. Phony Vandenberg."

"I like Tony," I said.

"I don't. He's nothing but a little kike from the Middle West whose family takes Vogue." I didn't make any reply and Greer went into a silent sulk for the next few miles. Eventually he poured himself another drink. "Going to visit his place?"

"Going to visit whose place?"

"Phony's place. His penthouse."

"I don't think I'll have time. My aunt . . ."

"That's good. Do you know where it is?"

"Sure. Two hundred Park Avenue."

"Right. There is no such address. It's Grand Central Station."

"Maybe you got the number wrong," I said. "Or maybe I did."

Silence again. Greer dozed while I tried to admire the bleak Eastern Seaboard landscape. On a gray November day it was not looking its best, but then I had never seen it before. Eventually we rolled through another pair of iron gates that looked just like the entrance to a boarding school and pulled to a stop at what turned out to be a boarding school—one for girls. Our party was joined by Greer's younger sister Posy. Posy Perry—her real name, unfortunately—was a remarkably pretty child of thirteen, her blond hair cut or uncut in the traditional way of New York's upper classes. She seemed frighteningly precocious and it was some years before I realized that she made up in vivacity for what she lacked in intelligence.

"Gig!" Posy said, stamping her foot on the running board. "You've been drinking liquor!"

"So what? And don't call me Gig." We were introduced. I tipped my new hat. Posy climbed aboard, the chauffeur tucked us all under a gray squirrel lap robe, and we were on our way to New York. Posy, with that remarkable poise of very social New York children, talked to me for just ten minutes, asking where I lived, how I liked school, what my father did, where I was staying in New York, and what I planned to do while I was there. She must have approved of my answers because when the interrogation was over she offered me a chocolate-covered peppermint, turned to Greer, ordered him to pull himself together, and then the two of them launched into a long private conversation involving junior holiday parties and mutual friends in New York all unknown to me. At last we were in New York, rolling down Riverside Drive, and I was too busy looking to listen. At the Plaza there was a frenzied little ballet involving the chauffeur, the doorman, the lap robe, my bag, and me.

"If you want a lift back, come up to our flat Sunday about three," Greer said. "You know where it is?"

"Eight eighty-eight Fifth Avenue," I said.

I tipped my new hat, tipped the doorman, wondered whether I should tip the chauffeur, thought better of it, and that was that.

My Great-aunt Harriet was a square-built old toad of a woman with a deep whisky voice. She was neither kind nor generous. She gave to whom, if and when it suited her own convenience. But she was bored and she was lonely. She needed something like a man to take her to places where women couldn't go alone during the thirties and I, on the brink of my seventeenth birthday, was the closest thing she could get at her age. But New York City, the Plaza, and a rich old lady like Aunt Harriet were new sensations to me and I tingled with excitement.

"You're not bad looking" were her first words. "At least you're tall and you've got nice skin. Did you bring a smoking?"

"A smoking what?"

"Dinner clothes. Black tie."

"Oh, a tuxedo." Then I remembered that my father always called it a dinner jacket and edited my statement. "No. I don't have a dinner jacket. In Santa Fe . . ."

"Well, you're not with the Indians now. Just a dark suit will do for tonight. Friday we'll go out and fit you up with something proper. But don't come whining to me for a Christmas present. I'm not made of money."

It was quite a weekend. Aunt Harriet took me to see the Lunts in Idiot's Delight, to see Ina Claire in Biography and Beatrice Lillie in At Home Abroad. For a total outlay of something like thirty dollars I was fitted out at Rogers Peet with a dinner jacket, a stiff shirt, two wing collars, a black tie, and some patent leather shoes. On Saturday night, with Aunt Harriet bedecked in lack-luster silver lamé, a fox-trimmed velvet cape, and a petitpoint bag, we heard Thaïs at the Met and danced sedately in the Rainbow Room. On my own, which was every afternoon while Aunt Harriet and three old crones fought over Ely Culbertson and Hal Simms at the bridge table, I went to the Metropolitan Museum, to see The Great Ziegfeld, to the Radio City Music Hall, and rode to Greenwich Village on top of a Fifth Avenue bus. By Sunday afternoon I was a polished man of the world. So cosmopolitan had I become that I took a taxi the half mile from the Plaza to Greer Perry's apartment, tipping both the doorman and the driver a dime.

The Perry apartment—that is to say the Mallory apartment,

Greer's mother having shed Mr. Perry and remarried—was sumptuous to say the least. I know now that it was a typical interior-decorated rich folk's New York flat down to the last silver cigarette box and Coromandel screen with nothing in it nearly so good as the stuff I had grown up with at home, but as I followed the real live butler through the Regency foyer and the Louis XV drawing room into the Georgian library I nearly genuflected in the presence of such taste, wealth, and beauty. I sank into a reproduction wing chair beneath an Augustus John portrait of a society goddess and pondered the many quirks of fate that had brought me there when, with a jangling of charm bracelets, the goddess herself clattered into the room. Like her apartment, Greer's mother was the standard society model—mutton disguised as lamb; fortyish with slightly lightened hair, a good girdle, and just a hint of flabbiness at the jaw.

"How do you do," she said in her silly good-finishing-school voice. "I'm Gig's mother. Oh dear, I mustn't call him Gig any longer. He hates it so. He couldn't say Greer when he was first talking and so we've called him Gig ever since. Now we've all got to learn to call him Greer again. I was a Greer. The children are having lunch with their father but they should be back any minute. What time was it that you've got to be back at school?"

"Ten o'clock," I said.

"Oh, then there's oodles of time. Of course I could always call the club and tell them to step on it. Wouldn't you like a drink?"

"Well, I . . ."

"Oh, do. I hate Sundays so. My husband always locks himself in upstairs with the *Times* crossword. I can never make head or tail of them myself. Just press that bell, would you, please? Thank you."

Mrs. Mallory told the butler to bring me a Coca-Cola—"or something stronger if you like; we let Gig drink at home because we want him to learn in the right way instead of sneaking off to some squalid hole-in-the-wall where you don't know what they serve"—and her "usual."

"Gig's told me so much about you. You come from, uh, out west, I believe. Minnesota."

"Santa Fe, New Mexico."

"Oh, yes. It's charming, I expect. A friend of mine built a house in Tucson—very modernistic but lovely. She has T.B. I don't suppose you know her—Eugenia Merrill?"

"I'm afraid not. Tucson's a long way from Santa Fe. In a different state, in fact."

"Oh yes, I suppose it must be. But I'm sure it's lovely," she said doggedly.

"Yes, it is nice, Mrs. Perry—I mean Mrs. Mallory. Very Spanish."

"Gig—dear, I must stop calling him that—says you speak Spanish. I adore Cuba. And then there's that book about Santa Fe? The one by Wilma Cantor?"

Mystified, I decided to hazard a guess. "Willa Cather?"

"Yes, that's the one! Who Killed the Archbishop. I never have time to read. It's sweet of you to help Gig with his Spanish. I'd love him to go into the diplomatic corps and of course languages help so much. I suppose you're just as upset over this Spanish Civil War as all the rest of us. I just hope General Franco puts those Reds right back in Africa where they belong. The idea! Just marching in and trying to take over a whole country! I love Madrid, don't you? But not as much as Paris." I wondered if I should set her straight on the war in Spain and thought better of it. "But one thing I just hate are bullfights. I think it's . . ."

What she thought of bullfighting, while undoubtedly unique, was never expressed. The front door slammed and Greer and Posy came in. Mrs. Mallory ordered chicken sandwiches, which nobody wanted, and watched us eat them while twittering away about the New York night clubs she considered suitable for a young man of seventeen. "I think the Rainbow Room is wholesome," she said. It was like granting the Imprimatur.

"I was there last night," I said, as one at last with the haute monde.

"Didn't you love it? I adore Veloz and Yolanda. They're really better than the Castles ever were. And those dresses! And the Stork Club is all right as long as Sherman knows Gig's coming and can keep an eye . . ."

"*Don't call me Gig!*"

"Sorry, darling. And La Rue. One place a mother *doesn't* have to worry is La Rue." This statement was made a good decade before the manager of that exclusive supper club was found in *flagrante delicto* with a fourteen-year-old girl. "Otherwise, Gig is simply going to have to wait until he's eighteen."

"Mother, I already am eighteen."

"Oh!"

"And besides, we've got to shove off."

"Oh, must you go, darling? It seems that I've hardly seen you at all."

"You were out every night, Mummy," Posy said.

"Well, there's Christmas. Now, Posy, *have* you got your retainer and *do* you wear it every night? You know what Dr. Jessup said: If you don't, your teeth will all go back to where they were and you'll have to go around wearing that bit all over again."

"Yes, Mummy."

"What lovely teeth you have," Mrs. Mallory said to me.

"Thank you."

"Gig's weren't bad but Posy looked just like a bulldog. I said to her father . . ."

"The car is downstairs, Mrs. Mallory," the butler said.

"Oh dear, is it? Well, it's been lovely meeting you. I'm glad that Greer—there, I *said* it, darling, Greer, Greer, Greer—has found some intelligent new friends. The boys he knew when he went to Browning were all so frivolous. Now bundle up."

Driving back to school in the car, Posy prattled on about a *ghastly* subdebutante dance held by a Miss Clementina Miller and how positively *drippy* all the boys had been and how she couldn't wait until the Junior Holidays at Christmas when at least there'd be some *decent* boys. One had little difficulty in deciding where she'd mastered the art of small talk. After Posy was dropped off, Greer emptied the whisky flask, stopped the car for a package of Sen-Sen, and slept all the rest of the way back to school. It had been some weekend.

I knew it was a corny thing to do with a really smooth article like Tony Vandenberg, but I'd seen and done and had so many new things during my four days in New York that I couldn't resist telling him about it. He listened patiently, but that's about all, and a third of the way through my breathless recital I realized that I was making a mistake even in trying to have anything in common with Tony.

"Your aunt lives at the Plaza? Well, I suppose it's all right for an old woman, but Hampshire House is a lot snappier." The Lunts, he said, were a couple of old hams. "Why, she must be forty!" Never having been to the real, professional theater before, I had found them staggeringly good. "Beatrice Lillie?" he asked, knitting his brows. "Beatrice *Lillie?* Oh, yes, Bea. Lady Peel." As for my evening at the opera, Tony asked where we had sat and seemed distressed that Aunt Harriet's seats were on the orchestra floor. "If only I'd known, you could have had our box."

"Vandenberg, does your family have a box on *Saturday* nights?" Perry asked.

"Sure."

"On *Saturdays?* At the *Met?* Couldn't you get one for Mondays?" With that, he slammed off to the can to work over his complexion. Tony turned a furious red and after that he was twice as brutal to me as seemed humanly possible. The Rainbow Room, he said, was a place for hicks; I should have insisted that Aunt Harriet take me to the Central Park Casino.

"It's closed," I said, having had its ruins pointed out to me from Greer Perry's apartment.

"I didn't mean that. I meant the French Casino. And as for having Thanksgiving dinner at Sherry's—well, why didn't your aunt stake you to Child's?" I had never seen the easygoing Tony like this before and I was hurt and mystified and getting angry. My trip to New York may have seemed old hat to him, but it had been a revelation to me.

"So what did the cowboy buy in the big city? The Brooklyn Bridge?"

Like a fool, I opened up my closet and got out my new evening clothes.

Tony went straight for the label. "Rogers Peet, eh? Well, it's not bad for ready-to-wear. But couldn't you get a double-breasted midnight blue?"

"Oh go to hell, Vandenberg!" I shouted and stomped out of the room just as the housemaster came in and said, "What's all the commotion in here?"

During the first weeks of December Tony and I spoke, but in a fairly stilted fashion and not more than absolutely necessary. The whole school was looking forward to the long Christmas holiday and, in the senior hall especially, every postal delivery brought its spate of invitations to what would be the first of many years of coming-out parties in New York and Boston and Philadelphia. Winthrop and Perry were especially in demand, each collecting a stack of engraved cards announcing that Mr. and Mrs. Chauncey Somebody and Miss Cynthia Somebody would be At Home at the Colony Club, the Somerset, the Ritz Ballroom, the Bellevue-Stratford.

"What's the matter, Vandenberg?" Perry said. "Won't your best friend tell you? I don't see the Gold Coast Good Time Charlie snowed under with bids."

"Hell, do you think I get my invitations sent to a dump like this? My mother's social secretary answers them back home in Chicago."

As for me, there were none. Santa Fe, New Mexico now boasts a population of little more than thirty-five thousand and, to my knowledge, no girl has ever made her debut there. If she had, my mother would surely have written to tell me how barbarous it had all been and not nearly so nice as the Queen Charlotte Balls in London.

But the fever of holiday gaiety in the air, the buzzing about parties and dances, new clothes, trips to Florida or Canadian ski resorts, did nothing to brighten Tony's spirits. He became, if anything, more arrogant, more patronizing, and his grades slipped perilously. A week before the school closed for Christmas, the housemaster came into our room to announce to Tony that unless all of his work was made up before vacation, he needn't bother coming back. If it had been Winthrop or Perry or even me, he would have called us into his study, but he obviously got a good deal of pleasure from humiliating Tony in public.

"That's tough, Tony," Winthrop said and blushingly made up a transparent excuse to get out of the room. Perry didn't say anything. He smirked at me, picked up a new brand of shampoo that smelled like mange cure, and clomped off to the showers. And then Tony did a strange thing. He burst loudly into tears. I was so surprised that I forgot how embarrassed I was and how unfriendly we had been.

"Tony," I said. "I'll help you. I've done all my work and I don't catch the train until the day after quitting time. You can do it. I know you can." And what's more, Tony could. Once he put his mind to doing a little work, I was amazed at the drive he had. On the last day of school, he turned in sixteen different papers—almost all of them entirely his own work—to the open-mouthed admiration of the faculty and to the thin-lipped disgruntlement of the housemaster. But the minute the work was done and accepted, Tony was back in Toyland again. He worked his way up and down the corridor shouting noisy good-bys, boasting of the LaSalle roadster he was going to get for Christmas, talking of parties in Chicago and Lake Forest (as many as three and four an evening), and describing the twenty-foot Christmas tree in the Vandenberg drawing room. After a solid week of working with me, it was almost as though he had been released from prison. What the hell, I grumbled to myself, why should I care whether he flunks out or not? I felt that my usefulness was at an end and wondered a little bitterly if I might not take up bridge and the rhumba so as to make a career as a sort of socially acceptable tutor to future generations of Tony Vandenbergs. Then the school emptied out for the holidays and once again Tony and I were alone together with Tony, as usual, doing all the talking.

Trying to fight off a sullenness that even at the time struck me as unreasonable, I set about my packing while Tony turned the full force of his opulence on me. He showed a slight interest in what train I was taking and said it was a pity that he wouldn't be in Chicago to entertain me during the long layover. "But," he explained, "I've got to wait for the car. My folks don't like me to take public conveyances."

"Which car this time? The Flying Wombat? The Diesel Dream? The Solar Speedster?"

"Oh, no. Just the Rolls. It's the most comfortable for a long trip."

The housemaster poked his head in the door. "If you're all packed, I'll give you a lift over to the station."

"Thank you, sir," I said. "That would save a lot of time."

"All right. But don't keep me waiting. I'm in a hurry."

"I'm all ready, sir."

I laid my new dinner jacket carefully on top of the hand-me-downs in my suitcase and was just about to close it when a small cellophane cylindrical box landed on the pile of clothes with a little plop. I picked it up and looked at it.

"W-what's this?"

"Merry Christmas, kid, and thanks," Tony said. "It's a feather boutonniere to wear with your tux."

II ♥

TONY

at home

That first Christmas back home in Santa Fe was a disaster. I felt, rather guiltily, that having been away to school I had suddenly outgrown the town, my friends, and my family. My parents especially appeared to be very, very old and pathetically out of the swim. My father and I had at least the school in common, but whenever we tried to talk about it—there being no other subject which we could discuss—all of the masters he had known were dead or retired and my enthusiasm for the place was markedly less than his. My mother was even worse. King Edward's abdication in favor of an *American* divorcee had been almost a personal affront to her and she was more Britannic than ever before, even to the extent of celebrating Boxing Day and

45

inflicting on her Indian maid of the moment an old family formula for polishing the furniture—"Once a day for a week; once a week for a month; once a month for a year." It created a servantless Christmas and my mother was a ludicrous sight bumbling around the kitchen in an elderly ball gown with her train tucked up into her girdle as she dished up inedible Yuletide messes of suckling pig, roast goose, plum and suet puddings.

Now that I could, I was expected to dress for dinner, and Tony's feather carnation created a family crise. Having had no truck with fashion for the last twenty years, my father found it a foppish abomination. My mother said, "But, darling, it makes you look like an assistant at Harrod's. Here when I have a conservat'ry full of flahs, to wear that artificial feather thing . . ."

"It isn't a conservatory. It's an old glass lean-to up against the garage and there's nothing in it but a lot of dead weeds!" I said. Oh, I was a little charmer!

"Leave the table!" my father said.

"It seems to me that this school of yours has done nothing for his manners," my mother was saying as I stamped out of the room. "Now at Eton . . ."

In a pathetic attempt to share in my dull little life, my mother feigned a great interest in my Christmas mail, going through the small stack of Scotties, snowmen, Santa Clauses, stylized reindeer, and such with ill-concealed scorn and asking about each boy from school who had sent me a Christmas card. Two invitations —one engraved in scarlet from Greer and Posy Perry asking me to a tea dance at the River Club in New York and another from Seth Winthrop and his twin sister requesting my presence at a skating party—impressed her as "teddibly nice." I was going to ask what was so nice about being invited to parties in the East when I was buried a million miles from nowhere in New Mexico, but fought down the impulse.

However, when Tony's Christmas card arrived, there were words, to say the least. His card was printed in shades of brown, black, and gold. It depicted in silhouette a young man gazing out on a vista of skyscrapers while the smoke from his cigarette ingeniously spelled out "Season's Greetings." On the inside "J. Anthony Vandenberg" was printed in gold and beneath that, in brown ink, Tony had written, "If you're ever in Chicago give me a call." His telephone number was thoughtfully included.

"Well!" my mother said, "I must say that this card is in the most dubious taste. Who ever heard of brown and black at Christmas? Now back home our cards always have . . ."

"Tony Vandenberg just happens to be the richest kid in school," I snapped.

"My dear, you will learn that wealth and taste don't always go hand in hand. Now back home there was this frightful man who had been in trade and thought he'd cut a great swath in the county by building a monstrous big house all in Spanish . . ."

"And speaking of houses," I said, "Lochby Court is pure Georgian and makes the places you're always talking about look sick!"

"Lochby Court, darling?"

"Yes. Lochby Court. It's Tony Vandenberg's house in Chicago."

"In Chicago? But, darling, how could it be Georgian in Chicago? There wasn't a Chicago when any of the Georges were on the throne. And then the whole city burnt down not sixty years ago."

"Sixty-five years ago. And Tony's family is descended from the Duke of Lochby."

"The Duke of Lochby? *Lochby?* I couldn't swear to it, but I'm certain there's no such title. Would you fetch me the *Peerage* and we'll . . ."

"Oh, to hell with it!"

"How dare you speak to your mother that way?" my father bellowed.

The vacation was not a success and I was happy to pack my

things again and get away from such hopelessly provincial parents.

As Mr. Robert Young used to say, "A pig can cross the country without changing trains, but you can't." The trip from Santa Fe to New York involved a five-hour wait in Chicago. To go from the West to New England meant an even longer layover. Although my mother had planned a further cultural foray into the museums of the city, I had ideas of my own. Tony Vandenberg was my friend. I'd helped him to stay in school. He was forever talking about visiting him in one of the many Vandenberg establishments. I even had in my pocket his Christmas card asking me to telephone him. Instead of traipsing through the Field Museum, the Shedd Aquarium, the Adler Planetarium for most of the day, I'd have a little fun. What harm would it do at least to *telephone?*

The Chicago telephone system proved so remarkably sophisticated that I almost gave up. It involved buying a five-cent slug and then using a dial. The exchange, as I recall, was BIttersweet. Eventually the operator took pity on me and got the number. My heart was pounding as I heard the ringing signal. Who would answer—Newton the butler, the social secretary, one of the footmen? After three rings a woman's voice shouted, "Hello?"

"H-hello," I said. Then I was in a quandary. How to ask for Tony in such a household? Should I say Mr. Vandenberg or Mr. Tony or just plain Tony? Finally I said, "May I please speak to Mr. J. Anthony Vandenberg?"

"Who?"

"Mr. J. Anthony Vandenberg, please."

"Oh, Jackie! Say, who is this, anyway?"

I gave my name and announced rather pompously that I was a friend from school. The wires sizzled with cordiality. "Oh! How nice! You here in town? . . . Well, Jackie's out getting a new suit but he'll be back home any minute now. Why don't you come on out? You know the address?"

48

"Oh yes," I said. I wished that my mother, with her incessant drumming of Mrs. Beeton's *Book of Household Management* into illiterate Indian girls, could see how democratic the servants were in the homes of the really rich.

"Well, I tell you whacha do. Get one of the Outer Drive busses—the double-deckers. Lake Shore Drive Limiteds, they're called. And tell the driver to let you off at the Drive and Belmont and you'll be right at the door. Can you stay for lunch?"

"W-why, yes. If it won't be putting you to any trouble."

"No trouble at all, honey. We've gotta eat anyway. See you in a few minutes. Toodle-oo."

To hell with your stately homes of England, Mother, I thought. This is real American hospitality!

The trip up the Drive from the top of the bus was impressive, with Lake Michigan coldly gray pounding against the shore to my right, the massive apartment buildings, equally cold and gray to my left. Eventually the driver called out "Belmont!" and I disembarked. There, spread out before me, was Lochby Court in all its eighteenth-century splendor and there, too, standing at one of the gate posts was the groom I had seen in the photograph, impressive in his bottle green tailcoat and white buckskin breeches. As I crossed the street a woman came out of the front door swathed in brown fur. Was it mink? Was it sable? "Do you think you can get me a taxi, Henry?"

"Sure thing, Mrs. Pletz!" he said and brought to heel a Yellow Cab with a shrill tweet of his whistle. "Yes, sir?" he said to me.

"Mr. J. Anthony Vandenberg, please. I'm expected."

"Dr. Vandenberg's office is around the corner on Belmont," he said.

"Not Dr. Vandenberg. His son."

"Their flat's around the corner, too."

"There must be some mistake. This is the house. Tony . . . Mr. Vandenberg . . ."

"No mistake, sonny. You just walk around that corner. You'll see a door says '400 Belmont Amyou.' That's where the Vandenbergs live. If you don't find 'em there, you come on back here and I'll help you. Morning, Mrs. Goodall." With a tweeting of his whistle he was off hailing another cab. There was nothing for me to do but to follow his instructions. As I rounded the corner I saw a realtor's placard attached to the side of the building.

L O C H B Y   C O U R T
3200 Lake Shore Drive
8 Room Apartment Available
Agent on Premises

Once around the corner the scene changed. While the façade of Lochby Court was all and more than it had been in the photograph, with a sweeping view of the park, the yacht club and lake, the Belmont Avenue side—if that was where I was; in my confusion I could be certain of nothing—was something of a letdown. The building still maintained its architectural airs and graces but the vista was a trifle bleak: the side entrance to a hotel, a barbershop, a drugstore, a hack stand, and a bus stop. It looked a bit like one of those painted street-scene backdrops in vaudeville. One of the ground-floor windows bore the legend "H. A. VANDENBERG, D.D.S."

I rang the bell marked "Vandenberg" and after an incoherent series of shrieks and screams through a speaking tube, the door buzzed and I mounted the stairs. A dark head swathed in tulle called down from over the banisters. "Up here on the top floor, honey. Sorry we don't have elevators on this side of the building." I reached the summit and there was the lady of the ermine and the opera box. "Come right on in, honey. I been hanging outa the windah like a regular slum woman. I didn't wancha to get lost or anything. In here, honey. The colored girl's just finished cleaning."

The first thing I could notice about the Vandenberg living room was, oddly enough, its splendid dentilated cornice. Tony had described, all too often, the moldings, paneling, and plaster work of Lochby Court. There was the cornice. It gave me some grasp on reality. Gradually, as if coming out of an anesthetic, I took in some of the other details of the room. It was small, although the proportions were good. There was the famous French furniture. I even found myself sitting on a piece of it. It was a sofa with a painted walnut finish, machine-carved cabriole legs, and fake tapestry upholstery—Louis le Grand Rapids. There stood the traditional Christmas tree—artificial and closer to twenty inches than to twenty feet. The Vandenberg collection of paintings? There they were—a reproduction of Hals's *Laughing Cavalier* over the chimney piece, a Leonardo da Vinci, yes, the *Mona Lisa*; a Rembrandt, *The Nightwatch*; a series of gifteshoppe Boucher ladies in swings hung in gilt compo frames over an upright piano. I felt dizzy and lightheaded and somewhere between laughing and crying. Nearby an incessant voice was haranguing me.

". . . feel like I already know you, Jackie's told Doctor and I so much about you. Can't be much fun to leave that fabulous big ranch of yours and the polo ponies and all to go back east to school, can it?"

"W-what?"

"I just don't know where the time has all gone to. It seems like only yesterday Doctor and I were down to the bus terminal meeting Jackie and now here he is, ready to go back again. Say! What train are you on?"

I was just barely able to tell her.

"Listen, I got an idea. Howsabout I send Jackie back on the train with you? This friend of mine . . . well, this gentleman is the president of this railroad and I know he wouldn't mind arranging a pass for Jackie just this once. I hate bothering him at business for a lotta favors, but that poor kid was so pooped out from the bus trip. . . . Gimme yer ticket, honey." With a rustling of her housecoat, Mrs. Vandenberg was across the room and mauling the telephone in the hall. "Mr. Willingham, please," she said. "It's Mrs. Van— Uh, just say Miss Rose is calling. Thanks, honey. . . . Will? Rose. Listen, dearie, I wonder if you could fix it so Jackie could go back by train tonight? Jackie's got this friend here and . . . *Him?* He's so busy fixin' teeth he won't even give it a thought. Have I ever asked you to do it before? . . . Well, what are you the president of a railroad *for?* Besides, that old bus . . . Thanks a million, sweetie. Here, I'll read off this other kid's ticket number. . . . I can't talk right now, Will, but I'll see ya Wenzdy like always. Now here's this other reservation."

While Mrs. Vandenberg was re-routing the railway system of the country over the telephone, I tried to make sense of all that I heard from Tony and what now appeared before me. Could it be some elaborate practical joke he was playing? Could this commonplace little flat on a side street in Chicago have been hastily thrown together in the half hour it had taken me to get here? Would Tony pop out from behind those faded portieres, face full of mischief, and shout, "Surprise!" and then lead me through the galleries and drawing rooms and music rooms and billiard rooms to the *real* Lochby Court where the Vandenbergs lived like kings? But no, Mrs. Vandenberg was back in the room, a cigarette gripped between her large white teeth. "This friend of mine is going to see what he can do about putting you boys in the same section on the train. Oh, and, honey, when you meet Doctor don't mention it to him. De-tails make him kinda nervous and upset. So did you have a nice Christmas? Jackie told me how all those Mexicans that work on your estate—rancho, I guess I should say—come and serenade you on Christmas Eve. That must be really beautyful."

She stopped talking and gazed at me expectantly with her fine dark eyes.

I was supposed to say something. But what? "I . . . I recognized you from the picture Tony—uh—Jackie, uh (you see we call him Tony) keeps at school. The one in the ermine. At least I *think* it's ermine."

"Oh that one! It's about a million years old. I used to model part time for Kagelbaum, that's this very fine furrier—at least he was; he's out of business now like almost everybody else. Oh, that photo was everywheres—*The Chicagoan*, *The New Yorker*, *Vogue*, *Town & Country*, all the swell magazines. One of the tails fell off while I was posing and Kagelbaum let me take it home to Jackie. That crazy kid's carried it ever since. Here's a couple more photos." She handed me two photographs in leatherette frames. In one she was stepping out of a very grand car (the Rolls, the Cord, the Cadillac, the Dusenberg?) displaying a well-turned ankle, an Empress Eugenie hat, and a fur coat very like my mother's old sealskin. In the other she simpered through silver fox fur framed by a pedimented doorway. "That one was taken right out in front, on the swanky side of the building," she explained. "I was some punkins in those days." She still was. Rose Vandenberg was what is called handsome— tall, statuesque, and all woman.

I thought I saw a famous profile lurking in the shadow of a drooping poinsettia across the room. I was almost afraid to ask, but it was up to me to say something. "Is that John Barrymore, Mrs. Vandenberg?"

"It sure is." She snatched up another photograph and handed it to me. It was Barrymore all right. The inscription read, "Harry—You saved my life. A million thanks, Jack Barrymore."

"Tony told me how Dr. Vandenberg saved Barrymore's life once," I said.

"Oh, it was a scream. We were all sitting around reading the *Trib* this one Sunday when the phone rings (the phone rings up here when it rings in Doctor's office downstairs) and I pick it up and say, 'Hello?' and this voice that sounds like somebody's strangling or something says, 'This is John Barrymore.' Well, I figure it's Doctor's brother Ernie. He's a real card. So I say, 'And this is Peggy Hopkins Joyce.' Well, whaddaya know but it really was Barrymore. He had this terrible abscessed tooth and he just picked up the classified and turned to dentists. So Doctor tells

53

him to come right on up and he'll take care of it. Well, we still think it's some kinda joke, but lo and behold in about thirty, forty minutes the doorbell rings and there's the Great Profile himself. He gave Doctor this autographed picture. Personally, I just wish he'd paid the bill instead."

That was the end of that anecdote and, for what felt like eternity, the end of all sound, save for the whine of a vacuum cleaner from another room of the apartment. Something had to be said. We both felt it and we both spoke at once.

"Sorry," I said. "Go ahead, please."

"Oh, nothing. I was just wondering what was keeping Jackie so long. He went down to the Boston Store to buy a new suit. We got him a tux for Christmas. He looks so cute in it. Honest, that kid and his clothes! Every penny he gets goes right on his back. And will he ever buy something sensible at the Hub or Rothschild's or someplace like that? He *will* not. He's always going to some little hole in the wall you never heard of and picking up all this collegiate junk. I said, 'Jackie, no nonsense this time. I want you to go down to the Boston Store and buy a plain blue serge suit that you can wear anywheres.' They're having this big sale—all the stuff they didn't move for Christmas. Wonderful bargains. I mean suits that cost twenty-five, thirty dollars marked down to fifteen-ninety-five. I understand you have all your suits made in London."

The photograph of John Barrymore fell from my hands with a clatter.

"It must be wonderful to travel. I'd like to go over there some time and take Jackie, too. It's really educational for a boy to get around and see how other people live. That's why we're sending Jackie east to school. It's not easy but I didn't want him to just go to old Senn High School with about a million other kids and not see anything or learn anything different. I said, 'Jackie's gonna have the best if I hafta scrub floors to see that he gets it.' Only with collections the way they are I don't know how we're gonna manage college unless he gets another scholarship." She laughed good-naturedly. "It must be a real eye-opener for you kids at school to see how the other half live. You with a ranch that covers half the state and your mother related to the Queen of England."

If the telephone hadn't rung then I think I would have fainted on the domestic oriental rug.

The telephone call apparently concerned some dental gold and the issue at hand was whether or not Dr. Vandenberg had paid for it. Mrs. Vandenberg had a forceful personality and showed it to its best advantage. "Now look, this isn't the first time you've phoned about this crummy ounce and a half of gold. . . . No, you can't talk to Doctor. He's got a patient. Anyway I'm the one that pays the bills and I paid yours just like I always do and I've got a canceled check to prove it. . . . Yes, I do have the check. It come back with the statement from the Harris Trust first of the month. . . . Yes, I can find it, but you'll hafta wait a coupla minutes while I dig it out. . . . No, I wanta get this thing settled once and for all. Now just hold the line while I find it. . . . Well, if you've been waiting for three months, you can certainly wait for three more minutes while I prove to you that I paid you. Hold the line." I heard her housecoat swishing off into the interior of the apartment and I decided to bolt.

It is difficult to explain my cowardice. I didn't care that Tony wasn't fabulously rich, that he was just about as well off as I was. In fact, it made me glad because I liked him anyhow and knowing that we were in the same boat lessened the chasm that had always yawned between us. That he was a liar of pathological proportions didn't especially bother me. I found it interesting though not really important. But what unsettled me was the thought of Tony's returning from a thoroughly ordinary errand to his thoroughly ordinary home to find me there like some sort of voyeur who enjoys catching people in sexual intercourse or on the toilet. Without stopping to consider what Mrs. Vandenberg would think, how she would tell Tony anyway—and at some length—about my astonishing arrival and departure, I gathered up my hat and coat and tiptoed toward the door. Out in the dim little hallway I could hear a voice over the telephone receiver saying, "Hello, hello, hello?" From another room the noise of the vacuum cleaner was joined by a high, off-key voice singing "Moon Over Miami," and from still another room the strident voice of Rose Vandenberg, "*Here* it is, damn him anyway!"

I reached for the knob and opened the front door. And I stood face to face with J. Anthony Vandenberg, bon vivant, playboy, and heir to millions.

For a long, agonizing moment we simply stared at one another. The thunderous silence was finally broken by the voice of Mrs. Vandenberg. "Here it is, paid in full. Just like I told you. Check number three-two-one-one; November tenth—I always pay the bills on the tenth, that's how I remembered—Harris Trust Company and it was deposited by you on the twel'th at the Continental Illinois Bank. Doctor may not be any fancy Michigan Avenoo dentist, but at least we pay our bills on time. . . . Good-*by!*" She slammed down the receiver.

"Why, Jackie, honey," she shouted. "You look like you seen a ghost. Isn't this ever some swell surprise though? I wanted to hide him in your room so when you opened the closet door to hang up your new suit . . . Hey, let's have a look at your new suit. Come on in here, honey. This is Jackie's room. It's got bunk beds because it's so small, but the next time you come through town, this is your home. Remember that. You two kids are used to sharing a room anyways. Now, let's see your new suit, hon. (Jackie's real hard to fit.)"

Mrs. Vandenberg was one hell of a woman. You could see where Tony/Jackie inherited his vitality. And it was she who saved the day. She was a great talker—the kind of person who can sit next to a total stranger on a plane or train and tell the whole story of her life in the course of a short trip. But as though her dialogue—or, more accurately, monologue—had been written by Satan himself, every statement she made seemed to be aimed directly at one of Tony's more grandiose fabrications. Cars: "Doctor used to have a cute little Chevy coop, but it's too expensive to keep an auto in the city." Servants: "We had a maid came in every afternoon and stayed through dinner but with Jackie away I can make do fine with the colored girl one day a week." Yachts: "Doctor has this little motorboat he keeps up at our summer cottage, but you couldn't get me on it for a million smackers." I gathered that of the numberless bits of Vandenberg real estate placed in the world's more desirable neighborhoods, only the fishing shack in Wisconsin had any substance to it at all.

Tony was silent and ashen during his mother's vivacious recital. As for me, I wished that the earth would open and swallow me up. Instead of deriving any malicious satisfaction or even a slight laugh at discovering Tony's real circumstances, I felt sick with embarrassment, and when Mrs. Vandenberg dwelt on the lies which Tony had obviously told her about me—our great wealth ("just imagine striking all that oil out in New Mexico"); my father's world-wide reputation as a physician ("having those Indian potentates going all the way out there just to see him"): my mother's exalted rank ("of course your folks'll be going over for the coronation, being related and all")—I had neither the courage to deny them nor the gall to carry them off. I felt dull and gauche and miserable and ashamed.

Mrs. Vandenberg cooked a bang-up lunch, sent Tony downstairs with a tray for Dr. Vandenberg, and then said, "Now, Jackie, howsabout taking in a show? Then we'll all go to some swellelegant spot for a little celebration before we put you boys on the train. I gotta surprise for yuh, Jackie. The choo-choo. No bus! Oh, and if they're still giving away chinaware at the Lake Shore, try and get me a cream pitcher. The colored girl broke our good one."

Going to the movies was a godsend. I recall vividly that the two films were Simone Simon in *Girls' Dormitory* and Johnny Weissmuller in *Tarzan Escapes*, but I couldn't have told you one thing about either picture ten minutes after they were finished. I was numbly grateful to be in a dark theater where I couldn't see Tony's stricken face and where neither of us would be expected to talk. We sat through both features, a newsreel, a travelogue, a comedy, a cartoon, and the previews of at least a thousand coming attractions. It was mercifully dark when we got out. On the way back to the Vandenberg apartment, for lack of anything better to say, I said, "I don't think Simone Simon is so hot, do you?" For the rest of the walk Tony talked shrilly and artificially about movie stars, running down only when we approached Dr. Vandenberg's dental parlors.

"I feel just like Mrs. Simpson or something, out with three such handsome fellahs," Mrs. Vandenberg said, beaming upon our three dark blue suits as we sat down to dine in a large, noisy German restaurant. Dr. Vandenberg had joined us. He was a thickset, taciturn man covered with pale red freckles and dark red hair. During the course of the dinner—a large, heavy one washed down with seidels of beer—he said that I had a nice set of teeth and, upon hearing how tasteless the food was at school, launched into a long, rambling anecdote full of fits and starts, retractions and detours about a boardinghouse where he had lived while studying dentistry. I laughed nervously several times at what I thought was the point of the story. (It proved never to have had one.) Mrs. Vandenberg carried on as always, sublimely unaware of the tensions that surrounded her. She complimented the waiter on the sauerbraten, asked if his feet ever got tired, introduced us all to him, told him that Dr. Vandenberg was a dentist and that if he ever had a toothache . . .

The wonderful thing about her was that she was always exactly herself. She would have been the same blooming Rose in Buckingham Palace or on a breadline. She requested "Ach Du Lieber Augustine" of the orchestra and sang happily along with the music. Tony looked as though he were about to die. "What's the matter with my Jackie-baby? He gonna miss his mommy? Here, this oughta perk up my boys." From a bud vase in the center of the table Mrs. Vandenberg broke off three weary carnations and tucked them into our buttonholes—all except Tony's, which was stitched together. "Honest to God, the way they make suits anymore! Now just look at his suit, Jackie. Genuine buttonholes —and made by hand I'll bet—even on the cuffs. And just see here, Jackie, Harry," she said, grasping my lapel, "the way this buttonhole is made, with a little thread loop sewn in behind to hold a flower." I was so ashamed of my inherited suit that I had never noticed any of its more esoteric details and knowing that they were there didn't make me like it any better. "Now that's real class tailoring. I know. Poppa used to be a cutter for Nadherny—that's this swanky tailor here in . . ."

"Oh, for God's sake, Mom!" Tony shouted, slamming down his napkin.

"Jack!" Dr. Vandenberg said.

"Now, Harry, just you leave Jackie be. It's only the excitement of going back to school and all. And we'd better skedaddle down to the station if you boys don't want to miss your train."

"Train?" Dr. Vandenberg said, as though our mode of conveyance were to be a camel caravan. "Train?" It was the most vivacity he had shown all evening.

"Oh, didn't I remember to tell yuh, honey?" Mrs. Vandenberg said smoothly. "The colored girl's got this brother that's a Pullman porter and has passes, so it's much cheaper than that old Greyhound bus. In fact, it's for free." She slipped me a conspiratorial wink and said, "Like to finish my strudel, Jackie?"

Through the machinations of Mrs. Vandenberg's highly placed acquaintance, my upper had been magically transformed into a compartment. I had never ridden in a compartment before and said so, hoping to clear the air if only a little. "That's nothing, honey," Mrs. Vandenberg said. "Jackie here has never even been on a sleeper before." She set to work explaining about the porter's bell, the brake cord, and the washbasin. And then she got a little teary, dabbing at her eyes and saying how she couldn't

59

believe the Christmas holidays had passed so quickly and that it would be like a century before Tony was home again. She rang for the porter. "Now you take good care of these boys, hear? And this is a little something for your trouble. Now don't you kids go wasting your money on a tip for him. He's already taken care of. And just leave your shoes outside the door to be shined. And remember the diner's two cars . . ."

"Board!"

"Rose, come on. The train's moving."

We sat facing each other, saying nothing and trying to avoid each other's eyes. With a little smile and a deprecating gesture, Tony began to speak in something like his old carefree fashion. "The house is in kind of a mess. We're redecorating some of the rooms and . . . Excuse me." He got up and left the compartment. Even Tony couldn't quite bring off so tremendous a lie. While he was gone, I prepared a nauseating little speech which was to say, in effect, that I liked him for himself and not for what he pretended to be. I wet my lips, ready to speak, but when Tony returned my courage failed me.

"Guess I'll turn in," he said, feigning a great yawn. "It's late." It was not quite half-past eight.

"Yeah. I'm bushed."

We undressed in silence, swaying with the motion of the train. "I—I think your parents are swell," I said, clambering into the upper berth. There was no reply. "Want the lights out?"

"Please," Tony said.

"Good night."

"G'night."

I lay awake for a long time staring into the darkness and listening to the noise of the tracks beneath us. Over the steady clickety-clack I thought I could hear the sound of sobbing.

TONY

at play

A more sensible person would have dropped Tony Vandenberg like a red-hot penny—and a bad penny at that. Not because he was poor when he had always pretended to be rich, but because he was a pathological liar. You can bolt your door against a thief, but with a liar you will always be helpless, never knowing when to believe him, always living in the shadow of doubt. But for some reason my discovery of Tony's real circumstances only made him more interesting to me. Instead of being forced apart by the sordid—no, not sordid, simply dismal—truth, it drew us closer together, as though I were somehow an accomplice in his great impersonation.

To give myself credit, I never once confided in anyone the

truth about Tony. This is not because of any nobility of character. It was simply because I disliked Greer Perry so much that I would not have given him the sadistic pleasure of knowing for sure the sorry circumstances of his enemy. But Greer, in his venomous dislike of Tony, was coming perilously close to discovering the sorry truth about him. He had already caught Tony in one lie and Tony's hideous Christmas card had supplied Greer with more ammunition. "Look at that," he whispered, showing me the silhouette of the young man whose cigarette smoke spelled out "Season's Greetings."

"What about it?"

"You can always tell. Jews never buy cards with 'Merry Christmas' on them."

"Neither do a lot of gentiles," I said. "I got plenty of cards from here saying 'Season's Greetings.' La Farge's said 'Cheerio' and he's a Catholic. Buckley's said 'Hi!' There was one from Armstrong with 'Hello there!' As a matter of fact, the invitation to your tea dance started off with 'Happy Holidays.' Did you mean Chanuka?" That was the end of that.

A fruitless search through the Chicago Social Register gave Greer enormous satisfaction. "I looked in the Chicago book and in the Locater. No Vandenberg. His father isn't even in Who's Who."

"Did you look me up, too?" I asked.

"Santa Fe doesn't have a Social Register. But if you wanted to be in it you could. Your mother's in Burke's Peerage. I found it in the library."

"No she isn't. She's in Burke's Landed Gentry, which is just as ridiculous as the Social Register. For God's sake, if you ever studied a textbook as hard as you do these silly snob catalogues you wouldn't have to pay me to do your work."

And another time: "Your fine friend Phony Vandenberg tried to borrow a buck off Winthrop."

"I hope he succeeded."

"Sure he did. I heard him. You know what an easy touch Seth is. Vandenberg's too smart to try it with me."

"So am I."

"But if he's supposed to be so rich, how come he has to go mooching money off other people?"

"Maybe his parents don't spoil him the way some people's do."

"You know what he said?"

"No, and I'm more interested in finding out what Hamlet said to Polonius. There's a test tomorrow."

"He said now that he was eighteen he had to write to his trustees for everything—even underwear and sweat socks and junk like that. Imagine!" The picture of a panelled board room filled with men in morning coats voting on a new toothbrush for a kid at school was not easy to conjure. Still, a lot of people—mostly Tony's sycophants—believed it.

I found myself in the position of an Alsatian priest in a film I once saw who was hiding a French deserter from the Hun. He disapproved of the deserter but he hated the Germans more and every time they came near the confessional where the refugee was hiding the priest had to think of something to distract them. "Perry," I said, "is that dandruff I see?"

"Where?"

"On your shoulders. Black sweaters seem to give you dandruff."

Armed with his bottles and lotions and scalp massagers, he was off to the bathroom and there was no more talk about Tony.

And there was no more talk *from* Tony. He still chattered away amiably enough but gone forever were the tall tales of daily life at Xanadu. I missed them. It was like being deprived of the movies. He still had his coterie of slobs hanging on his every word, but whenever I came into sight his conversation ground to a halt. Even the housemaster grudgingly said that Vandenberg seemed quieter.

But that winter Tony had his first opportunity to display the considerable social gift that would be with him for the rest of his life. Within a radius of thirty miles were half a dozen girls' boarding schools filled to the rafters, like our school, with frustrated teen-agers on the verge of maturity and panting for any contact with the opposite sex. Thus there was some sort of dance held almost every Saturday night and headmistresses, desperate for anything male, were forever laying siege to our school. The only requirements for attendance were testicles, a B average, and a dinner jacket, and these pallid evenings, starting at eight and ending at eleven, were at least a change from the movies and the village diner.

Tony shone like a beacon. He was an intrepid dancer, not especially good but fearless and tireless. One had only to listen for a shriek of slightly shocked laughter from a corner of some crepe-paper-hung gymnasium to know where Tony was holding forth. "Just like all the rest of his race," Greer Perry once said, "loud, aggressive . . ."

"Heil Hitler," I said and moved over to where the fun was. But, ethnic groups aside, Greer did have a point about Tony. I have never seen anyone work so hard in the name of pleasure. During those winter months I must have danced with a thousand girls without remembering or even ever knowing the names of more than a dozen. Not Tony. He appeared at every dance armed with a little black Fabrikoid notebook and jotted down the name and address of every girl he met. Once back in the monastic hush of our school, he proceeded to do research on all of them and none too subtly, employing the Greer Perry tools of Social Register, Who's Who, and just plain asking questions of boys from the same towns. The girls with the richest fathers and the glossiest social standings were eventually transferred to a red book—genuine leather this time—and it made quite a volume. The other names were quietly discarded.

Tony also inaugurated a sort of society-cum-gossip column in our school paper. He called himself Cholly St. Grottlesex and his literary style, based roughly on that of Maury Paul, Walter

64

Winchell, and Louella O. Parsons, was enough to curdle milk. Granted, there was little of interest to say unless one wished to defy the laws of libel and good taste by reporting an unnatural incident that occurred between a faintly effeminate boy in the second form and the assistant tennis coach (whose resignation was immediately accepted) and, besides, our newspaper was carefully censored. But Tony's column faithfully reported such news items, separated by ellipses, as: "Chaddy Donohue of Choate and Miss Walker's B.U.T. Barbara Baxter!!! Wow! . . . Is Seth Winthrop thataway about Evelyn Wakefield? . . . Hotchkiss hotshot 'Red' Rogers is ca-razy for Maisie (the very social dotter of the M. Bidwell Brents of Noo Yawk & Noopawt) . . ." Well, it was frightful, but it became the underground dope sheet of almost every school in New England since Tony thoughtfully clipped his own column each week and sent forth copies to rival feature editors and to all the girls who had made his red book. By the time spring vacation rolled around Tony Vandenberg had become the Lucius Beebe of the acne set and had even garnered a round dozen invitations to holiday dances in New York.

I had done so well as unpaid companion to Great-aunt Harriet that she summoned me to the Plaza for Easter vacation. "A splendid cultural opportunity," my mother wrote, "and far less expensive than transporting you all the way to New Mexico and back again. You may accept. Enclosed is a small cheque for incidental expenses—precious little, but more than we can afford."

The spring holiday parties amounted to a dry run for the coming debutante season and even I, although far from being the sensation that Tony Vandenberg was, had received a couple of invitations to parties in New York. Perry said one of them was decidedly second-rate and that the other was "a Catholic dance." It conjured up a picture of nuns and cardinals sedately trucking to the ecclesiastical strains of Benny Goodman, but to make me feel better about the shoddiness of my social life, he said that I would be permitted to escort his sister Posy to a very junior dance at the Cosmopolitan Club. For some reason I was grateful.

Tony was in a swivet about his many invitations—all *third*-rate, according to Perry—and desperate at the prospect of having to refuse them. "Don't worry," he said (I hadn't given it a thought), "I'll get to New York some way. I don't know how, but I'll manage."

Tony's ways and means were made clear to me about a week later when I received a large pink envelope in the mail. The letter, printed with a big, smudgy silver "R," was a real shock. It read:

Honey—

Are you ever a peach asking Jackie to stay with your aunt in New York! He's never been before & this will be one swell chance for him to really see the Gay White Way with an experienced fellow like yourself.

Doctor & I sure will miss seeing our boy but we couldn't let Jackie lose out on a trip like this! Here is a check for $25 for Jackie's carfare etc as Doctor & I don't want he should be a dead wait [*sic*].

Thanks a million & have a swell time.

Sincerely,
Rose M. Vandenberg

Tony/Jackie and I then had what was to be the first of our many frank conversations. "Just what the hell are you trying to pull?" I said brandishing his mother's letter. "I can't drag you along to Aunt Harriet's. I hardly know her and she certainly doesn't know you. Even if she did, there isn't space enough. I have to sleep on a sofa in her sitting room as it is. So just write home and say the trip is off."

"Oh, I wasn't going to stay with you. That's just what I told my folks. I'll move into some little hotel and they'll think I'm at the Plaza with you."

"For two weeks on twenty-five bucks? Plus train fare and meals? New York's expensive."

"Don't worry. I'll manage." He stroked the soiled ermine tail.

Manage he did. Tony lived in a Y.M.C.A. but he did little more than sleep there. Actually he spent a great deal more time in Aunt Harriet's suite at the Plaza. As I have said, my great-aunt was not a very nice old woman and by no means fun-loving or gay. But she was bored and extremely susceptible to flattery and it was in this territory that Tony scored. He came to call almost daily and always just before lunch, even armed once or twice with a clutch of expiring roses. He complimented her outrageously on her fairly fusty clothes—crackling old mink tippets, dowdy navies and mulberries and bottle greens from McCutcheon's, and some ancient tea gowns by Jessie Franklin Turner—the beauty of her dark, viewless suite and the Cinderella quality of her tiny size-9B foot. The old megalomaniac simpered with delight and often asked me why I hadn't the get-up-and-go of my nice little friend. "He's a Crackerjack!" Aunt Harriet growled pleasurably.

So smitten did Tony seem with Aunt Harriet that he even volunteered to get out of going to holiday parties for the sheer pleasure of spending a little more time in the old harridan's company.

"I'm taking the boy here to see God and Suzanne tonight, not that he knows anything about the theater," Aunt Harriet said one day as she got up from her frugal room-service luncheon (in contrast to her and my poached-egg-and-vegetable plate, Tony had ordered squab and a vanilla soufflé). "Pity you can't join us."

"Gee, what a shame. Susan and God! Gertie Lawrence is one of my mother's dearest friends," Tony said, avoiding my glance. "As a matter of fact, maybe I can. There's this big dance at Sherry's, the Easter Cotillion"—there was no such party—"but I think I can get out of it. I'll just send a note to this girl, Marilyn Rockefeller"—there was no such girl—"if I may."

"Good! You just sit down at the desk there and I'll call the scalper."

Tony scratched off a hasty letter to his family. When I looked for a sheet of writing paper later that afternoon, all of it was gone. But little notes from Tony Vandenberg, written on Plaza stationery, arrived at good finishing schools for some months to come.

The only blight on Tony's visit came when the girl who was going to take him to the Senior Get-Together (a dance almost as chic as the Colony or the Metropolitan; even Greer Perry had to admit that) came down with German measles. Tony's voice from a telephone booth at the Y was a thin, high wail of despair. But he managed to turn defeat into triumph with Aunt Harriet. "Let him go off to his kiddie party," Tony said. "I'm going to take you out on the town tonight."

"Well," Aunt Harriet snapped, "it's nice to know that at least somebody cares what an old lady does with her evenings. I accept."

As I was leaving for the dance, Tony arrived in black tie with a real—not feather—carnation and armed with a box of orchids from the florist in the lobby. (The orchids were a great cause célèbre after Aunt Harriet got the bill for them. I was blamed for them and had to pay her back. But that is another story.)

There was no living with Aunt Harriet the following day. She had dyspepsia and an epic hangover. Between her moans and belches I learned that Tony had taken her to the Pierre for cocktails, to Twenty-one to dine, around Central Park on a romantic jaunt in a hansom cab, and downstairs to the Persian Room for supper and dancing. It had cost her a great deal of money and like the poor relative of nineteenth-century fiction, it was somehow all my fault. "I can't afford these visits of yours," Aunt Harriet said, shifting from one haunch to another and breaking wind. "You take too much advantage of a poor old widow eking out her last days on a miserable little pension."

We wound up the spring holidays with luncheon at the Colony, the only fashionable establishment in New York which Tony had not been able to achieve during his fortnight of free-loading. There was a pretty pantomime over grabbing the check. Aunt Harriet—by this time he was calling her Hattie—got it, just as I got to tip the cloakroom attendant for Tony's pseudo-camel's-hair coat. "Be a good kid, would you, and get this? I haven't anything smaller than a buck." Aunt Harriet kissed him good-by and even shed a tear over his parting. As a farewell gift she gave him a set of gold and diamond cuff links that had belonged to her late husband. Tony, she said, would wear them "with an air." She asked him to stay with her any time—just any time—he happened to be in New York. There was no mention of my returning.

"Hattie's a pretty game old bag," Tony said as we rattled back toward school on the day coach. "Christ but I'm hungry. I wish we'd swiped some rolls from the Colony."

"The dining car's just up ahead. We could get a Coke and a sandwich."

"Can't afford it."

"What do you mean? You said something about having nothing smaller than a dollar."

"That dollar's all I've got left and it's for Seth Winthrop. I borrowed a buck from him more than a month ago and I've got to pay him back."

"Why the sudden attack of ethics? Turning honest in your old age?"

"Haven't you heard? His twin sister is coming out up in Boston this June. The Winthrops are giving this big party at their mansion. After all, Seth and I are old friends. We room together."

"I see."

With his amazing gift for trivia, Tony became a guide to chic New York. He was Jimmy Walker, Grover Whalen, and Mayor LaGuardia rolled into one. In two short weeks he had managed to store away more useless information concerning smart shops, fashionable restaurants, exclusive clubs, and good addresses than the average native New Yorker learns in a lifetime. He was insufferable to perfectly nice boys whose only fault was that they happened to come from places like Philadelphia, Washington, Baltimore, Providence or Boston, or—even worse—the suburbs instead of Manhattan Island. He could and would tell you which was the Good Side of El Morocco, what floor of Brooks Brothers was devoted to tailor-made suits, the age and origin of the merry-go-round horses at Armando's, whether to use the Forty-eighth or Forty-ninth Street door at Hattie Carnegie's—important facts like that. To the gauche and naïve, Tony was very impressive and his shabby little newspaper column began to read like one of the more fulsome issues of *The Park Avenue Social Review* until one outraged alumnus wrote a scathing letter asking if this were the red-blooded alma mater of his boyhood or Miss Hewitt's Classes. As he was a generous contributor, the column was dropped and apparently every boarding school kid in the East was desolate about it except Tony. By then Tony had established himself as the social arbiter of the *jeunesse doré* and inventing further scoops and exclusives had become a drag. He had passed his college boards and had been accepted by Williams with even—God knows why—a small partial scholarship thrown in because of his "journalistic achievements." Williams wasn't quite the Yale or Princeton that Tony had had in mind (Harvard had never appealed to him nor, for that matter, did education) but it had a lingering reputation as a rich boys' college and, for Tony's purposes, it was far better than living at home and going to the University of Chicago or Northwestern. His guns were trained now on Seth Winthrop and on receiving an invitation to Seth's sister's party. The obvious charm Tony exuded made me a little sick, almost as sick as listening to Greer Perry say everything possible to prevent the Winthrops from inviting Tony.

As things turned out, both Greer and Tony were wasting their time. Seth was too nice to be swayed by Greer's slime-slinging and too sensible to be influenced by anything Tony might do or say. Tony shared a room with Seth just as the rest of us did. For some reason, that made him automatically one of Seth's friends and put him automatically on the party list. On the same day,

Tony, Greer, and I each received invitations for Abigail Winthrop's dance and letters from Mrs. Winthrop herself asking us to stay at the house for the weekend of Abigail's launching. Tony was beside himself with joy, and a fast and furious correspondence must have been exchanged with the Vandenbergs again as to the ways and means of Tony's going up to Boston right after commencement.

I was able to deduce this from yet another pink letter sent to me by his mother. "Doctor and I are sure disappointed to miss the graduation excercises, but if we can give Jackie a little pleasure with the money it would cost, I say it's worth it. Enclosed is $5. Please take the poor kid out for a fancy meal right after the graduation and tell him it's from Doctor and I." A crumpled five fell out of the letter and I was all for cramming it down Tony's throat. Word got around school that the Vandenbergs were cruising the Aegean on their yacht.

My own parents were very frank about not being able to come east for the big occasion, especially my father, whose disappointment must have been boundless. As for the visit to the Winthrops, they gave me their permission but no financial backing and I had to pad Greer Perry's final English theme by seven hundred words in order to raise the money to go.

I endured the commencement exercises in the Willingham Chapel, moved only by the joy of knowing that I would never have to return to my father's school again. Tony was fed at the local inn and the next day we made for Boston and what amounted to our debut in real debutante society.

Tony prattled away excitedly about the wide swath he expected to cut, the clothes he was going to wear, the new steps he was going to introduce. Things social had taken such a hold on him that he sounded faintly like a girl anticipating her first dance, but there was something just a little sinister about it. As usual he had come prepared with facts, figures, and estimates as to income and position. It made me feel both uncomfortable and

71

angry to hear him plot his campaign so coldly and I was annoyed that he chose me as his confidant. Perhaps it was because I was the only one of his new friends who knew anything like the truth about him, but I couldn't help wishing that he'd keep his aspirations to himself.

Tony was, if anything, disappointed by his first glimpse of the Winthrop house. Tony had always spoken of it as an estate. The Winthrops called it a farm. He had undoubtedly expected some imposing pile of fake Tudor or bogus Renaissance. Instead, the Winthrops lived in a white clapboard house that had been added to over the centuries as need and affluence dictated until it rambled amiably and exquisitely over the undulating countryside.

Anyone with a practiced eye could tell from the fanlight over the front door, the ancient Chinese wallpaper in the hall, the glowing old furniture on the faded Turkey carpets that it was a gem of a place, marvelously comfortable and unobtrusively elegant with no detail overlooked. It was one American house that my mother would have approved of. If it had been a museum or a movie set, Tony would have liked it a lot better.

Mrs. Winthrop herself greeted us at the door. She was a rawboned handsome woman with her graying hair drawn back in a neat knot. She wore a cotton dress, a cardigan with the sleeves pushed up to her elbows, and pearls—real, I feel certain.

Leading a convoy of silent Irish maids, she brought us to the room we were to share. It was a minor masterpiece in mellow maple and much too good for a couple of punks like us. Nothing had been overlooked, from the silver-backed brushes on the chest of drawers to the vase of fresh field flowers to the carafes of ice water to the embossed letter paper in the Governor Winthrop desk. "I hope you boys will be comfortable here," she said. "If there's anything you want, just ring. Seth and Abby and some of her friends are down at the pond swimming. I know they'd love to have you join them." With that she was gone.

"The old folks at home," Tony said, flopping down on his bed.

"If the Winthrops are supposed to be so damned rich, why don't they spend a little of it?"

"Listen, shit for brains," I snapped, "if you knew your ass from your elbow you'd realize that the bed you're mucking up with your four-ninety-five shoes is worth about ten times as much as anything you've ever seen before. As for the rug you just dropped your ashes on . . ."

"Okay, okay. But you'd think they'd live in something with a little class instead of this old ark. As for Seth's old lady, she didn't look so bad at commencement, but coming to the door in some old housedress and . . ."

"What the hell do you expect, some mausoleum out of the funny papers with a butler in knee breeches and suits of armor standing around the hall?" I realized then that it was just what he had expected so I shut up.

"I guess you'd call the Winthrops kind of conservative," Tony said, blowing a cloud of smoke upwards through the net canopy.

"I guess you would," I said, as I began unpacking my clothes.

"You know that new book about Boston that everybody's talking about—'The Late John Something'?"

"*The Late George Apley?* Sure. I've got a copy right here."

"Let me look at it, would you?"

"You going to lie around reading a book on a beautiful day like this? Seth and a whole bunch of dames are down there swimming."

"Don't wait around for me. I'll be along in a little while. Oh, and just reach me my good luck charm, would you?" As I started down to the brook, Tony was curled up on his bed flipping through the pages of *The Late George Apley*. "Be seeing you," I said. He didn't even hear me.

My enormous admiration of Seth Winthrop had been the deciding factor in my coming to Boston. I had never met his twin sister, his family, his friends, and had no expectation of cutting any ice with them at all. I was not disappointed. With the prewar xenophobia of Boston society, they tended to look upon all outsiders with the darkest suspicion and even—to a certain extent—among the young, anything that smacked of extravagance or frivolity was considered not quite nice. Greer Perry, to my surprise, was doing none too well. He was, if anything, too obviously rich, too New York smart haberdasher to fit in comfortably and his white satin bathing trunks, disclosing a slight roll of blubber at the waistband, were regarded with obvious disapproval, although Seth's Boston friends were far too well mannered to say anything about them. Standing there in my drab navy blue shorts and an old Basque shirt, while Seth made punctilious introductions, I realized that for once I was going to fit in, sartorially speaking, far better than my more stylish classmates.

Abigail Winthrop, a pretty version of Seth, had been sent to Foxcroft (a false note; one would have expected Emma Willard) and so had the handmaidens who surrounded her. Being in Virginia, Foxcroft was too far removed from our school for us to have had any contact. All I knew about the place was that it was the most expensive of all girls' schools, surely the most uncomfortable, and a place where the horse was worshipped second only to God. As the owner of a fifteen-dollar Palomino pony, I achieved a brief celebrity among Abigail's horsy chums, chatting a little self-consciously about gaits and heaves and spavins until I became conscious of a rapt silence. Following the general gaze, I saw Tony approaching the pond.

As he had done so often at school, Tony had counted too heavily on the hurried skimming of a book, his ermine-tail talisman, charm and bluff to carry him through. If he had mounted the Winthrops' staircase as the breezy boy from the Windy City, he descended it as a Proper Bostonian straight out of vaudeville, complete to a copy of *Walden* under one arm.

Pulitzer Prize winner or not, *The Late George Apley* had been inadequate as the textbook to transform Tony into a Bay Colony blueblood. Like me, Tony had had only three months' experience in polite society and that on the subdeb circuit and only in New

York where Society was a little less polite and lot more fun. If he had only been bright enough to be himself he might have injected a shot of real adrenalin into Abigail Winthrop's non-cohesive group of guests, for Tony could be both amusing and charming. As it was, he was ludicrous.

When he remembered, his A's broadened, his speech became a pained drawl, and his old bounce was drowned in a languorous lassitude. Names dropped like autumn leaves—Cabot, Lodge, Saltonstall, Adams, Winslow, Sears, Otis, Gardiner: all the most obvious choices. At first Seth Winthrop laughed good-naturedly, assuming, I suppose, that this was some sort of elaborate gag planned by Tony to enliven a fairly drooping circle, but when there was no let-up even Seth fell into an embarrassed silence.

"It's the Society for the Preservation of New England Antiquuities," somebody said. There was laughter—more laughter than the remark warranted—and they were laughing at, not with, Tony. Still he did not stop. Names fell thicker and faster. The Vandenbergs, I learned, were really an old Boston family who had settled in Chicago just after the Civil War and to my horror I discovered that Tony was claiming relationship to half the Brahmins of Beacon Hill. In a place as inbred and incestuous as Boston it was an egregious error.

". . . my cousin Carleton," Tony was saying. "I must look him up while I'm here."

"Look him up?" Abigail asked blandly.

"Yes. It's been ages since I've seen him."

"I should think it had been."

"Of course we lunched together this winter."

"Did you now? In what cemetery? He was Pa's uncle and he's been dead since 1928."

"I didn't mean the old Carleton. I meant Carleton, junior."

"That's odd. Uncle Carleton was a bachelor."

The young people around the pond snickered audibly and Greer Perry's face was a study. Seth, always the good egg, changed the subject to the horse he had been given as a graduation gift.

Not satisfied to sit back and listen, Tony, unaware that riding is to Foxcroft what beer is to Milwaukee, lunged into the conversation with a full-blown account of the Vandenberg stables—the hunters, the racers, the polo ponies. A malicious look went around the group. Questions were put to Tony that would have stumped a jockey, and the harder he tried to bluff his way out, the deeper in he got. Greer Perry reintroduced the nickname Phony, this time aloud. It was taken up and used openly for the rest of the weekend.

And at dinner that night Tony also proved himself wanting. His entanglements with the beau monde had been confined to public restaurants and large dances heretofore, but confronted with the artichoke and the finger bowl, Tony was at a decided disadvantage. He very nearly strangled on the former until Mrs. Winthrop, kindness itself, reached out with her own knife and fork and performed the proper surgery. At dessert, Tony was so busy impressing her with his great friendship with Dr. Koussevitsky that he helped himself to a meringue and dropped it with an enormous splash into his finger bowl. The table was in an uproar. Tony's message had made the rounds.

In the horrid way that people have of excluding someone they sense to be an outsider, the party broke down into impervious little groups after dinner. Filled with high spirits and bravado, Tony moved from one to another, but at the bridge table the three inept players who had been talking and joking and forgetting what happened to be trump when I had bid a small slam were suddenly deep in concentration when Tony appeared. A game of backgammon miraculously became a lifelong vendetta not to be interrupted by conversation or kibitzing. A dumpy girl devoid of looks or charm discovered upon Tony's approach that she had to retire immediately to write to a mother who lived a scant ten miles away. Greer Perry even said, "Look, Vandenberg, Mary Elizabeth and I have a lot to catch up on. So, if you don't mind . . ." Mr. and Mrs. Winthrop finally took pity on him, but Tony's conversation was perhaps too highfalutin for a man who wore leather patches on his elbows and called himself a farmer. After a few mystifying statements from Tony about the senior Vandenbergs sailing to Mexico City on their yacht, Mr. Winthrop explained that he was an early riser and excused himself. His wife was not long in following. After that, Tony counterfeited a consuming interest in a copy of Miss Edith Wharton's *The Age of Innocence* and slumped on a sofa in the library pretending to read it. When I went upstairs to bed, Tony was sleeping—or a reasonable facsimile thereof.

The house was abustle the following day with florists and caterers coming and going, with a dance floor, a marquee, and a bandshell being erected to the ruination of the Winthrops' velvet lawn. Seth's mother, again in a cotton dress and pushed-up sweater, announced that the young people could do whatever they wanted as long as they did it elsewhere. An outing on horseback with a picnic to be consumed as far from the house as possible was her suggestion. It was eagerly taken up, especially by the Foxcroft girls who gushed away about Miss Charlotte and the Santini seat until even I felt a little apprehensive about riding forth in their exclusively equestrian company. "I can't wait to see you in the saddle, Phony," Greer said.

But Tony had other plans for the day—a relative to be visited in Boston. Like a fool he added that it was a Saltonstall, which caused Mrs. Winthrop to put down her list of urgent errands attendant to Abby's dinner dance and analyze the exact degree of kinship. It was pathetic to hear Tony trying to wriggle out of his preposterous lie and he was rescued only by the arrival of a sealed package from Shreve, Crump & Low—a small string of pearls for the debutante from her godmother. By the time the shriekings of "Oh, how divine!" were over, Tony had telephoned for a taxi and had extricated himself for the day.

It was late when he returned with half a dozen mysterious packages under his arm.

"Where have you been all day?" I asked.

"Brooks Brothers."

"Does Boston have one?"

"Certainly."

"Well, you missed a great outing. Abby's pals ride like Comanches and . . ."

"Good. Now if you don't mind getting the hell out of here, I think I'll dress for this hick-town shindig."

"What do you mean hick-town shindig? It's going to be a terrific party. The governor's coming and the ambassador to . . ."

"I'd like to know just what the hell you know about a decent coming-out party, cowboy."

Resisting the obvious answer, I tied my tie, put on my dinner jacket, and went downstairs. Abby Winthrop's party looked very decent indeed. No Babylonian excesses, but no corners cut either. Flowers were everywhere. A big orchestra and a small relief band kept the music going incessantly out on the lawn and, for good measure, a popular Harvard boy, whose position that evening was a nebulous combination of guest and performer, hammered out old show tunes on the piano in the music room. Waiters loaded down with champagne were forever at one's elbow and the Winthrop maids in full force circulated with canapés. If there was something wrong with this party, I couldn't imagine what it was.

Looking around at the assembled guests and their party get-ups, however, I was reminded a little of the annual evening entertainment my parents held for the gentry of Santa Fe. I mean the whole affair would have been better if they had all taken a little more trouble with their dress. As shabby as his standards were, Tony did have a small point about Nice Boston on a spree. Abby received with her parents, and as rich and grand as they were, there was a decided air of the jumble sale about them. Pretty Miss Winthrop wore a dress which everyone in the family said had been made for her great-grandmother by the House of Worth. There was no reason to doubt it. Its lace was the color of an old horse's tooth and it kept shedding seed pearls as though they were meant to be favors for the guests. During the evening the whole rig began to disintegrate so alarmingly that Abby was sent upstairs to change into something less venerable but more practical. Mr. Winthrop was got up in a yellowing old mess jacket and pumps more down-at-the-heel than even my father's. The hostess was a blaze of jewels (even at seventeen, I just knew that Mrs. Winthrop wasn't the sort who would wear paste) in a high-rumped old evening dress that seemed to be made out of curtain material. Except for the youngsters, who hadn't had sufficient time for their clothes to develop the patina of ages, the rest of the guests were dressed to match. While I confess to being a trifle disappointed, I felt right at home in my Rogers Peet Prep Department dinner jacket; more at home, say, than Perry who was got up in a pristine white sharkskin jacket with red cummerbund and matching tie. Greer was also more than a little drunk, eyes glazed and swaying slightly.

Tony's Grand Entrance—that is the only word for it—occurred late and during a lull in the general hubbub. It was right out of the last act of *Easy Virtue*. He appeared at the top of the Winthrops' imposing stairway in white tie and tails and for some reason—don't ask me why—an opera cape with a scarlet lining. To compound the felony, he carried a top hat, an ebony stick, and white kid gloves. The houseful of people stood in shocked silence as he made his way downward.

On the fourth step from the bottom, one of Tony's brand-new pumps slid on the stair carpet, his feet shot out from under him, and one shoe flew through the air, landing with a clatter on the floor below. With a terrible sound of splintering wood, Tony grabbed at the banister and saved himself from falling into the crowd below, but three of the balusters of that ancient staircase were ruined forever. There was a sound of applause. It was Greer Perry. Mystified but dutifully, the rest of the Winthrops' guests joined in. "Ladies and gentlemen," Greer bawled, slurring his words badly, "introducing Phony Vandenberg the Great, who will entertain us with feats of legerdemain." Some of the young people, particularly the members of the house party who by now quite disliked Tony, laughed. Nobody else did. Greer's was the sort of stunt that might have gone over in New York. It only perplexed Boston.

"Mr. Vandenberg," Mrs. Winthrop said, rising above the damage to her stairway, "I do hope you haven't hurt yourself."

She was interrupted by Greer who lurched up and, with a flick, undid Tony's white tie. "Phony, old boy, white tie after April and in the country? Impossible! Or is this what you wear to the B'Nai B'Rith ball?"

"Shut up, Greer," I said.

Tony looked as though he had been struck. His ostentatious costume among the soft shirts and greenish old dinner suits of rural New England was bad enough without this frontal attack by Greer Perry. Even Tony, after what had been an outstandingly unsuccessful two days, hadn't the gall to carry it off.

Not satisfied with being sensationally unamusing, Greer fingered the material of Tony's lapel and said in a terrible Yiddish accent, "Det's a nice piece goods, Abie."

"Stop it, Greer," Seth said.

Mrs. Winthrop, forever the great lady, stepped into the fray. "Mr. Vandenberg, may I introduce . . . Oh, but of course you know Dr. Koussevitsky."

The reunion never took place. "Excuse me," Tony said. He turned and bolted up the stairs, his one shoe slipping and sliding on the carpet. Dinner was announced.

The marquee on the lawn was filled with tables for ten. There were only nine at one of them. Tony did not appear for the rest of the evening. It was after three o'clock when the party broke up. When I went upstairs to our bedroom it looked as though the secret police had raided it. Dresser drawers were open, hangers were strewn all over the floor, and the closet had been stripped of all but my own poor duds. There was no sign of Tony. The wastebasket was filled with crumpled wrapping paper, messy nests of twine, and a dozen cardboard price tags each reading "Filene's Basement."

IV ♥

TONY

at arms

Going to different colleges, Tony and I had little contact during
the next four or five years. Our meetings were infrequent and
they took place mostly at holiday dances in New York. In those
days any male enrolled in a "good" college had no trouble getting
onto every canned debutante list in the city. In fact, it was
difficult to stay off them and, in cold cash, the free liquor and
groceries which a boy could consume during a season were worth
about a thousand dollars even then. Some sort of dreary ethic
kept me from going to a dance unless I actually knew the girl
who was giving it. Not so Tony. He was seen everywhere except
at rare parties such as Rosemary Warburton's where, for some
quaint old-fashioned notion, it was considered proper for the
guests to be at least vaguely known to the girl's family.

After his total defeat in Boston, Tony went at society as though it were the First Crusade. Somehow and somewhere he had boned up on every last fine point of etiquette no matter how archaic, and I marveled to hear him mouth such outmoded bylaws of the game as "White tie after the Horse Show," "Red carnation only with black tie," "One says whisky and soda, never highball," or "You never notice the clothes on a really well-dressed man." Bit by bit he had been able to drop the pretense of wealth. Those who had heard of it and believed in it accommodated Tony by spreading the great lie with nothing lost in the telling. Those, like Greer Perry, who couldn't or wouldn't credit it, talked just as much. It created a controversial figure of Tony and the actual truth made very little difference to him or to his present social set. He was being talked about and that was what was important.

I, too, heard less from Tony than about him. For a year or so he took the greatest possible advantage of my Aunt Harriet's weakness for flattery, stopping with her at the Plaza while I holed up at the Y. But after borrowing fifty dollars which he never repaid, running her telephone bill up to an astronomical figure, and meeting some far more prominent people with comfortable guest rooms in large apartments and townhouses, Tony began stopping elsewhere.

Money? It began to be more abundant when Dr. Vandenberg switched to orthodontia and moved his practice to a prosperous suburb. Tony was also able to convince a couple of decidedly second-string gossip writers that he was as thick as thieves with the young smart set and he received five dollars for every juicy item he supplied—not, unfortunately, always true—which was printed. His photograph began to appear with monotonous regularity in magazines like Life, Look, Click, and Peek doing the Big Apple and the Lambeth Walk, swallowing goldfish and masticating phonograph records. For the millions who didn't know, Tony Vandenberg was old-line society and flaming youth rolled into one adorable bundle. It took a whole world war to halt his progress. And even then World War II furnished a sort of international playground for our boy.

There had been a fairly colorless kid at school named Bashforth. A class behind Tony and me, he had followed Tony to Williams. Bashforth was totally unexceptional but for being very rich and for having a grandmother who was even richer, slightly eccentric, and titled.

Lady ffynche (that's right, two small f's) had, at the turn of the century, been an apple-cheeked Swedish girl from Minneapolis whose father had amassed enough money to buy her a peer for a husband. "A very old title," my mother had said, "but always poor as churchmice." The historic ffynche poverty ended with the Minneapolis misalliance and over years of marriage and widowhood, Lady ffynche had become as much a symbol of England as Queen Mother Mary herself, emulating that great dowager even to the toque hat and the dubonnet Daimler. She was not, however, a staunch enough Briton to withstand the rigors of total war. With the first blitzkrieg Lady ff. shot back to America and set up a sort of unofficial British Embassy in her apartment at the Marguery. Not Winston Churchill, not even my mother could hope to compete with Lady ffynche in pure, unadulterated Englishness. Bundles for Britain and the English-Speaking Union were as nothing compared to the Anglo-American alliances formed and supported by the Anne Morgan of Minneapolis. With money to burn, with a few genuinely important contacts in London and Washington, and with unlimited chutzpah, Lady ffynche was not long in forming an international monument to herself, the ffynche Fund for Comforts Overseas. Like the Red Cross, the American Field Service, the Y.M.C.A., and the Salvation Army, the ffynche Fund had quasi-military status, but unlike those other valiant bodies of unarmed volunteers, it served no known useful function other than to hog up a lot of press coverage for Lady ffynche and the more colorful of her recruits.

It was the kind of organization that had received so much publicity that whenever it was mentioned people automatically

83

said, "Oh yes," for fear of being thought ignorant of burning current issues, although few knew exactly what the hell it did do. The alleged function of the ffynche Fund was to furnish free candy, cigarettes, sewing kits, and entertainment to the Allied troops fighting in the Western Desert, and a lot of blood-and-guts stories with titles like "Bringing the Ballet to Tobruk" were written by a paid press agent in New York and planted in such mass media as *Collier's* and *Liberty* with appropriately dramatic illustrations of Lady ffynche's fleet of Ford trucks making their fearless way through a perfect inferno of exploding shells. By the time the United States entered the fray, the ffynche Fund was too respectable—as well as too small—to attract the notice of any prying senator in Washington.

Concurrently with the establishment of the ffynche Fund and the Selective Service Act, Tony Vandenberg became a good deal fonder of Lady ffynche's drab grandson than anyone would have had reason to expect. Not only did they suddenly begin to share rooms at Williams but Lady ffynche's opulent apartment in the Marguery became Tony's home away from home. Well versed in the arts of pleasing rich old ladies, it was not long before Tony had carte blanche in the Marguery restaurant (he took me there to lunch one day) and became what Lady ffynche described as "a puffeckly splendid sawt of Ameddican boy—top drawer—just the sawt of chep I want over theah with the Fund."

Tony graduated from college in June of 1941, as did I, splendidly educated but unprepared to earn a living. With his draft board and the still swollen rolls of the unemployed yawning before him, it was not surprising to read in Cholly Knickerbocker's column that "the buds of Gotham are all drooping with the news that popular Williams grad J. Anthony ('Tony') Vandenberg has turned his back on the social whirl to go overseas as a volunteer in the fashionable ffynche Fund on bare subsistence pay. His destination is secret. Bon voyage and bon chance, Tony! We wish there were thousands more like you." His "bare subsistence pay" amounted to a hundred dollars a month plus full keep and uniforms from Brooks—or a better deal than he could possibly hope to find in the job market in 1941. (Lady ffynche had rather inflated ideas of what life's meanest necessities cost.) His destination was about as secret as the pyramids. The ffynche Fund, like the war itself, was in Cairo by then. From his first-class quarters on a brightly illuminated hospital ship, Tony graciously granted an important exclusive interview to *Park East Magazine* for which he was very British, very secretive, and very, very brave. By the time Pearl Harbor was attacked Tony was established on the banks of the Nile, discomfited by neither the sound of gunfire nor compulsory military training.

My next meeting with Tony took place on the veranda of the old—the *real*—Shepheard's Hotel in the spring of 1943. Africa was virtually in the hands of the Allies by then, and short of drinking and some administrative work, there was nothing much doing in Cairo. It had become one teeming rest camp, as I suppose it must have been for Tony all along. At least he didn't *look* especially war-torn. Instead, he looked like a caricature by Osbert Lancaster. Fascinated, I watched his royal progress up the steps of the veranda. He had grown a brick-red mustache that, when waxed, had a wing span of nine inches. His uniform, even in a city of staggering turn-outs, was stunning in the truest sense of the word. The ffynche Fund, being technically a civilian body with officers' privileges grudgingly granted to its personnel, had no required official uniform and in a city like Cairo, overflowing with officers' shops and little hole-in-the-wall tailors and shirt-makers, Tony had gone wild. "Merry Widow" Aussie hats, thirty-mission Air Force caps, berets, kepis, and highland bonnets were his to choose from and he had chosen at least one of each. When I first saw him he was in his most British phase—pale suède desert boots, smartly tapered shorts, a Sam Browne belt, an ascot, a fly swish, and a solar topee. On each of his shoulders were two pips, very British Army looking which, on closer scrutiny, turned out to be the cuff buttons from our boarding school blazer. He was very suntanned and the shorts showed off a pair of nicely muscled calves.

Nodding curtly to the waiters, bowing amiably to a Greek brigadier general, Tony marched across Shepheard's veranda with his nose in the air. The temptation was too much. I stuck my foot out into the gangway and Tony fell flat.

We had a lot to catch up on. Tony, naturally, did most of the talking and it was fascinating to listen to. Not that his conversation was especially interesting. It was the delivery. The *eether, tomayto,* and *rether* of Chicago had become *eyether, tomahto,* and *rahther.* What he had to say seemed miraculously tailored to include such disparate Briticisms as contróversy, labóratory, aluminium, and petrol, although his speech pattern lacked consistency throughout. He slapped back three drinks at terrifying speed and then looked at his watch. It was one of those elaborate and expensive chronometers that tells the second, the minute, the hour, the day, the month—everything but the time of your next bowel movement—and said, "Great Scott! Nearly time for monger. Do come back to HQ with me. I don't eat there often but Lady Effeff has found a smashing chef and they lay on a fust-rate spread."

The ffynche Fund was housed in an impressive building of Franco-Egyptian-rococo persuasion in the Garden City district. The place looked like an old embassy which, indeed, it was. There were a couple of jeeps, a staff car, and one of the ffynche Fund's Ford trucks in the courtyard. A sleepy Egyptian in coveralls was tinkering with the motor of one of them. Adjacent was a tiny office, empty. A bulletin board hanging over a desk delivered the information that one truck was in Palestine with a folk music group, that another was in Syria with chocolate, that someone was in hospital with malaria, and that somebody named Purdom was on leave in Beirut.

"Sorry, old man," Tony said, leaping between me and the bulletin board, "but you really shouldn't be reading this. Classified, you know."

86

"It looks very important," I said.

"Come along and I'll introduce you to the other types."

Except for the unoccupied office and the vehicles in the courtyard, there was no evidence of any activity whatsoever. I followed Tony through a series of cavernous rooms, sumptuously furnished and echoing with emptiness, into a sort of palm court where half a dozen volunteers of the ffynche Fund, each dressed in a different combination of Allied uniforms, were slopping down gin and lime. From an adjoining room one young man was having a difficult time in French on the telephone with what turned out to be a belly dancer he either was or was not sleeping with. I couldn't be sure. Eventually one of many Egyptian servants announced luncheon.

The table was presided over by Lady ffynche's first in command—an old English auntie with a hyphenated name who had been a chorus boy in one of André Charlot's revues, secretary to Sybil Colefax, and co-owner of a tea room-cum-antique shop in Brighton. His qualifications hardly seemed suitable for heading a compassionate unit charged with dispensing millions of dollars' worth of aid, but a bit later I decided that as far as the ffynche Fund was concerned, they were perfect. Luncheon consisted of hors d'oeuvres, sole with crayfish sauce, salad, a vanilla mousse, and white wine. The horrors of war! At the end of the meal the commander-in-chief of the ffynche Fund rose and his underlings straggled to their feet in a halfhearted attempt at respect. "Sit down, girls," he said. "I'm off for my massage." Addressing me he said, "There's the most divine Turkish bath on the Sharia Sharkis. D'you know it at all?" He winked broadly.

"Afraid not. I just got here."

"Pity. Well, do try to dine with us tonight. We're having chocolate soufflé."

"Will you be using the staff car?" Tony asked.

"No, darling. I thought I'd hire a carriage. It's so *fin de siècle*. À *bientôt*, dears." One earnest young man, a conscientious

87

objector from Sewickly, bristled with indignation. The rest took it as a matter of course.

"Well, I'd better be going and let you get on with—with whatever you have to do, Tony."

"Oh, not at all. Where are you staying?"

"At the Y.M.C.A. I have just a week's leave and . . ."

"The Y? What can it be like?"

"You certainly ought to know, Tony."

"But you can't possibly bunk there with a lot of American GI's. Tell you what, why don't we go off to the Gezira Spawting Club for a quick bathe, then we can collect your gear and I'll put you up in my digs?"

"Here?"

"Good God no! I can't bear sharing a bahth. I've taken a little flat on the Kornish el Nil—just along the embankment here. Nice view."

Tony's apartment looked like a Shriners' convention hall, dancing with tile, filigree, mosaic, and mushrabia work. There were potted palms, brass trays, hassocks, ottomans, camel saddles, and divans covered with oriental rugs. It seemed large for one person and very, very grand. Tony clapped his hands imperiously. A servant wearing a red fez and a long white galabia darted in. Tony rattled off something that was a mixture of English, French, and Arabic. "Mustafa will put your kit in Tatty's room."

"Tatty?"

"Tatham Purdom, the chap with whom I share this flat. An Ameddican. He's our music expert. Southern. Fine old family and really out of the top drawer in spite of going to Juilliard."

"You're sure I won't be putting him out?"

"Not a bit of it, old man. He *is* out. Tatty's been in a bit of a flap lately. Just put him on the train for Beirut and a spot of rest."

"Wounded?"

"No, gyppy tummy. What would you like to drink? I've

Scotch, Irish, gin, and a fairish *eau de vie*." We sat out on Tony's terrace watching the little feluccas sail up and down the Nile as the sun sank behind the desert. It occurred to me that Tony had been away from his job most of the day. "Don't you have to be getting back to the ffynche Fund?" I asked.

"Whatever for?"

"Well, I don't know. At least for a chocolate soufflé."

"Oh dear me no. I rarely dine with the mess. Mary's likely to get her nose wet and things become too sticky for words. That's why Tatty and I moved out."

"Mary?"

"The C.-in-C.—our leader. You met him today. Frightfully amusing, rilly, but unless he's got a date . . ."

"Oh. But you mustn't let me keep you from your work."

"But you're not at all, dear boy."

"Is this some sort of holiday?"

"Not a bit of it. I'm simply waiting about for transport back to Blighty."

"Where?"

"Blighty. The U.K. London. Lady Effeff has a smashing house there. Belgravia. I've got this do with Edith Sitwell."

"With Edith Sitwell? What for?"

"Why, to entertain our brave boys at the front, naturally. What else?"

"Singing? Dancing? Bumps and grinds?"

"Oh dear no. Reading her poetry—*Façade* and that sort of thing. Lady Effeff is frightfully keen on raising the standards of entertainment. She wants T. S. Eliot, G.B.S., Angna Enters, Raymond Duncan—people of that caliber."

"Don't you think the Tommies would be a little happier with something along the lines of Gracie Fields?"

"Well, yes and no. Tatty was the first to bring chamber music to the Western Desert. Monteverdi. Lady Effeff was ever so pleased."

"Were the troops?"

"It was an interesting experiment." Quickly changing the subject, Tony said, "It's nearly dark now. Where would you like to dine? La Taverna? The Petit Coin de France? The Continental-Savoy? I'll tell you what, we could go to Les Ambassadeurs. It's a bit like the Versailles in New York. Goodish cabaret. Quite the smartest spot in town next to Shepheard's and not so many bloody Yanks. Wait, I'll book a table."

While Tony was changing for dinner—U.S. Army pinks, Guards' cutaway dress jacket, French kepi, bronze chukka boots, and swagger stick—I discovered that the last of my cigarettes was gone. "Could I bum a cigarette, Tony, until I can buy some?"

"*Buy* them? Don't talk such utter madness. Here, take one of these. They're Fuad Premier Dorés. You may not like them." I didn't. They were long, thick, gold-tipped ovals that tasted like camel dung. "Then I'll fix you up with whatever you like." He unlocked the door to what I'd suspected was a cupboard. It wasn't. It was an entire room, larger than any in his flat, piled to the ceiling with cases of cigarettes and chocolate. "What do you fancy—Luckies, Camels, Chesterfields, Old Golds, Kools? Or perhaps you prefer British. I've Players, Gold Flakes, State Express, Benson & Hedges, Peter Jacksons. . . ."

"What's this—the ffynche Fund warehouse?"

"You might say that," Tony said with a little smile. "Here, give me a hand with a couple of these crates, there's a good fellow."

When Tony, reeking of musk, was completely satisfied with the splendor of his costume and the luster of his hair, he tucked a long, flat gold cigarette case into his breast pocket and a scented handkerchief into one sleeve. Then he jabbered something incomprehensible to Mustafa and supervised the loading of four cases of American cigarettes and five jerry cans filled with gasoline—forgive me, petrol—into the trunk of the ffynche Fund staff car. "Good-oh," he said. "Off to Les A!"

For quite the smartest spot in Cairo, Les Ambassadeurs struck me as being located in a fairly woebegone neighborhood as Tony steered the car into a dark little cul de sac. "Is this it?" I asked.

"Les Ambassadeurs? Certainly not. Just sit tight. A little business to transact." Tony disappeared into a sinister-looking doorway. In a few moments some even more sinister-looking Egyptians unloaded the trunk of the car. I waited apprehensively and, for something to do, opened the package of cigarettes which Tony had given me. They were Lucky Strikes and under the cellophane wrapping had been inserted a neat card:

Thumbs up!
A gift to the ffynche Fund
with best wishes from
THE GARDEN CLUB OF GARRISON, N.Y.

Tony reappeared with a fistful of Egyptian pounds and piasters. "Do you know Alex at all, old man?"

"Alex who?"

"Alexandria."

"No. I came by way of Suez."

"Like to go tomorrow—just overnight? I've a spot of business there."

I was awakened at dawn the next morning by a bumping and thumping and, from the street below, Tony yelling shrilly at Mustafa. Looking down from my window, I saw one of the ffynche Fund trucks being loaded. On my way to the bathroom I noticed that the door to the storeroom was open and that the room beyond was empty.

Breakfast was served on the terrace—café au lait, croissants, brioches, and rose-petal jam from Groppi's. For so flamboyant a dresser, Tony today was wearing something that looked almost like mufti. He was frenetically gay but I sensed a certain nervousness beneath his chatter. He kept looking at his glittering golden wristwatch and at last he said, "Now we can go. The Rollo Bank will be open."

"What's so special about the Rollo Bank? Going to pull a heist?"

Tony looked stunned for a second and then he laughed. "It's simply that I want to put some money into my account. I hate carrying a lot of currency. These wogs would as soon rob you blind as . . ."

"From the way you live I shouldn't think that excess cash would be much of a problem."

"Well, now that I'm past twenty-one my trustees send a bit over from time to time. Just pocket money, you know."

"In cold cash? By V-Mail?" Then I gave it up. The tried and true old photographs of Lochby Court, of Rose Vandenberg in ermine, of the cars, were scattered about the salon of Tony's apartment, this time in silver picture frames. I supposed that six thousand miles away from the dismal truth, the Vandenberg legend was flourishing again.

Tony flipped one of his gold-tipped cigarettes over the railing. "Got her! Well! Shall we be off? All packed? Dress uniform? Plenty of bathing costumes . . ."

"I have only one."

"I can lend you some. Let's be gone."

Tony gave me explicit instructions for guarding the truck and its cargo while he put his money into the bank. Then we were away from Cairo streaking northward across the desert. Unlike its Humber staff car, the ffynche Fund's trucks were uncomfortable and hot as hell. After jolting along the macadam highway for nearly two hours I spotted a large N.A.A.F.I. canteen marked "Halfway House." Dying from heat and thirst I said, "Here's a place we can stop. I'll sock you to a beer or tea or anything else you like."

"Capital idea, old man," Tony said. He slowed down the truck and began turning into the car park. It was filled with British M.P. jeeps. Spewing a shower of gravel, the truck lurched, gained speed, and then bounded back onto the Alexandria road. I was thrown first against the door and then against Tony. He was a livid color.

"Hey, what's the matter?"

"Oh, I forgot. It's a frightful place. Ghastly. We're nearly at Alex anyhow."

"Yeah. Just about eighty-five more miles, or one hundred and twenty-seven kilometers if that signpost can be believed."

"Tell me," Tony said, "what do you hear from any of the kids from school?"

The ffynche Fund in Alexandria was a far cry from the establishment in Cairo. It was, Tony told me as he stopped the truck, manned by one volunteer—a real misfit from a London council school, a fanatic whom nobody could stand.

"Don't worry," I said. "You needn't introduce me."

"That's just it. You're going to have to introduce yourself. The bloke is named Epply. Most unattractive. It's all on the troisième étage—that's the third floor," he translated considerately. "The door's always open. Oh, and be a good fellow and don't tell Epply about the truck. Just say we came by train or got a lift or something like that. I'll be back in about half an hour."

"Can't I give you a hand with all those cigarettes and chocolate bars?"

"I wouldn't think of imposing, old man. Anyhow, certain security measures must be observed. Cheerio!"

The building was squalid and a beehive of activity. All the doors were open and the noise was overpowering. On the ground floor a Dr. Maloof, Dental Surgeon, was pulling a tooth, apparently without anesthetic to judge from the screaming; on the first floor a baby was wailing and an unseen couple were having a real set-to in Greek; the second floor featured one radio broadcast in French and from the set across the hall a plaintive love song in Arabic, both loud; on the third floor one of the genteel voices of B.B.C. was announcing the correct Greenwich time. Across the landing, from behind a scabrous door bearing an elegant sign

"The ffynche Fund for Overseas Comforts—Alexandria H.Q."
an ailing gramophone was playing the Don Cossacks' recording of
"It's a Long Vay [sic] to Tipperary." The door was ajar. I
knocked. It swung wide on its sprung hinges. The room looked
empty so I walked in.

As I entered from the hall, the "bloke named Epply" came
into the room from a rickety balcony overhanging the street.
"Most unattractive" barely began to describe him. He was albino
blond, very tall, and very thin except for a pendulous little pot
belly. He walked with a stoop and his legs had a tendency to
bow. His skin was milk white peppered with angry red pustules.
Plagued with adenoids, his thickish lips were always parted,
displaying a disordered set of large, yellow teeth. He was dressed,
if you can call it that, in a set of British-issue mesh underwear
which hung on him like a camouflage net.

" 'Oo are you?" he asked.

I told him and then said, "You must be Epply. I've just come
for the day with Tony Vandenberg. He'll be along shortly."

"What'd he do with the lorry?"

"Lorry? What lorry? We came by train. The Royal Egyptian."

"Don't give me that. I saw the lorry with my own eyes and I
know where that fancy Yank's goin' with it, too. To flog a load of
cigs and Cadbury's just like 'e always does. I suppose you're in on
it, too."

"I really don't know what you're talking about," I said.

"Hah!" Epply snorted eloquently. He shut off the music with a
screeching of the needle against the record. "If I 'ad my way
about it, I'd turn the 'ole lot of you in, that's what I'd do. The
workers back in civvy street doing without so a lot of layabouts
down in Cairo can swank about getting rich off the sweat of their
toil."

"Mind if I sit down?"

"Suit yourself, bloody Yank. I come all the way to fucking
Egypt expecting to do something for the Tommies and what do I
get? I ask you, what do I get?"

"I have no idea."

"Bloody fuck-all, that's what. Sit around in this stinkin' wog flat for six bloody months like the forgotten man. Supposed to be passing out cigs for the troops and I haven't hardly had a packet of V's to smoke myself."

"I have some Luckies if you'd care to . . ."

"I've got to get on with my washing." He slammed out of the room. I was pleased and surprised to know that anything around the place, including its tenant, had ever seen soap and water. He was certainly a change from the orchidaceous group of ffynche Fund followers in Cairo. It was not difficult to see why he didn't care for them and vice versa.

Looking about the sordid little room I saw a mug of cold milky tea, a soiled shirt which Epply probably did not consider dirty enough to launder, Epply's unmade bed, some phonograph albums of Leadbelly, the Almanac Singers, and the Chorus of the Abraham Lincoln Brigade, an untidy row of books featuring the works of Marx, Engels, Lenin, Silone, and other companions of the left hand, and a lot of flies. My only conclusion was that Lady ffynche and Volunteer Epply had been drawn to one another sight unseen.

"Six bloody months," Epply shouted, slapping through the room with a handful of dripping socks, "of doing nothing but maintaining my vehicle"—he pronounced it "veetle"—"while the rest of them toffs in GHQ play at being officers. Now if anyone in the Red Army . . ."

"Epply, dear boy!" It was Tony. He had changed his clothes somewhere and now wore breeches, boots, and a bush jacket.

"Oh, it's you, Vandenberg, with another load of cigs to sell. You and your whole rotten class make me sick to my . . ."

"Epply! Have you taken leave of your senses? My friend here and I hitched a ride to Alex simply to deliver your mail. And here it is—The London Daily Worker, a letter from the Bermondsey Boys for Social Action, two issues of The Young Marxist, and one or two personal things."

"Gimme those."

"What's the magic word?"

"I'll magic word your arse. And where's the lorry and the supplies I been writing for ever since . . ."

"Lorry? What lorry? I told you, my dear Epply, that we came by . . ."

"I saw it with me own eyes while I was 'anging out my wash."

"Hhhhhanging, Epply, hhhhhanging. Now let's try it again, Eliza. In Hhhhhhereford, Hhhhhuntingdon, and Hhhhhhamp-shire hhhhhurricanes hhhhardly ever hhhhhappen."

"Come off it! Where's my rations?"

"Rations, Epply? *Rations?* You're only issued rations if you're out in the blue. You know that. Pretty soft life you've got here, I should say."

"*Soft?* Nothing to do and nothing to eat."

"You're to mess with the Coldstream Guards. Splendid bunch."

"Pack of bloody snobs. I'd almost rather take my monger with you do-nothings in Cairo."

"And our meals are miserable without you, Epply. You *know* they are."

"Now what about the lorry? I seen it, I tell you."

"Well, yes you did, Epply. But it wasn't a lorry with supplies from Cairo. I was sent up here to collect this one and drive it back. It's just off the Western Desert and . . ."

"No lorry of Lady ffynche's has been closer to the Western Desert than the officers' beach at Mersa Matruh. It's a crying shame and a disgrace it is. I, for one, feel like writing a frank letter to the *Worker*. And as for you, Yank, with your shady dealings in . . ."

"Speaking of beaches, Epply old boy, how's for a nice swim at Al Agami? You look a bit peeky. I'll take you out for a nice tuck-in and . . ."

"Not to some posh officers' club, you won't. Them and their old school ties!"

"Not a bit of it, old darling. We'll go to some nice proletarian workers' café and you can pass out pamphlets to the waiters. Hop to it now. Put on something very dashing, as always, and we'll be waiting down below."

"Well—well, I shouldn't desert my post. . . ."

"Nonsense. I'm sure it's Whitsun or something like that back home in Golder's Green or wherever. You deserve a jolly hol."

"Oh very well. I'm that sick of bully and biscuits."

"Shall we say ten minutes?"

"Make it fifteen. Or do I need to shave?"

"Not a bit of it. Just wear a heavy motoring veil. Cheery-by, comrade!"

Tony pounded down the stairs with me in pursuit. We got into the empty Ford truck. Tony started the motor and sped off. "Hey! What about Epply?" I said.

"Screw him! Lousy red! Now for lunch and that swim. Would you be interested in meeting King Farouk?"

"Not in the least."

"Very well. I just thought I'd ask. Today I feel that I can treat you to a very *good* lunch."

Lunch was splendid. The waiters all seemed to know Tony. He tipped each of them with a packet of Players and never paid the bill as none was presented. We swam at Sidi-Bishr and then checked into the Cecil Hotel. There were no vacancies, the clerk at the desk claimed, but when Tony produced two cartons of Chesterfields, the man suddenly remembered a small suite that had just become empty. Tony changed into something vaguely reminiscent of *The Student Prince* and led the way swiftly through the blacked-out streets (Cairo from sunset on was a blaze of light; not so Alexandria) to yet another Officers Only restaurant. From there we went to a posh brothel where Tony was also well known. After watching an *exhibition* more comical than erotic, Tony handed me a packet of English condoms. They

97

were called Mister and the motto was "Soft as a fairy's cheek." Then we parted company.

I came downstairs first, felt in my pocket, and discovered that my last cigarette was gone. A nearly naked cigarette girl came out with a tray containing a vast array of American and English brands. For the better part of a pound I bought a package of Luckies. Like the ones the night before, these also contained a card. This one:

V . . . —
TO OUR BOYS EVERYWHERE
The Junior League of Grosse Pointe
Distributed through the ffynche Fund
for Overseas Comforts

Back at our hotel Tony took a full bottle of Scotch from his gleaming camel leather bag and poured two drinks. He put out the lights, opened the blackout curtain, and we got into bed. "Sleepy?" he asked, as though my welfare concerned him more than anything else in the world.

"Not especially."

"No more am I." Pause. He lit a cigarette with his solid gold flame-thrower. "Your parents?"

"What about them?"

"Still alive and kicking?"

"Very much so. My father is senior air-raid warden of Santa Fe, New Mexico. It's a top-secret position and one fraught with danger."

"Did I ever know what he did—in real life, I mean?"

"I think you did. He's a doctor—by appointment to many Indian potentates. Remember?"

"Quite so! I'd forgotten. Does he specialize?"

"Sure—in sick Indians and poor Spiks and anyone else who can't afford to pay for proper medical attention."

"Salt of the earth, those good old-time G.P.'s. I wonder if you could write and ask him something."

"Probably. What?"

"Well, you see I'm considering having my circumcision altered."

"Your *what?*" I said, spilling the drink down my chest. Tony repeated his amazing statement. "For purely aesthetic reasons," he added.

"Who's to know, unless you go around exposing yourself?"

"Well, you see, old man, it comes to a little more than that. It's different with you, but for me—having a name that ends with 'berg' . . . Well, it's given rise to a certain amount of unpleasant confusion, and being circumcised . . ."

"Are you out of your mind? Just look around you."

"The Moslem faith is quite like the Judaic . . ."

"Not here. Back home. Practically everyone is. It's S.O.P. with every boy born unless the doctor or his parents, for some reason, specify . . ."

"Yes, I realize all that. But I happened to fall into conversation with this refugee plastic surgeon in Cairo. . . . "

"That must have been some conversation."

"He did a number of restorations on wealthy Jews who had to get out of Europe. It was either that or the gas chamber."

"I don't think you're likely to be offered so dramatic a choice."

"His operations were almost seventy per cent successful."

"What happened to the thirty per cent that failed?"

"I mean they got past the Gestapo examiners without detection. They looked just like anyone else."

"Yeah, the old joint may *look* all right, but will it work?"

"And then being as Nature intended one to be has a certain classical quality. Greco-Roman sculpture . . ."

"So has a leaf. You can pick one off any fig tree for free and it can't possibly hurt."

"What do you think your father would say?"

"I know what he'd say—just what I'm saying only ten times as many words and Latin ones at that. And even if this—this skin graft—were as simple as a nose job, where would you get all the money? And don't give me that crap about your trustees."

"I think I could manage that. You *will* write your father?"

"Well of course I'll write him, but he'll hit the ceiling. He . . ."

"Promise?"

"Promise."

"Good night." Mission accomplished, Tony rolled over in his bed and went to sleep.

I was awakened by a loud noise outside the hotel in the East Harbor. Probably two destroyers crashing into one another. By squinting at my watch in the pale gray light I saw that it was only five o'clock. However, I was awake for the day. I had plenty of cigarettes but no matches. Silently I opened the drawer in the little nightstand between our beds and groped about in it trying to find Tony's lighter. My hand struck a large, soft wad. Pulling it out of the drawer I saw that it was money. Hundreds and hundreds and hundreds of Egyptian pound notes.

Back in Cairo Tony stood over me, breathing down the back of my neck, while I wrote to my father, couching Tony's problem in as delicate and nebulous terms as possible. After that, he was in his usual frenzy of activity. This is not to say that he did anything that even resembled work. During the next four or five days, he graced the headquarters of the ffynche Fund only twice—once to pick up his mail and once to collect several bottles of liquor and a few cases of cigarettes. But it would be unfair to accuse him of being idle. I chaperoned him through countless fittings at his tailors—a lavenderish-gray British battle dress "for autumn, in case we push on to Italy," a flowing cape probably inspired by something Erich von Stroheim wore in *La Grande Illusion*, some almost sheer slacks for the long summer ahead, a cossack-style coat with an astrakhan collar, and a number of other odds and ends. There were boots and shoes and slippers to be bought and several trips to Onnig's for gold cuff links, that essential of the battlefield—an alligator-covered flask with gold fittings, and gold identification bracelets (two). "Does your blood type vary from day to day?" I asked.

"One is for Tatty Purdom. I promised to pick it up for him."

Tony also gave a cocktail party in my honor. At least he told me it was in my honor, just as he had told two of the other guests that he was giving the affair for each of them. I was introduced as *leff*—not *lieu*—tenant to quite a lot of people I could never have hoped to meet in my humble circumstances. They were mostly English, ranging in rank up to brigadier general, and they were almost all called Captain Lord Somebody, Major Sir Ronald So-and-so, Seaman First Class Lady Daphne Something. Let me tell you, I was impressed. There were a few Americans on hand from none but the finest families and Tony, with more subtlety than before, was dropping the names of the fancier people and places he had been associated with. To add a little luster to plain old me, he even dropped the name of our school, which was apt to impress people who hadn't actually gone there.

"Oh," said an Arrow Collarish lieutenant commander, "I wonder if you ever knew a friend of mine—Seth Winthrop?"

"Know him?" Tony said, all toothy charm, "we all roomed together. As a matter of fact, Seth and I are cousins."

It was too much for me. "Then you undoubtedly know that your cousin Seth is dead."

"That's right," old Arrow Collar said. "In the Pacific. He's been awarded the Congressional Medal of Honor—posthumously of course. It was all written up in the overseas edition of *Time*."

Tony had been so busy being English that he had never looked at anything American beyond the Cholly Knickerbocker columns which some sappy girl in New York clipped and mailed to him every day. The news came as a thunderclap. Tony staggered, clutching at a cabinet for support. Silently, swiftly the understanding guests bade their adieux and tiptoed out as though leaving a bier. I picked up my gear from the bedroom and followed.

"Where are you going?" Tony said, by now quite restored and pouring another drink.

"Back to the Y. So long, Tony."

Hundreds of miles away from Tony and Cairo, I began to miss him. As irritating as he could be, there was at least some sort of activity whenever he was around. The war in the Middle East, which had been as good as finished for some time, ground officially to a halt in May of 1943 and there was nothing to do over the long, hot summer except to invent ways of keeping everybody busy and to wonder where and when we were going next.

It would have been an ideal time for the ffynche Fund to have shown up somewhere with a few of their famous comforts and a traveling camp show or two. But as far as I could learn, very little had been seen or heard of the Fund. There had been a performance of *The Duchess of Malfi* (in English) presented to the First Greek Brigade stationed at Sidon and a reading of *Oedipus Rex* (in Greek) dramatically staged in the ruins of Palmyra for some Australians. The Free French had been treated to an inaudible performance of *The Marriage of Figaro* in Italian and a stockade full of Italian prisoners of war at Tripoli had rioted during a concert presentation of Charpentier's *Louise* in French. In the big, comfortable cities, however, the ffynche Fund showed more evidence of effort. Owing to the exigencies of transportation, a sell-out performance of Alben Berg's *Wozzeck* was held at the Cairo Opera House with neither costumes nor scenery, and in Oran a gala revival of the Gertrude Stein-Virgil Thomson *Four Saints in Three Acts* had a stage full of Florine Stettheimer's famous cellophane settings but no cast. Noble as its purpose may have been, the ffynche Fund didn't seem to do anything that the N.A.A.F.I. and the U.S.O. couldn't do a lot better. As for their cigarettes and candy, I was, to my knowledge, the only man in uniform who had ever received any. Those who had ever run across the ffynche Fund damned its membership as a pack of rich playboys out on one long, larking goldbrick. Even more damning, not one man in a thousand had ever *heard* of the ffynche Fund.

But I heard from Tony almost daily and on pale blue onionskin engraved with his name and A.P.O. number. Like his speech, his spelling had become British most of the time and, as a gesture to the Continent I suppose, he was religiously crossing his sevens. The letters were, at first, cajoling, saying that I had misunderstood what he had said about Seth Winthrop. There was a long, lame explanation—something about "cousins" and "dozens." It made no sense and, by that time, no difference. Eventually Tony's letters became more importunate. The ffynche Fund, traditionally in the vanguard of any military action, would not linger in the Middle East forever. Hadn't my father the common decency to reply to my letter?

My father had. His answer was a masterpiece of outrage and, coming from a man totally devoid of any sense of humor, one of the funniest things I've ever read. As I had prophesied, the good doctor went into the subject thoroughly, quoting from a dozen medical textbooks and inserting his own furious opinions at the beginning and end of every paragraph. "Your astounding question of the seventeenth inst . . . appalled at the very idea . . . a question of plastic surgery which, heretofore, I had connected only with the so-called lifting of the faces of actresses . . . not my field at all, nor one which has received either my interest or approval . . . circumcision, to which your 'friend' is so strongly opposed, was created in the Holy Land, where you are now, to the best of my knowledge, stationed, as a bulwark against filth and disease five thousand years ago . . . centuries of endeavor on the part of the keenest minds in medicine . . . the questions of vanity, capriciousness, and folly quite apart, so wicked and foolish an operation would be costly, unspeakably painful to any potent male, and almost certainly foredoomed to the most abysmal failure . . . etc. etc. etc."

After reading my father's treatise several times, I scrawled "Maybe it would be easier to have your nose done instead" across the top of the first page—there were twelve—and sent it on to Tony in Cairo. It was the last I heard of him for some months.

On September 3 the first Allied troops landed on the Italian mainland and once again the Middle East was in a furor of confused and confusing troop movements. A week later I found myself in Cairo on the exciting assignment of waiting for transportation to Europe. Bored and idle, I went around to Tony's flat. Only his servant was there, jabbering away at me in his patois of Arabic, English, and French. About all that could be drawn from his recital was that Tony was out and that the servant hadn't been paid for some weeks. Unsatisfied, I went next to the ffynche Fund headquarters. The courtyard was in a fever of activity as crates of cigarettes, chocolate, and some of the better pieces of furniture being loaded into the Ford trucks. The air was thick with shouts and curses as the ffynche Fund vehicles backed into one another. A raddled old redhead, tears streaming down her cheeks, stood in the doorway of the house shrieking to no one in particular. "But what am *I* to do? I've come all the way out from New Zealand with my modern dance troupe and now you're going away. You can't just leave us stranded."

Like a jack-in-the-box, the head and shoulders of the Commander-in-Chief popped up through the sun roof of the staff car. "Here, you, Ali Mohammed, careful of that harpsichord. It's eighteenth century. *Écoute, Ali Mohammed, le harpsichord, le piano*—whatever you call it in French . . . Dickie, *tell* him, for pity's sake. And *hurry!* We're hours late getting started."

"Uh, pardon me," I said.

"Can't you see that I'm up to my . . . Oh! It's *you!* Well, if you're looking for your friend Tony Vandenberg, you won't find him here. Not while there's work to be done and danger to be faced." He disappeared back into the tonneau of the car. In a moment he was beside me, very picturesque and total war in a Field Marshal Montgomery beret and, in spite of the heat, a snow white trench coat. "But now that at least you're here, I'd like to give you just one small piece of my mind about your Ameddican gangster methods."

"What the hell are you talking about?" I almost added Mary, the only one of his many names I could remember.

"Oh do please come off it, Yankee laddy. The game, I'm afraid, is veddy much up. It must have been lovely for young Mr. Vandenberg while it lasted—thousands and *thousands* of pounds' worth of our supplies flogged on the black market—here, in Alex, in Port Said, and Suez, any place where he could find some *unscrupulous* wog who'd pay enough for a load of our goods. Oh, don't go all wide-eyed innocence with me, blue eyes. You knew *all* about it. Epply, over there, was only too happy to give your little scheme away." He made a sweeping gesture toward a loaded lorry. Epply was standing before the rear-view mirror pressing a pimple on his chin. At the sound of his name he looked up and flashed a malicious ocher smile. The Commander-in-Chief shuddered and continued his diatribe. "Your Mr. Vandenberg, *malheureusement*, is beyond the jurisdiction of the military police, but never fear; I intend to press civil charges that will keep him rotting in an Egyptian jail for some time to come. Poor Lady ffynche! Her life work dragged through the mud! I haven't had the nerve to send her a cable, but when I get to Italy . . . No, no, *no*, Ali Mohammed. Not that wretched statue, the Houdon bust. Dickie! *Tell* him! When this scandal gets out, it's going to *kill* poor Lady ffynche. I hope you're satisfied, you murderer!"

"I haven't got anything to do with your lousy ffynche Fund. If you don't believe me, ask Tony. Where is he, anyhow?"

"My dear, do you mean to say you don't *know?* Why, naturally, he's malingering in hospital with some cock and bull story—if you'll forgive the expression—about a circumcision or some such fantasy. As you well know, it's *the* classic golden brick (I *believe* that's what you Yanks call it) of all time."

"What hospital?"

"I don't know and what's more I don't care. I only hope they've snipped his whole *thing* off. And now, if you'll forgive me, Mr. Dillinger, *I* have important work to do. Hours behind shed-ule, no decent villas available in Naples. Oh, get out of here!"

As I made my way out of the ffynche Fund courtyard, Epply sneered, "Just you wait, Yank, you and your whole de-cay-dent class are going to get it."

More out of curiosity than compassion, I spent several days canvassing the hospitals in and around Cairo. Finally Tony was found in a British Army hospital out in Ismailia. The toothy nursing sister who interviewed me told me in sepulchral tones that Mr. Vandenberg was suffering considerable pain and mental anguish, but that a visitor might do something to cheer him up. I would be allowed into his room—Tony had naturally been given a private room—only if I would promise to be very quiet and to leave quickly. But she issued a whinnying little giggle as she opened the door for me.

Tony lay naked in bed, the sheet over his middle propped up by some hidden framework. His handlebar mustache had been shaved off and he looked very young and very vulnerable.

"Tony?" I said in little more than a whisper.

His eyes rolled lugubriously in my general direction. "So it's you. My only friend. The only one who cares if I live or die."

"What's happened to you, Tony? Didn't you ever get my father's letter?"

"Yes. But I didn't believe it. After all, he's just a little country doctor." I could feel myself beginning to bristle. "But as for that lousy refugee charlatan! One thousand pounds he charged and the whole thing is a washout! If you could only imagine the pain . . ."

"Thank God I can only imagine it. But, Tony, I'm afraid that your—your surgery is just the beginning of your troubles."

"What do you mean?" he moaned.

"I mean that you're going to be in real hot water. I'm not sure that I understand it, but it seems that the ffynche Fund is missing quite a lot of supplies and Epply . . ."

Tony groaned. His tremulous hand reached out for the ermine-tail good-luck charm on the bedside table.

"That faggoty fuehrer of yours was pretty steamed up about it. That's how I found out you were laid up. They've gone on to Italy now, but when he gets there he's going to cable New York and . . ."

Tony groaned piteously. "They're trying to frame me. That Communist Epply and the whole rotten outfit have it in for me because . . ."

The door opened. It was the nurse again. "I say, Mr. Vandenberg, this *is* a red letter day! Another nice Ameddican come to visit. I'm afraid you'll have to leave, sir."

A pale disheveled Southerner darted into the room. He wore most of the components of what had originally been the ffynche Fund uniform and flapped a crumpled overseas military newspaper.

"Tony! Thank God you're all right."

"All *right?* Listen to me, Tatham Purdom, if you knew what I'd been through while you were away trying to get Wanda Landowska . . ."

"Tony, don't you know what's happened? The whole ffynche Fund . . . everyone except you and me . . . the ship they were on was hit by a U-boat. They've all been lost at sea!"

Tony sank back on his pillows with a soft little sigh. I marched out of the room and slammed the door behind me.

V

TONY

in Sodom

In the middle of a muddy field somewhere north of Naples I received many months' worth of mail. Tony Vandenberg figured prominently. He had made it back to the States, along with Tatham Purdom, as the last relict of the ffynche Fund. Somehow he had been able en route to write an eyewitness account of the watery demise of his comarades which was published in *American Magazine* with illustrations almost as imaginary as the text.

Lady ffynche, I read, had given a banquet for Vandenberg and Purdom at the Waldorf, complete with speeches, medals, and eulogies to the defunct heroes of the Fund. Mr. Purdom then joined his widowed mother in the deep South, leaving Tony alone to bear the burden of nation-wide adulation. He was interviewed by the press, on radio, and on that novel little flickering box, television. Like most wartime phenomena, Tony's fame was short-lived, commencing with dinner at Gracie Mansion and culminating with luncheon at the White House. Forty-eight hours later someone else came along to capture the public's fancy. After that I heard nothing more of Tony until World War II was a thing of the past.

Our next confrontation occurred in the autumn of 1945. I was living in New York and more or less gainfully employed as the most junior of editors at the publishing firm of Harold Dean Associates—"a little Knopf," as Mr. Dean called it. While giving an expense-account lunch to a very unimportant author and her very important agent in the old Ritz Grill, I ran into J. Anthony Vandenberg, exuding an air of charm, authority, and wealth. To my embarrassment, he threw his arms about me and kissed me on both cheeks as though he were presenting the Croix de Guerre. Back on native soil he was less British and more American, but not much. "Dear boy! A sight for sore eyes. Just seeing you makes me feel young again." For the benefit of my luncheon companions, whom I had not bothered to introduce, he dropped the names of our school, a couple of Grade A debutantes whose parties we had attended, and two or three of the better clubs and restaurants in Egypt. Perhaps, as it sent my stock up with the authoress and her agent, who pronounced Tony "utterly delightful," I should have been grateful. Somehow I wasn't.

"I've got to dash," Tony said, "but do come round and see us. Tatty—you remember Tatham Purdom—and I have bought a townhouse. Tell you what: Stop by for cocktails tomorrow. Here, I'll write it all down for you." He scrawled the time and place on a pristine parchment visiting card with a gold fountain pen, caroled out "Au revoir!" and then he was gone. Reading it over in my office later, I learned that J. Anthony Vandenberg was now John Anthony van Denberg and that I was expected "6-ish."

Dressed in my one postwar suit, I arrived on the following evening. It was a splendid old bow-fronted brick house on West

Sixteenth Street, not in the Village but of the Village. At least I knew the butler who opened the door to me. He was an astonishingly competent old Negro who had tended bar at almost every literary cocktail party I had gone to that fall, although for a time Tony persisted in referring to him as "our man."

The high-ceilinged rooms of the place, had they been preserved, would have served future generations as a flawless example of *haut décor* of the mid-forties. The walls of the foyer were Chinese red, the drawing room bottle green, the dining room Wedgwood blue, and the bedroom a daring black. The woodwork was naturally picked out in dramatic white. Much had been made of the antiquity of the large, Victorian bathroom. "Witty" nudes hung against its flocked wallpaper. Gilt paint and red nail varnish had been used on the claw-and-ball feet of the tub. A long plush cord and tassel dangled from the water box above the toilet.

The rooms were furnished in a style known as "pansy auction" with heavy emphasis on massively framed mirrors, gargantuan chandeliers, and bits of thrift-shop baroque all sprayed white. In the last three months I had been to a dozen such parties in a dozen such places. But through the smoke and the chatter I felt that there was something different about this one. Suddenly it dawned on me. There were no women present.

Tony, followed by two yapping little poodles, bore down like a tornado, embracing me and clapping at my biceps with the palms of his hands as though he were plumping a pillow. The dogs, Flotsam and Jetsam, were then introduced and, with a great deal of coaxing and threatening, offered their right forepaws to be shaken. Their claws were painted gold.

"Adorable, aren't they?" Tony said.

"Nauseating."

"Oh, you're terrible! Tat!" he called. "Come over here. There's someone I want you to meet."

I had, of course, seen—not actually met—Tatham Purdom two years before at Tony's deathbed. He was still tall, thin, and pale and a lot more Southern than I had remembered. He and Tony were dressed alike in charcoal gray suits, pink oxford-cloth shirts, black knit ties, and black tasseled loafers. "Ah'm so please," Purdom said. "Tony's told me so much about you. All of it good, of cawse," he added with a nervous little laugh. I wondered.

"Now let me get you a drink and then we'll make the rounds. We have Scotch, you'll be amazed to learn."

"I'm not amazed a bit. I'd be surprised if you hadn't."

Armed with a drink, I was propelled by Tony from one loose little group of young men to another. As had always been his custom, Tony added a bit of biographical material about each guest, just enough to make him sound bigger and better than he actually was and, hence, making Tony seem a bit grander for knowing such important people. In this particular crowd, however, I soon discovered that So-and-so, "the actor," was now and had always been at liberty. Somebody, "the decorator," had just begun attending the Parsons School of Design on the GI Bill of Rights; Someone Else, "the painter," painted on weekends and poked at a comptometer the other five days; the many young men who were "in publishing" were working in various Double-day Book Shops until something better happened along. Greer Perry's remark about Tony's attracting second-raters came back to me when I, a second-rate editor in a second-rate publishing house, achieved something like star status at the party. Of the forty or fifty young men who were there, at least half were writing books and they conscientiously took down my name and the name of Harold Dean Associates and asked for permission to submit their manuscripts. As Mr. Dean had always told me to scout at parties—and anyplace else—I was delighted to think that so much material would be coming into the editorial department. A feather in my cap.

But the real sensation of the evening was Jackson Balderston, "the poet." He was a handsome, aesthetic Negro the color of café au lait and the only genuine celebrity in the room. Like a Hollywood starlet who achieves fame without making a single film, Jackson Balderston was widely known at least by name. I had read it in the letters-to-the-editor pages of *The Saturday Review of Literature*, in *Time* and *The New Republic*. I had seen announcements that he was to participate in various symposia at the New School, the Rand School, the Y.M.H.A. His name appeared toward the top of the lists of intellectuals protesting this or deploring that. Everyone had heard it, everyone knew vaguely that he wrote, but no one had ever read any. At least I had not. Tony and his guests clustered about him like flies at a honey pot. Even Tat Purdom, albeit a little self-consciously, paid court. Only the Negro butler gave Jackson Balderston a wide berth, serving him either very slowly or not at all. It didn't matter. Tony was only too happy to dance attendance. As Balderston was leaving—"I've got to meet with this committee to see about starting a new magazine of *belles lettres*"—he shook my hand warmly. "You know you're the only publisher I've ever met who hasn't asked if I wouldn't submit a manuscript."

"I assumed that you already had a publisher, Mr. Balderston."

"Well, yes, of course. I guess you could say I have a wide acquaintance in publishing. But that doesn't mean I might not be ready to consider another offer."

"I'll be happy to read anything you care to send in."

"I may surprise you some one of these days. Well, ta-ta, Tony, Tatty. I'm off."

After Balderston's departure, the other guests—all a little drunk by now—broke up into chatty groups, jabbering excitedly among themselves. It was as though they'd all experienced some new thrill in meeting a Negro socially.

The first wave of departures took place in black chesterfield coats and yellow chamois gloves but no hats. The boys began to avail themselves of the chairs and sofas. Some sat cross-legged on the floor. The conversation became general, centering on their favorite women. In alphabetical order they ranged from Arletty to Zorina, touching—*en passant*—on Tallulah Bankhead, Ingrid Bergman, Elisabeth Bergner, Marlene Dietrich, Hermione Gingold, Katherine Hepburn, Greta Keller, Patsy Kelly, Gertrude Lawrence, Lotte Lenya, Beatrice Lillie, Mabel Mercer, Elvira Rios, Margaret Sullavan, Maggie Teyte, Mae West, and culminating in a full-voiced moan of ecstasy over Greta Garbo, the goddess of them all. My opinion that Miss Garbo was a rotten actress and that all of her pictures, except possibly *Ninotchka*, had been lousy on every count might better have been left unvoiced. I felt a distinctly glacial atmosphere enveloping me.

From the panegyrics to established performers, the talk deteriorated to the Hollywood washouts—those highly publicized actresses who never quite made the grade. The names of Toby Wing, Rochelle Hudson, Olympe Bradna, Sigrid Gurie, Tala Birell, Andrea Leeds, Gloria Stuart, Anna Sten, Lili Damita, Rosemary, Lola, and Priscilla Lane—a fairly standard list—were all bandied. Apparently it was a favorite game, untarnished by repetition. But when I suggested Elissa Landi as an all-time money loser, I was indignantly put down. Miss Landi, several people told me, was a Hapsburg and/or a Bourbon et Parme, a deathless beauty and a great star. It was obvious that I was on the wrong wave length.

More farewells. The conversation took another turn. This time it concerned the failings of women I did not know, or so I thought for a while. "She," "Miss," and "Mrs." were constantly employed. It took a little time for me to realize that they were discussing the gentlemen who had recently left.

Under the circumstances departure seemed unwise, but I was bored and I was hungry. I got to my feet and interrupted Tony at the bar where he and Tatham Purdom were having a serious discussion as to how the ice might or might not hold out.

"Thanks for everything, Tony," I said. "But I've got to be shoving off."

"Oh, don't go. Please."

"Afraid I must. I've got to get back to my squalid quarters to pack."

"Going away, old boy?"

"No. I've overstayed the five-day limit in my hotel and I've got to move on to a new one."

"Do you mean you're looking for an apartment? Well, why didn't you say so? We've got a smashing one up on the third floor you might like."

"You mean it hasn't been snapped up yet? With the housing shortage as acute as . . ."

"Nobody knows it's vacant. We don't want to take just anyone. It's for rent, furnished."

Looking around Tony's room at the overscaled lamps with great drum shades of gold paper, the battery jars burgeoning rhododendron leaves, the white matchbooks printed with "T 'n' T," I said, "Furnished? Is it very expensive?" It was, but cheaper than living in a series of flea-bag hotels. It would also have the virtue of permanence.

"The party's breaking up. Stick around. You can have a little bitey with Tat and me and then we'll go up and see the apartment. Besides, we've so much to catch up on and I *do* want you to get to know Tat."

In twos and threes and fours the party broke away, the uptown guests heading for little suppers at Copain, P. J. Clarke's, or 1–2–3; the Village people bickering amiably over Julius's, Chumley's, The Old Place. Names and addresses were exchanged along with promises to telephone. Movement, small talk, movement, small talk—and eventually the last of them was gone.

While their faithful old retainer of four long hours' service tidied up the remains of the party, we retired to the black bedroom. The bed, now cleared of its load of velvet-collared chesterfield coats, was covered with a huge Nazi banner gathered at its four corners with large gold tassels. Flanking the bed were two enormous Santos with chipped-off noses, missing digits, and great cracks and splits in the carved folds of their robes. They had been converted into lamps under huge black marbelized shades. On the wall above the headboard a pyramid of red votive lights flickered eerily. "The garden's back here," Tony said, wrestling with the accordion folds of some old louvered jalousies which had been disinterred from several decades of paint jobs and stripped down to their natural wood. "It's going to be very pretty when Tatham gets around to fixing it up. Sit down while I get out of these clothes." I sat in the only chair—one created from the horns and hooves of cattle, upholstered in scarlet corduroy, and a conversation piece if ever there was one—and thought of all the things I wouldn't do to any space I might or might not rent in this building.

While Purdom, bearing trays, spun up and down a spiral staircase connecting the parlor floor with the kitchen below, Tony slithered into a golden brocade dressing gown ("I got the material in Damascus for next to nothing") and some needle-point slippers worked with the emblem of the ffynche Fund.

Our suppers were very artistic to say the least and the most—white Wedgwood and milk glass with very good old silver and ingeniously folded red bandannas for napkins on black lacquer trays. But the meal of not-quite-thawed Birdseye shrimps and peas in a sauce of bottled Welsh rabbit over scorched English muffins left something to be desired. A Chilean riesling was poured. "Tat loves to cook," Tony said.

"Well, now you know what I'm doing," I said. "What about you?"

"Oh, not much, old man. I've been awfully busy with the house. (We just moved in.) But I've got my investments to look after and I'm mulling over two or three interesting offers. Tatty's the real breadwinner. Ever tune him in?"

Mr. Purdom, I learned, was a musicologist with a vast library of rare records who carried on a twice-weekly program of interviews and musical esoterica from a small, highbrow radio station in New Jersey. I promised to listen. In his anemic way, Tat was nice. Gentle.

The vacant apartment was a predictable Williamsburg green, its Salvation Army furniture done over in Royal Stewart plaid. "Masculine," Tat said. As Tony pointed out, it was long on

115

charm, with a Victorian marble fireplace, louvered windows overlooking what would someday be a blooming garden, and solid walnut doors hidden beneath many coats of scarlet lacquer. As I pointed out, it was very expensive. As Tony pointed out, it was within walking distance and would save a fortune in carfare. Ten cents a day, as I pointed out. Still and all it was much nicer than anything else I would find—if I could find anything at all, Tony pointed out. Knowing that he was right, I agreed to take the place.

"How shall I make out the check?" I asked.

"Tatham Purdom, that's capital Tee, ay, tee . . ."

"Just make it out to cash," Tony said quickly. "Two months' rent, please. It's a round figure and since you won't be taking the rent off your income tax for professional space, there's no reason why Uncle Sap should know. Officially Tatty and I occupy the whole house."

"Tony, do you think that's . . . ?" Tatham began.

"When I think of all the wartime profiteers screwing the people out of millions when we were facing danger overseas," Tony said righteously, "I don't have many qualms about taking money that is rightfully ours. You 'tend to the music. I'll keep the books.' Now let's go downstairs and have a drink and maybe a little music."

Tatham brightened. "Ah found a wonderful old Scarlatti . . ."

"None of that crap. I'm in the mood for classical music. Let's hear 'Manhattan Tower.'"

While Tatham, all too eager to please, whirled down the spiral stairs to coerce his electronic monster of a record player into producing a little music, I glanced at Tony stretched out on a white Recamier sofa. "Well, Tony," I said, "you seem to have landed on both feet. Tatham is very nice."

"Isn't he?" Tony said, a beatific smile on his lips. "Yes, old man, for the first time in my life I'm happy. Truly happy. What do I care for public opinion when I've got all this? The pure love between two men . . ."

Given the intelligence of a bivalve, I would have asked for my check, put on my hat, and left; would never have come to this silly party in the first place. An imbecile could have foreseen that total involvement and complete lack of privacy were as good as written into the lease of that overpriced little upstairs apartment. But, as always, the spell of Tony was too strong for me. Tony Vandenberg, dancing darling of the debutante world, had embarked upon a new metamorphosis as Tony van Denberg, exquisite, aesthete and—I felt fairly sure—kept gentleman. I was too fascinated, too curious to do what any sensible person would have done. I wanted to stay around and watch.

Little by little I settled into the house on Sixteenth Street. The fireplace smoked; the cold water was labeled "hot"; the oven wouldn't always light and couldn't be controlled when it did; one window couldn't be opened and another never quite closed. Otherwise the place was all right.

The cocktail parties—Tony once or twice had the nerve to refer to them as "salons"—continued with only minor changes in personnel and one after another the party-propelled manuscripts began to flutter into my office. They were all thinly disguised autobiographies and after the first three I knew just where to turn to find what:

Page one—"John [or Ralph or Christopher or Brooke] was not like other boys. . . ."

Page three—"His gentle mother was a beautiful woman, warm, understanding, and gay. . . ."

Page seven—"He hardly knew his father, a stern man who had little time for his family. . . ."

Page ten—"When the other boys chose up teams for baseball or football he was not invited to join in their fun. . . ."

Page fourteen—"The scoutmaster [or Latin teacher or chauffeur or curate] laid his hand gently on John's [or Ralph's or Christopher's or Brooke's] arm. 'You're trembling,' said he. . . ."

In the hands of a competent hack writer any one of them might have sold a million copies to the drugstore trade, but these pitiful attempts at self-flagellation were simply drab, dull, and not at all what Harold Dean Associates happened to be looking for. Tony took each rejection letter as a personal affront and it became politic for me to avoid facing his crew of disappointed authors at the weekly Purdom-Vandenberg (or van Denberg) gatherings.

My literary plum of the season—the magnum opus of Jackson Balderston—had yet to burst into fruit. I secretly doubted that it ever would. Why would a giant like Balderston, known and sought after by every big publisher in New York, ever demean himself to come to a little place like Harold Dean Associates? But come he did, heralded by an intimate telephone conversation during which he said that he would like to bring the manuscript in himself "to discuss terms and explain it." That should have warned me. Would Jackson Balderston be available to explain his book to each of the thousands of readers who were presumably perishing to snatch it off the stalls? But I was younger then. Dean Associates were in a flurry of expectancy. Curtains and a bowl of chrysanthemums were installed in my office and Mr. Dean himself, a man of indestructible elegance, stood waiting in the wings to pay a carefully rehearsed impromptu visit during the interview.

The great day came and with it, just forty-five minutes late, Jackson Balderston himself, tab collar, tightly furled umbrella, and mouse gray chesterfield with velvet to match. I didn't see how Mr. Dean could ever hope to compete with such splendor.

Gesticulating airily with enormous tortoise-shell spectacles, Balderston got the conversational bit between his small white teeth and held it there for better than an hour. "Henry Seidel Canby calls my book neither poetry nor prose and John La Touche thinks . . . to quote Gerald Sykes . . . Diana and Lionel Trilling think . . . naturally it isn't finished yet—just fifty pages and an outline . . . Jacques Barzun . . . an advance of twenty-five thousand . . . Bunny Wilson always says . . . similar to some of Gore Vidal's work but written on three levels

. . . Anaïs Nin, the darling . . . at Djuna Barnes's little pied-à-terre in Patchin Place . . . Luther Green and adorable Judith . . . too dishy . . . a dust cover by Buffie Johnson and my photograph by George Platt Lynes on the back . . . my great chum Paul Bowles . . . Brion Gysin and Lisa Sergio . . . Heavens, I must dash. I'm having tea with Cole. Cole Porter. Could you let me have a five? I seem to have come off without a sou. Au revoir!" He shot his cuffs, displaying links the size of silver dollars, and bustled out, leaving his spectacles behind. They were filled with window glass.

If his visit had been exhausting, it was nothing as compared to his manuscript. In essence it was just like the others that had flowed in from Tony's cocktail party, only worse in that it was pretentious, obscure, raunchy, and racial. It began:

Black my hands, black my feet, black my face and hair. Black my lips and black my tongue. Black my bowels and groin . . .

I sighed and settled down to read the rest of it. No worse hodgepodge had ever come my way before. Too insecure to trust my own judgment, I passed Balderston's well-thumbed manuscript on to the senior editor and eventually up to Mr. Dean himself. The opinions were unanimous. "Pity," Dean brooded, pressing his fingertips together. "Terribly big name of course, but the writing . . . well, I'm afraid it isn't . . . well, to be quite candid about it, it's a perfect shower of shit. Pity."

A few evenings later Tony pounded furiously at my door. "Well!" he snorted, all but stamping his foot. "I gather that you and that half-assed company of yours had a wonderful time humiliating a great artist."

"What are you talking about?"

"My friend Jackson Balderston. Throwing his work back in his face just as you have with all the authors I've sent you. If it means nothing to you to humiliate a poor Negro, you might at least consider *my* feelings. He just telephoned—in *tears*. He's going to kill himself."

"Good!"

"Just because he happens to be black . . ."

"I don't care if he's Kelly green, his book was unreadable."

"If Jackson were a white heterosexual, you wouldn't have dared. But because he's colored and gay . . ."

"If Jackson were a white heterosexual, you wouldn't know him, Tony. But because he *is* colored and gay, you and that pack of queens who turn up here every week have taken him up like a burning issue. He's as much an adornment to your parties as the flowers or those mangy poodles."

So towering was Tony's indignation that he was not even listening. "I could have sent him to Random House or Knopf or Harper's or any *real* publisher. They'd have taken him to lunch and treated him like royalty."

"They all *have* taken him to lunch, Tony. I've checked. And from the condition his manuscript is in, I think he wrapped the left-overs in it."

"Very funny! Oh, hahahaha!"

"It's a fact, Tony. Jackson Balderston's book has been turned down by fifteen other publishers that I know of."

"Publishers, bah! You're nothing but a lot of cheap, commercial printers—the whole lot of you. Here I invite you into my home, introduce you to a sensitive artist, a brilliant Negro, creative, a famous name . . ."

"What's he famous for, Tony? Tell me one thing he's ever done. Just one."

"I'm not going to tell you *anything*. From now on you can publish your crummy books without any help from me. Good *night!*"

I was not invited to the next cocktail party but, then, neither was Jackson Balderston.

After that the atmosphere was frigid, with Tony barely nodding if we met in the hallway. Tatham, however, baked an almost impregnable mincemeat pie and brought it upstairs. "Ah just ran up to say merry Christmas and good-by for a little. Ah've got to go down home to spend the holiday with Mothah right after today's broadcast. Be good now, heah? And look in on Tony once in a while. He'll need cheering up while Ah'm gone."

"I think Tony can take care of himself just fine, Tat. But merry Christmas—and thanks."

I spent that first peacetime Christmas with Aunt Harriet. It was far from peaceful. She had aged tremendously and did nothing but complain, accusing chambermaids of stealing things that were right out in plain sight and me of neglecting her, forgetting that I telephoned once a day and usually got hung-up-on for my trouble. Otherwise the holiday season passed as usual. I went to too many parties, gained weight, got engaged in a drunken moment, and disengaged the following day when we both realized that it had been not love but liquor. I confess to have given Tony not so much as a thought.

But Tony came sharply back into focus at a few minutes after eleven one cold clear night when I was awakened by the jangling of the telephone.

"Hello?" I said, not bothering to stifle a yawn.

It was Tatham Purdom, both raising his voice to cope with the interference on long distance and lowering it as if he had something to say in the greatest of confidence.

"Listen, Ah hate to make you pile outta bed at this un-godly houah, but Ah've been tryin' to reach Tony since eight o'clock. The line's been busy, busy, busy and now the operatah says the phone must be off the hook. Tony's so careless."

"Yeah."

"Well Ah'm taking the plane up tomorrah mawning because I have to be back for my broadcast but the thing of it is this." His voice dropped to little more than a whisper. "Mothah is coming back with me. And there are just some things downstairs that Mothah doesn't need to see."

"I'll bet there are. Tony, for example."

"So heah's what Ah'd like for you to do, if you don't mind: Go downstairs and let yourself inta the apartment. . . ."

"How can I do that?"

"I'm *telling* you. You know that big pier glass down in the front hall?"

"Mmm-hmmm."

"And you know the big vase of mag-nolia leaves sits on the mahble shelf in front of it?"

"Yeah."

"Well, Ah always keep an extra key hidden undah that vase for the cleaning woman or in case Tony or Ah should go out and leave ours behind. So if you don't mind, Ah wish you'd go downstairs, let yourself in, and leave a note for Tony wheah he'll be absolutely *certain* to see it. Mothah and Ah should be theah a little aftah ten tomorrah and . . . Excuse me just a second. . . ." At the other end of the line I could hear an indistinct voice that was distinctly querulous and then Tatham saying, "Ah'm just calling the airline, Mothah, to make sure they have a seat for you." Tatham's voice was back in my ear again, loud and authoritative. "Very well. That's Flight Ninety-three for La Guardia tomorrah. Thank you kindly." He rang off before I could say anything else.

I scrawled a note for Tony on a large sheet of wrapping paper. "Delouse the house. Your mother-in-law will be here at 10 A.M. Good luck." I could see light shining beneath Tony's front door so I was certain that he was out, leaving a few lamps on to discourage prowlers. Finding the key, I opened the front door, went in, and headed for the bedroom to deposit my note on the Nazi banner. Flotsam and Jetsam barked sleepily. I switched on the bedroom light and gasped. But I wasn't the only one to gasp. A tousle-haired brunette sat bolt upright in the bed. She emitted a little shriek and pulled the sheet over her bosom. "What *is* this? A *raid*? Is he *married*?"

"Technically speaking, no," I said.

Tony came to life with a series of snores and snorts. "What the hell?" he growled sleepily, blinking his eyes.

"I was sound asleep and all of a sudden this potty comes in like the Grestapo or somethingue," Tony's friend said indignantly.

"What the hell?" Tony said again, this time almost awake.

"Tony, I'm sorry. Your telephone's off the hook."

"I know it is. I took it off myself. And the reason was that I did *not wish to be interrupted.*"

"I'll bet you didn't. Well, I didn't wish to interrupt you and . . . and your friend. Tat's been trying to reach you. He called me, finally. He'll be here around ten in the morning—*and so will his mother.*"

With that, Tony bounded out of the bed, naked as the day he was born. "You've got to get the hell out of here," he said to his companion. "My roommate's coming home."

"You told me this was your house. That you lived here alone."

"You misunderstood me, baby. The guy that owns it . . ."

"It looks like I misunderstood a lot of things. I should of known the minute I saw this place—all these fancy rooms, those goddamned poodles, that gold bracelet of yours . . . a real queer joint. Fairyland."

"Oh, shut up and get out of here!"

"With him lookingue?"

"Sorry," I said. "Well, I've delivered the message. Now if you'll excuse me—and I'm sure you will . . ."

"Wait a minute," Tony said, struggling into the new dressing gown, one of a pair that Tatham had bought at Clyde's, and followed me into the living room. "You've got to stay and help me."

"You seemed to be doing just fine with Miss—uh—I didn't quite catch the name. Terribly nice girl, though. Sweet. Where did you pick her up, the Debutante Cotillion?"

"Ah! She's a dog."

"Good for you, Tony. That 'pure love between two men' you were telling me about . . . I'm glad that Miss—uh—Miss Dog has done nothing to defile it. Good night."

"Don't go! You've got to help me clean this place up. Look at it!" It was a mess, all right, with dirty glasses and ashtrays everywhere, stacks of show tunes replacing Ted's Elizabethan madrigals and seventeenth-century court dances.

Tony's recent bedfellow clumped out of the bedroom in her galoshes. Her head was tied up in a scarf and she wore a red fox chubby. She sniffed rhetorically. "I suppose you know it's snowingue."

"Is it?" I said in my most conversational tone.

"So what?" Tony said.

"Well, amcha at least gonna gimme cabfare?"

"Cabfare? All the way to Jackson Heights? You came by subway."

She let out a yip that could be heard to Battery Park.

"Oh, all *right*. Have you got any dough, chum?" Tony asked me. "I seem to be fresh out of change."

"Me, too," I said, turning out the pockets of my robe.

"Well, maybe I can scrounge up something." He slammed off to the bedroom and returned with five singles. "Here. I'll call you later this week."

"In a pig's ass you will! I won't be answeringue."

"Little whore."

"Would you kinely look at who's talkingue, ya big faggot!" She snatched up her purse and marched out, slamming the front door.

Uncamping the Purdom-Van Denberg premises for a living symbol of Confederate motherhood sounded a lot easier than it was. "Here," Tony said, thrusting a bottle of nail polish remover at me, "get that stuff off the dogs' claws while I take down the pictures in the loo."

"I will not! You put that muck on those helpless mutts. You get it off. *I'll* take down the pictures." The "witty" photographs —some nudes of Tony and Tatham frolicking on a lonely beach, a worm's-eye view of Tony sunbathing on his terrace in Cairo, a unit of ffynche Fund volunteers lined up for short-arm inspection, and a blurred shot of Tatham relieving himself somewhere on some desert—left large, unfaded squares on the red plush wallpaper, but the squares were probably preferable to the pictures. The bed had to be freshly made. The amusing towels marked "His," "Hers," and "Its," were replaced by the smart black towels Tony had bought at Wanamaker's, and then *those* had to be replaced by the baby blue towels Mrs. Purdom had sent as a housewarming gift. A modest collection of pornography was swept off the bookshelves. Tat's Bible with "Read a chapter every night. I'll be praying for you—Mother," scrawled on the flyleaf had to be located and put conspicuously on one of the bedside tables. A photograph of Jackson Balderston was replaced by the folding leather frame that contained a study of Mrs. Purdom and the late Mr. Purdom on their wedding day. Rose in ermine and Lochby Court were considered not only suitable but essential to the decorum of the place. Some Parian-ware satyrs, a large poster warning against venereal disease, and a bottle opener shaped like a penis were jettisoned. By daybreak the establishment looked, if not exactly manly, at least respectable.

"Thanks a million," Tony said, gripping my hand. "Promise you'll stop in for cocktails tonight. I'll have to find some straight people to invite in. You know—some butch types, a few girls."

"What about that charmer who just left? A little flat-chested, but a lady to her fingertips."

"If you ever tell Tat about her I swear I'll . . ."

"You'll what?"

"I know you won't. You're too good a friend."

So curious was I to see Mother Purdom that I waited at the top of the stairs that evening until two of Tony's and Tatham's less obvious cocktail-party gentlemen arrived and then, certain not to be the first human sacrifice, I all but burst through their front door.

Tony had described the aristocracy of the Purdoms so often that I more or less expected something along the lines of Queen Alexandra—tall, stately, lean as a wand, with perhaps a black velvet change-of-life band around her throat and just possibly billows of high-piled white hair. (Mrs. Purdom's bridal photograph circa 1915 had been disappointingly unrevealing.)

The real-life Mrs. Purdom was short and plump as a pouter pigeon. She had a huge head covered with sparse frizzed henna hair, broad meaty shoulders, and a huge bust tapering down to matchstick legs and tiny feet. Visualize, if you can, a marcelled ice cream cone and you have Mrs. Purdom's silhouette.

Somewhere between fifty and death, she was insistently Southern and given to a kittenish flirtatiousness not at all compatible with her age and shape. She used make-up extravagantly, if not well, leaning heavily on rouge. Under public scrutiny her face was a seething mass of simpers, grimaces, and moues, but her beady little eyes, looking out through beaded little lashes, were hard as agates. She was quite the go-getter in the small town which she all but owned. She ran Purdom Brothers (department store), the Purdom Palace (hotel), the Purdom Pantheon (movie house), the Purdom Arcade (office building), a lot of miscellaneous real estate, and a large working plantation—all at maximum profit, she said. There was no reason to doubt her, not with those eyes. Superficially she was pleasant enough, giggling away with the cocktail-party boys, who were old hands at turning on the charm with the mothers of their friends. They were forever telling one another about dear old Grace or Maude or Blanche who was a perfect scream or a pure camp or a real darling. Flattery, it seemed, would get one everywhere with Mrs. Purdom. Her weakness had not been lost on Tony, a past master in the arts of blandishment, but Tony was obviously lost on Mrs. Purdom.

He was being the perfect host, forever jumping up to light Mrs. Purdom's cigarettes (she smoked only at parties, with sweeping gestures of her pudgy little hands, triceps swinging, as she blew great clouds of smoke high into the air) and replenishing her drinks ("a bubbon ole fashion' with plintya fruit an' sugah"), but for these services he received but perfunctory thanks. Whenever he spoke, Mrs. Purdom listened attentively with a hard, blank stare, greeting his sallies of charm and wit with a slight twitch of one corner of her mouth and then pointedly launching into a fresh conversation that somehow never happened to include Tony. It did not make for an especially comfortable evening. I noticed it. The cocktail-party boys noticed it, and Tat, most of all, noticed it. He looked drawn, ill at ease, and paler than usual, wincing visibly each time Mrs. Purdom addressed him as "Son" or, as the liquor took its hold on her, "Sonny." If Tony sensed her dislike—and it was impossible that anyone as astute could not—he gave no indication of it. Instead, he redoubled his efforts, all but flying to her side with blazing matches and fresh drinks—every drink a good deal darker than the last.

The other guests trickled in at intervals, each a little surprised and self-conscious at being there; each laughing about the temperature, as though it were somehow comical; each asking Mrs. Purdom dutifully if it were her first trip to New York. It was, she said, implying that it would be her last.

Other merrymakers were the lady veterinarian who periodically dewormed the poodles, looking downright sissy in peacock blue with a lace jabot; a vaguely pretty girl from the Purdoms' home town who lived at the Barbizon for Women and worked at the Museum of Modern Art; Lady ffynche, supported on the left by her dull grandson and on the right by an ebony cane; and—most surprising of all—Posy Perry, twenty-one, very blond, very beautiful, very late, and very silly. I had had no idea that Tony even knew her.

Like all of Tony's parties given to impress if not to enjoy, it simply did not jell. None of the guests really knew each other and they seemed happy to keep things that way. Because of her great age, wealth, and title, great deference was paid Lady ffynche. It did not evidently please Mrs. Purdom, who was pretty obviously accustomed to being the queen bee at social functions back home. Her corrugated lips, the rouge now coursing the creases in little red rivulets, were pressed into a thin line of disapproval as Lady ffynche described the valor of Tat and Tony during the war, the emotional blow at the demise of the ffynche Fund, and her burning desire to return to England as soon as rationing was ended. "That's all well an' good, Miz Fitch," Mrs. Purdom said, clearly having no truck with foreign titles or entanglements, "but hah dyew thank Ah felt, as a mothah, not knowin' from one day to the nixt whethah Sonny was alahve or day-ud?" I had no reason to question her claim to motherhood, but it was easier to picture Mrs. Purdom suckling a litter of jackals than a real, live baby. "As for England, Ah wouldn't lift a fangah to help 'em again if they was . . ."

"Another drink, Mrs. Purdom," Tony said, dancing like a marionette.

"Ah have had enough to drank," Mrs. Purdom announced. I thought she'd had a bit too much myself.

"Are you warm enough, Mrs. Purdom? Wouldn't you like to sit here by the fire?"

"Ah am quite comfortable, thank you." There was a pause, then Mrs. Purdom signaled the part-time butler and said, "Uncle, a bubbon ole fashion' with plintya fruit an' sugah." The snub to Tony was obvious to everyone—even Tony. And then, just to make her feelings abundantly clear, Mrs. Purdom turned to Tat, who was looking a little like St. Sebastian at the time. "Sonny, run inta mah room an' fetch mah fox. It's chilleh in heah, heah? Chilleh." The atmosphere, if not the room, was icy and even the two die-hard mother-charmers conveniently remembered that they had been invited to another party to meet Jean Cocteau.

My duty done, my curiosity more than sated, I decided that it was high time to clear out. "Posy," I said, "unless you have something else to do, would you have dinner with me? I want to hear all about Greer." (I didn't.)

"Oh I'd love to," she said with an air of desperation, "but it's got to be an early evening. Honestly I haven't had more than three hours' sleep since . . ."

"Don't worry. It will be."

We went to an ex-speakeasy in the Village called "Sixty-eight" because it is at 59 Fifth Avenue. Posy thought it was cute—"just darling." Too late I realized that, for all her surface sophistication, she was a very stupid young woman. She talked mostly about how onerous it was to come out in wartime; how poky her debut had been; how the only boys around had either been babies or fairies; and how severely poor Mummy—now a Mrs. Thaxter—had been criticized in the press for the ostentation of Posy's party. Posy was, she said, bored to death and would simply have to get a job or something like that to keep from going mad.

Greer Perry had done something very secret and heroic with the Navy in Washington during the war—Posy didn't know exactly what—and now, "by Mummy's pulling all kinds of strings," was in Rio de Janeiro with the Foreign Service and "practically engaged to this Brazilian girl called Maria Luisa de Something or other. I can never remember those Spanish names. Maybe you saw her picture in the the Latin American issue of Vogue. Quite attractive." I said that was nice.

"Tell me about Tony van Denberg," Posy said, lowering her lashes over a stinger. "I barely know him. Oh, I saw him around town a few times last year. He went to school with you and Gig, didn't he? So he must be nice. It's so hard to tell nowadays. I mean with all the uniforms still around. I nearly died when he called up and asked me to that deadly party. I mean if you hadn't been there I wouldn't have known a soul. Tony's attractive. But that awful old Southern woman. Deadly!"

The party and Mrs. Purdom had been deadly, but Posy was deadlier. I took her uptown to the family seat, still firmly established at 888 Fifth Avenue, regretting the cabfare with every click of the meter, refused to come up and have a nightcap with Mummy and Mr. Thaxter, promised to telephone, and shot back to my own apartment.

Tony was seated in the one comfortable chair in my living room, smoking my cigarettes and drinking my liquor. "I said I had a date and let myself in with the pass key," he said. "I hope you don't mind."

"Perfectly all right. After all, I surprised you last night."

"*That* little tramp?"

"What's happened to Scarlett O'Hara?"

"Tat's taken her to the Lafayette for dinner."

"Yummy!"

"I hope the old cunt chokes on it."

"Wah, Toneh! Sech a way to talk Ah nevah in all mah bawn days *did* heah! You were bein' so all-fired sweet to ole Miz Puddum Ah lak ta bust."

"Oh, come off it! For Christ's sake, I do everything but go down on her and she treats me like some kind of carpetbagger."

"In a way you are."

"What do you mean?" Tony's tone was sharp.

"I mean you've taken Sonny away from the ole plantation. As far as she's concerned, you're just a damyankee interloper who . . ."

"Maybe you're right. When the old cow got *good* and drunk she said about a hundred times what a shame it was that Tatham didn't go back home '*where he belongs*' and settle down with some nice girl."

"That nice girl naturally being Mrs. Purdom herself?"

"Well, at least she hasn't caught on," Tony said. "And what's more, she's not going to. Talk about square!"

"Square, yes. Stupid, no. Miz P. is nobody's fool. I'll bet Tatham will be glad to dump her at her hotel and . . ."

"*What* hotel? She's sleeping right down below in the bedroom."

"All three of you?"

"Lan's sakes, Sonny, whin you-all got that great big ole house up theah in Noo Yawk whah should Ah go spind a lotta moneh in some *ho*-tel," he mimicked angrily. "No. She's moved in bag and baggage. Tat and I are holed up down in the basement where he keeps his old records. 'Tony's room' he calls it."

"Poor Tatham."

"Poor Tatham hell! Don't think it's any lead pipe cinch living with him and his long-hair records and his banging away on the piano all day. As for his cooking . . ." I sneezed loudly three times. "Gezundheit!"

"Sorry. I seem to have this cold coming on," I said.

"Well, in that case, I'd better clear out. If there's one thing I don't need right now it's to catch somebody's cold. So long."

"Good night," I said. "And good luck." I emptied the rest of the whisky into a glass of hot water, drank it, and went to bed.

The next morning I woke up sick—really sick: sweats, chills, shakes, and all the rest of it. Harold Dean Associates seemed downright pleased that I wouldn't be able to make it to the office. "I *quite* understand," Mr. Dean said. "Until New Year's has come and gone and all this holiday nonsense is finished and done for, nobody's doing any work anyhow. Why don't I send the messenger over with a few manuscripts? With no interruptions you can get a lot of reading done—clear out all the unsolicited material and start the new year with a clean shelf. Take care, and don't *think* of coming in until you're fit."

After our moronic messenger, bearing the burden of two dozen manuscripts, pressed the wrong doorbell, my exact condition and whereabouts were known to the entire household. There would have been fewer interruptions at the office but I was dogged about reading—or trying to read—enough of each author's offering to write an intelligent reason for not publishing it.

I began with a toxic little jollification entitled *Around the World in a GI Bra*. It was the first of what would be an endless series of smart-assed war reminiscences, this one submitted by a WAC, the convulsed recipients of whose letters must have urged her to attempt writing professionally. It was a large collection of old jokes badly told.

. . . I was just getting rid of the *valet de chambre* in my best high school French when Margie yoo-hooed from the john.

131

"Oh my aching back! Helen, what in the blankety-blank is this?" I went in, hoping to finally dislodge her so I could shampoo the tics and chiggers of "la belle France" out of my "crowning glory." Margie was pointing at a little hunk of plumbing that looked like a foot bath. "Is that to wash the baby in?" asked she. "No, dopy," I ha-ha-ed, "that's to wash the baby *out!*"

There was a rap at the door and Tatham entered with a breakfast tray. As always the arrangement was artistic—fluted napkin and bud vase—and the food abominable. Owing perhaps to the presence of Mrs. Purdom, the meal was depressingly Southern. "Thanks, Tat, but I really don't think I can."

"Feed a cold and stahve a fevah."

"I have both."

"Please. Or I'll be offended." He sat down and watched me eagerly as I moved the mess around with a fork and finally settled for the Nescafé. "Mothah thought you were very nice."

"That was sweet of her. How's everything going down below?"

"Well, Ah don't exactly know. Mothah doesn't say much. Tony's already out. He's just killing himself to do things for Mothah. He's trying to get seats for *Life with Fathah* and *Carousel* and *Up in Central Park* and *Ah Remembah Mama* and those sorta wholesome shows he thinks Mothah would like."

"Yes, a nice dark theater where nobody can talk is probably the best idea," I said, recalling the day I had spent with Tony in Chicago nearly ten years before.

"Mothah's very fond of you."

"Meaning that she's not very fond of Tony?"

"Well, Ah can't exactly tell. She hasn't *said* anything. She *did* say that she was coming up to visit with you. She knows what it's like to be sick and have no one come to see you. She hasn't been well herself. Maybe you could listen to my broadcast together."

"That's nice of her, Tat, but I may be quite contagious and I have a lot of work to do. Well, thanks for the breakfast and say hello to Mrs. Purdom for me."

The historical novel was still going strong at the end of 1945. Even Harold Dean Associates had hit the best-seller lists in a small way with a long novel dealing with the French Revolution and Mr. Dean was anxious to publish any other rousing historical that was "well written, accurately researched, indicative of impeccable scholarship and has enough hay scenes to keep the slobs reading." Six of the manuscripts piled at the foot of my bed were overblown pieces ranging in period from the fall of Babylon to the siege of Richmond. The one I chose had something or other to do with the signing of the Magna Charta.

Princess Margit arranged her sable-lined mantle gracefully over her new blue silk bliaud. The buds of her firm young breasts had flowered over the English summer into full-blown roses. She often stroked them with her white, tapering hands, shuddering with delight. "Forsooth, sire," she murmured, scarce concealing the smile that played at the corners of her delicate coral lips, "prithee jest not with so simple and unread a maiden as thy humble daughter. Od's bodkins, but what thou hast just said must indeed be a conundrum to fuddle my poor head." Her father strode across the rushes strewn on the floor of the common room. "Nay, daughter, 'tis no idle jest. Sir Orplid hath bade me give him thee in wedlock. His equerry awaits beyond the moat for . . ."

"Jesus H. Christ!" Tony bellowed, slamming into my apartment without knocking. "One more snide crack out of that old bitch and I'll throttle her!"

"What now?" I asked, happy to put down the bulky manuscript.

"Nothing suits her. Here we move into this really chic house and she's tramping around the drawing room running the whole place down. 'Lan' sakes alahve, with so many gawjus ole places down home Ah surely don't know why Sonny bought this ole roomin' house. Sonny could have his pi-yuck of inny position he wanted down home, yit he comes up Nawth heah to talk to a lot of old opra singahs on the radio. It's not lak it was In-Bee-See or inny station innybodeh evah hud of. We've got the grayundest li'l ole radio station down home an' jes gawjus music. Now till me, what do you-all do fer a livin', Mistah van Dinbug?' She's driving me right out of my box."

"It won't be long."

"It's been long already and she'll be here till after New Year. I don't know when she's leaving, but one of us has got to go."

I couldn't help laughing. "What are your plans for New Year's Eve—Guy Lombardo at the Roosevelt Grill? A festive supper at the Jumble Shop? Times Square at . . ."

"I got seats for Song of Norway and . . . Oh, shut up. Here Tat's always told me what a gay old bat she is. Loves to get dressed up and have a few drinks and . . ."

"She didn't seem to be leading any prohibition movement last night."

"Yeah, but she practically snapped my head off. I'm supposed to be good with the old girls. I'll never forget that Aunt What's-her-name of yours in the Plaza. But this one's driving me out of my own home and . . ."

"And right up to mine. Aren't you afraid of catching my cold?"

"Hell, at this point I don't care if you've got leprosy. Oh, and if she should ever ask you what I do, tell her I'm an editor at your place—sort of an executive editor who can come and go all day long. That's what I told her. Well, I'm off for a decent lunch. Take in a movie or something. So long."

Casting aside the historical novel as one that would never see a printing press, I dipped into the memoirs of a general—a man I had never heard of, which was surprising as, to judge from his manuscript, he had, quite without help, won both world wars, albeit hindered by such upstarts as Pershing, Kitchener, Foch,

Montgomery, Eisenhower, MacArthur or Patton. With Franklin Delano Roosevelt dead, buried, and well beyond refuting any of the general's statements, I also got the impression that when the general wasn't spang in the middle of a battlefield, he was at the White House supervising all civilian activity as well.

It was around midnight, 6 December 1941, when F.D.R. called me on the secret telephone line only the two of us knew about. "Butch," the Chief said, "afraid we're in for a bit of trouble." "What is it, Frank?" I said. "It's the Japanese. You were right, Butch. They're going to attack."

A world in crisis was interrupted by yet another tray, this one borne by Mrs. Purdom herself. It contained a curdled eggnog, rigid with rum, and a peanut butter sandwich. "This is very good," I lied. It was better than anything Tatham had ever served up, but then it is difficult to do very much to a peanut butter sandwich. "Ah made it mahself," Mrs. Purdom simpered. "Ah truly don't know innythang about keepin' house. Ah was always waited on hand and foot like a queen. But the war come along and the Niggrahs Ah'd stood ovah and taught ivvry blessed thang they knew all walked out for jobs in a definse plant. That's the thanks you get."

Mrs. Purdom sat down, lifting her short skirts high to display her scrawny little legs, and lighted one of her social cigarettes. I knew that I was in for a long visit. Mrs. Purdom, amiability itself, was filled to overflowing with chitchat, non sequitur following non sequitur, as she spoke admiringly of her clothes (junior miss dresses in a size too small, usually sticky pastels and always cut low over her tremendous bosom) and her jewels (large globs of aquamarines, tourmalines, amethysts, and other semiprecious stones, worn in matching sets of earrings, brooch, and "dinner" ring). With an airy kick of a crossed leg, she deplored loudly the difficulty of finding shoes small enough to fit her. She was shod today, as always, in two-tone suède sandals very high of heel, toes jutting out far beyond the limits of the last, insteps bulging painfully between vamp and ankle strap. How much better for all concerned, I thought, if she had hated me and adored Tony. I sensed, however, that she had not puffed up the stairs to discuss her clothing problems. There was not too long a time to wait until, with her annoying accompaniment of smirks and fluttering gestures, Mrs. Purdom got down to the business at hand.

"Ah believe that you ah Mr. van Dinbug's oldest and dearest frind?"

"Not quite. I've known him for nine or ten years. We were in school together."

"And his family?"

"I met Dr. and Mrs. Vandenberg," I said, lapsing into the old spelling of the name, "once. They live in Chicago."

"*Doctah?* He's a dintist and they live in Ivvanston, Illinoise. And they are as poah as Job's tuckey."

"I didn't go into their finances."

"Well, *Ah* did. Through the credit depahtment at Purdom Brothahs, Ah have means of findin' out. As for this boy, he has nixt to nothing. Fifteen to twenty thousand in the bank."

It sounded like quite a lot to me. In the hope of shutting off further confidences I said, "It's time for Tat's broadcast, Mrs. Purdom. Wouldn't you like to hear it?" I snapped on the radio.

"Uh, good afternoon, uh, this is Tatham Purdom, your, uh, opera analyst. It is my, uh, very great pleasure to have in the, uh, studio this, uh, afternoon that distinguished, uh, Spanish countertenor Señor Alejandro de los Santos. . . ."

"That don't sound like Sonny."

It did and it didn't. On the air Tatham did what he could to soft-pedal his accent, but his speech was slow, full of throat-clearings, pauses, ums and ahs. He was not what you'd call "a natural."

"Uh, Señor de los Santos, you are of course best known for your, uh, delightful, uh, interpretations of Purcell and Lully, but now I, uh, wonder if you could, uh, tell our audience something of the, uh, very high range and scope of the, uh, countertenor voice."

In a piercing falsetto Tat's guest launched into his spiel, his English all but unintelligible. "Tonk you, Meeser Purdom. Dere is olmose no contertenors leeving today. Only vairy few. Wain Ai study in Modreeth oz vairy yong man, mai, how-you-say . . ."

"Who's that forrun woman talkin' ta Sonny?"

"It's a man. A countertenor." I had expected so doting a mother to sit rapt, drinking in her son's every profundity. Not Mrs. Purdom. "Sonny could own the radio station down home. If Mistah Purdom hadn't passed away they'da bin nonna this music school nonsince. Tatham woulda gone ta the university. Maybe the Citidil. With all mah bizznizzizz he could run . . ."

". . . feel sure you agree, uh, Señor de los Santos," Tat was saying with unusual passion, "that one of the real outrages perpetrated against the, uh, true lover of seventeenth-century music is, uh, the obstinate refusal—the almost pigheaded refusal, if I may employ such, uh, strong language—of impresarios today to produce such operas as *Orfeo* or Lully's magnificent *Alceste*, which offer the, uh, countertenor a golden and, uh, rare opportunity to . . ."

"Now take this old house," Mrs. Purdom was saying. "Have you inny ah-dea how much mah boy pawed into this rat trap?"

"I only rent an apartment here. I don't know what it cost them."

"*Them?* Cost *them?* Well, Ah can tellya hah much it cost yoah fon frind. Not a cint. Not one red pinny! But mah son took the moneh his daddy left him and . . ."

". . . exquisite *Ode for St. Cecelia's Day* and John Blow's masque, uh, *Venus and Adonis* stand alone in the, uh, little available literature for the, uh, countertenor voice. . . ."

It had occurred to me that the domestic arrangements downstairs were perhaps something less than fifty-fifty. It was also

137

none of my business. I said so without much hope of being heard above the radio and Mrs. Purdom.

". . . *Jubilate in C Major.* And, of course, your matchless interpretation of Purcell's sublime masque, *The*, uh, *Fairy Queen.*"

". . . milkin' mah boy dry, *that's* what he's doin'.'"

". . . very great treat indeed, this rare recording of the final act of *Dido and Aeneas.* Alejandro de los Santos sings the role of Aeneas and on this, uh, record you will also hear the haunting aria, 'When I Am, uh, Laid,' Dido's farewell, sung by . . .'"

". . . stand by silently an' watch the wool pulled ovah mah boy's eyes. . . .'"

There was some scratching and clicking, then a lot of cellos and viols and a piping voice screeching over the loudspeaker.

"Now Ah ask you, what do you think?"

"Mrs. Purdom, I think it's none of my business."

With that she became all coy and girlish again. "Well, Ah know you won't breathe a wud of what we've been discussin'." *We?* "Ah'd better get on downstairs now and fix mahself up for Tatham and tell him how much Ah enjoyed his broadcast."

For the next couple of days, while I took aspirin, blew my nose, and read my way through more historicals and two uplift books with the working titles of *Heal Thyself* and *Take Up Thy Bed*, Tony, Tat, and Mrs. Purdom visited sporadically. Tony said that he was about to put ground glass in Mrs. Purdom's grits. Mrs. Purdom said that she was about to have the law on Tony. Tatham said that things were going as well as could be expected. In the evenings they took Mrs. Purdom to things like the revival of *The Red Mill* and I was intrigued to hear Tony and Tat raise their voices in "Every Day Is Ladies' Day with Me" from the floor below.

On Saturday afternoon the house was blissfully still. Tatham was in New Jersey for his broadcast, Tony was just "out," and Mrs. Purdom had been sent off on her own to take in a matinee.

It was growing dark and I had just switched on my lamp to finish off a manuscript of bucolic recollections called something like *I Remember Life with Father in Mother's Boardinghouse and Chicken Every Sunday* when the door burst open and there stood Mrs. Purdom, hair awry and brandishing a leatherbound book. "Ah hate and despise to bothah you, but it has been a most distressin' twinty-foah hoahs. We wint to see this show *Bloomah Gull* last night and out on the stage comes this Niggrah to sing this song about bein' free and who should stand right up and applaud but mah own boy! Ah could have died! Then today Ah wint to a matinee bah mahself—some trash called *Deep Ah the Roots*—and in the middle of it this white gull kisses a coal black Niggah! Ah walked right out."

"It's a shame Katherine Dunham's *Carib Song* just closed, but *Show Boat* is coming back."

"And whin Ah got back home what should be waitin' at the front daw but anothah Niggrah, uppity as you please. 'Is Tatty home?' he says to me. Callin' mah son by his *Christian* name!"

"That would be Jackson Balderston. They're great friends," I said, hoping that the shock would shut her up. Of course it didn't. I couldn't believe that she had come charging in to discuss the race question and I was right. This was but a preamble to what she really wanted to say.

"Ah was so undone Ah had to have a drank and while Ah was lookin' for a bottle, Ah found *this*. Mah boy's diary. Believe me, Ah come to you only because Ah'm most distressed by what Ah've read. You are a well-bred gintleman and . . ."

"I'm well bred enough not to read other people's diaries, Mrs. Purdom." It made no dent.

"What Ah had begun to suspect and feah in mah hot of hots is all true. That low, unprincipaled swine has se-duced mah boy, dragged him away from his home and his mothah to live a vile, unnatural life that . . . Ah jes can't go on. Wuds fail me."

I was grateful for that but at a loss for anything to say. Pointless to point out that nobody had seduced anybody; that her son was what he was and that if he had not found Tony he would have settled for someone else, possibly better, probably worse. Nothing I could say would do any good. Mrs. Purdom had the facts before her in black and white. Now she was outraged motherhood, blind to any shortcomings, no matter how obvious, her child might have.

"Mrs. Purdom," I said, "you've got to remember that Tatham is twenty-seven, twenty-eight—older than Tony. If this is the life they choose to lead, I don't see that you can do anything about it."

From the distraught little mother role she had been performing so badly, Mrs. Purdom became the woman of steel I had always known she was. "Oh, Ah can't, can't Ah? Well, we'll see. *We'll just see.*"

My chances for just seeing were a lot better than I had expected. At that moment Tony entered without knocking—as usual. "Well, for once there's a little peace and quiet . . . Oh, Mrs. Purdom. I didn't know you were up here."

"Ah'm morally certain you didn't. But now that youah home, Mistah van Dinbug, Ah would lak a wud with you."

"Would you mind not having it here?" I said. "I have work to do—and besides, I've been sick." The air was frosty with their mutual loathing as they left.

I turned in early that night, filled with foreboding and hot lemonade. I was just falling asleep when there was a loud pounding at my door which, for once, I had locked. There stood Tony, dapper in a trench coat and a pork-pie hat.

"What are you doing here? I thought you three musketeers were off to yet another night of wholesome theater—*Oklahoma.*"

"I got out of it. Said I'd picked up your cold. I've seen it anyhow. I've really come to say good-by."

"Going somewhere?"

"Palm Beach."

"So, Mrs. Purdom got the best of you after all?"

"No. I got the best of her. And it's probably better this way. It wouldn't have lasted. Those things never do."

"You mean you and Tat are splitting up?"

"He doesn't know—yet. I left a note."

"I see."

"And that reminds me. What I came up here for was to ask if I could store a few things in your apartment for a little while. I don't know when I'll be back but . . ."

"Go ahead, Tony. Just put them here in the living room. But do it quietly. I'm going back to bed."

"You're true blue, pal. Really T.B."

"Just one question, Tony. How much did Mrs. Purdom pay you to run out on Tatham?"

"Well! If you weren't sick, I'd bust you one right in the . . . What kind of person do you think I am anyway?"

"I haven't got time to tell you, Tony. Good-by."

The coroner's verdict was "accidental death from an overdose of barbiturates." Mrs. Purdom was in a state of hysteria, thrashing about the big black bedroom, moaning and sobbing and, now and again, screaming out that Tony had murdered her son. She was just able to telephone her bank and stop payment on the check she had given Tony before collapsing and being carted off to the hospital. It didn't really matter. By the terms of Tatham Purdom's will, John Anthony van Denberg was his sole heir.

VI

TONY

in love

The beginning of 1946 was a time of fairly feverish activity. The firm of Harold Dean Associates was gobbled up by a much larger publishing house that wanted, for some reason, our list of prestigious money-losing authors and the tweedy presence of Mr. Dean himself. The new firm, however, did not seem to want any more junior editors and so I was out of a job. Just about then Aunt Harriet died, naming me as her heir because, as with all deaths in my family, there was no one else to leave the money to. Aunt Harriet's trust fund died with her, so that her passing did not automatically make me a man of means, but in addition to her dowdy dresses and jewels, there were sufficient stocks, bonds, and cash in her bequest to allow me to take off a couple of years and try my hand at writing a book of my own. And at the same time, Tatham Purdom's house on Sixteenth Street was sold by its absentee landlord to a fecund couple of well-off bohemians given to thong sandals, leather clothing, and constant pregnancies. Since they had six children under the age of seven and another obviously on the way, they were only too happy to have me break my lease and clear out. As my few bits and pieces were being carted out, the dark walls and white woodwork of Tony's love nest were already being stripped down to the bare brick.

Living and working in old—not New—Mexico, I was more out of touch with the sort of civilization Tony fancied than ever before. By watching my money carefully I was able to afford a tiny house on the sea at Yucatán, a motherly maid-of-all-work, food, cigarettes, and typewriter ribbons. Fashions changed, the O.P.A. was abolished, other Americans went to the polls to re-elect Harry S Truman, but they did so without any help from me. I was hard at work and knew only vaguely what was going on in the United States.

But my exile was not in vain. By the spring of 1949 I was the author of a published novel with the second one finished and scheduled for the following fall. I had a slim scrapbook of favorable reviews and my first book had been bought by the movies. A photograph of me squinting into the sunlight and duly credited to Maria Pilar Diaz (my maid, who had clicked the shutter of the camera and had gained local immortality as the only citizen of her village whose name had ever appeared in print in the Yanqui press) had appeared in *Time*, the *Saturday Review*, and all of the suitable literary supplements. For the first time in my life I had money in the bank and a very modest fame. I was—to quote my agent—on my way. To prove it, a thickish packet of junk mail was being forwarded by my publisher once each week—letters from clipping bureaus offering their exclusive services; invitations to speak at book-and-author luncheons; galleys from other publishers requesting my favorable comment; a threatened plagiarism suit from a crank in Brooklyn; an application blank from *Who's Who*; and, eventually, a plump envelope addressed in Tony's extravagant handwriting.

Dear Old Pal—

Where have you been hiding yourself all these years? I've missed you, kiddo. But I saw your picture in *Time*, read the review of your book, and now proudly say to everyone I meet, "I knew him when." No kidding, it's great about your book. Haven't read it yet (I've been busy as a bird dog) but I certainly hope to. I also see in Winchell that you sold it to Hollywood. Terrific! You must really be in the chips!

I'm sending this letter to your publisher and hoping that it doesn't end up in the circular file, because I've got some news, too, and I want you to be the first to know it.

I'm getting married!!!! What's more, you know the girl and I'm sure that—after you come out of your faint—you'll see how right we are for each other. It's Posy Perry!

What I'm really writing to say is that the wedding will take place on Saturday, June 25, and *I want you to be best man.* I know you're rich and famous now, but remember, you're my oldest and dearest friend, so don't let me down. You can stay here with me (I have a little *garçonnière* on Park and 55th) until the week of the Big Event when we all move out to Perry-go-Round in Southampton. Call me (collect) and say YES!

Bestest,
Tony

P.S. Posy and I only want one thing for a wedding present—an autographed photo, with something really personal written on it. We're starting a whole gallery of pictures of our famous friends.

From the snowstorm of clippings that fluttered out of Tony's envelope, I gathered that I was not quite the first to know. Articles announcing the forthcoming P-V nuptials had appeared in the *Times, Tribune, News, Mirror, World-Telegram, Journal*

American, and Sun, and the Chicago newspapers had graciously granted equal coverage. It all sounded very grand—a truly top-drawer society engagement—complete with town and country addresses, a list of the schools attended by the happy couple, the names of grandparents (hers, not his), clubs, the bridegroom's brilliant war record, and the proposed date of the wedding. What interested me most was to see that Dr. Vandenberg had managed to die and that Rose Vandenberg was now a Mrs. Willingham of Chicago, Palm Beach, and Santa Barbara. With his father out of the way, Tony was now Mr. van den Berg.

My better judgment told me to refuse Tony's invitation but my curiosity wouldn't listen. An all-expenses-paid bid to go to New York and discuss a series of articles with the editor of a big monthly magazine arrived in the same mail. It was too much for me. I sat down immediately and wrote Tony that I would be there.

From then on the mails were hot with bulletins from Tony, each enclosing a sheaf of clippings concerning his forthcoming marriage. In their columns Cholly Knickerbocker and Charles Ventura had informed a rapt public that I, a best-selling author, was to function as Mr. van den Berg's principal attendant. My book had sold respectably but never that well. However, Tony wrote that the added impetus of being mentioned on the society page would undoubtedly move thousands of the "right people" to load up on copies of my novel. Somehow it never did.

In another letter Tony also asked me to write a story or an article of three-to-five-thousand words for his new magazine, *East of Fifth*. The magazine paid almost nothing to its contributors but the prestige of appearing between its covers would be invaluable. Not just anyone was asked to write for *East of Fifth*, as not just anyone was allowed to subscribe.

You can't turn your back on New York for very long without having the face of the city change. The same was true of Tony. He was very much a figure of fashionable New York, billed in the press as "Tony van den Berg, publisher and smart man-about-town." His little garçonnière was little indeed. It was a one-room-and-foyer "efficiency" apartment at the rear of a low block of converted brownstone houses even then scheduled for demolition. Some of the apartments in the building were spacious and charming. Tony's was neither. It was simply a cheap way to achieve the dubious prestige of a Park Avenue address. The entrance to Tony's flat was on East Fifty-fifth Street and the address of *East of Fifth*, "The Journal of Smart Manhattan," was 101 East Fifty-fifth. It did not take a cartographer to figure out that Tony's living quarters and his magazine's editorial and business offices were one and the same place.

Tony looked buoyant and blooming as ever. His hair was a trifle longer at the sides and he was nicely sunlamped, although from the way his clothes fit I gathered—with a certain malicious satisfaction—that he had grown heavier.

"Putting on weight?" I asked.

"Certainly not!" Tony said, moving to the mirrored wall in his foyer. "Why? Do I look fat or something?"

"No. Your suit just looks a little—well, tight."

"Oh, come to the party! You've been off with those peons too long. This is the newest thing. Italian. In London they call it Edwardian."

"Like the Teddy Boys wear?"

"What the hell would you know about it anyway? Come on in and have a drink. We've got a lot to catch up on."

"Efficiency" certainly described the place. Tony was able to cram a lot of living and—to hear him talk about it, at least—a lot of business into one medium-sized room. The telephone was his most valuable piece of equipment, all calls being taken by an answering service that tried to sound as secretarial as possible while Tony listened in before deciding whether to speak to the lucky caller or not.

Except for the telephones—there were four—with their ranks of pushbuttons and flashing lights, the place was stark simplicity, its fittings made mostly of glass and brass, blond wood, steel, flush doors, and foam rubber, with the essentials of living hidden behind screens or curtains or flopping down out of the walls. A sluttish part-time secretary came and went at Tony's convenience. She was sent home on my arrival.

"Very functional," I said, wondering just where I was to be bedded down. A squat crystal bowl filled with ice and Scotch was placed in my hands. "Now tell me about Posy."

Tony's face took on an other-worldly look. His eyes rolled, suggesting the dangerous possibility of a catatonic seizure. "You'll never believe this, but I'm wrapped in a blanket of love."

I didn't believe it, but I wasn't going to ruin his performance by saying so. Tony in love was too good to miss. "How did you, uh, young people happen to get together?"

"Well, naturally, I've *knaown* Posy for some years. At school with Greer and all." Naturally he hadn't. Greer Perry had to be out of town—out of the country—before Tony would have so much as dared to telephone Posy. Fate and the Foreign Service had intervened nicely. "Well, I mean I kept seeing her around town at parties and the poor child was so bored with that usual deb routine. Posy's a ve-ry intelligent girl, incidentally."

It occurred to me that from what I had seen of Posy, any intelligence would have to be entirely incidental. "Go on," I said.

"Anyway, I was down in Palm Beach on business . . ."

"You mean after Tatham killed himself?"

"Uh, yes, poor Tat. Suicide was never proven. I always begged him not to take sleeping pills. Anyhow," he continued briskly, "I was down there on business and Posy arrived with her mother. It's a terribly shallow existence they lead down in P.B. (Palm Beach)," he explained, "and Posy and I were sort of drawn together."

"Two intellectuals cast up on the beach."

"I suppose you might say that." He went on quite seriously. "At that time she was engaged to Morgan Wyckoff—I don't suppose you know him."

"No, I don't."

"Typical. Lawrenceville, Princeton, Navy. Drinks too much and, if you ask me, a tiny bit queer around the edges."

"You should know," I said, but Tony didn't even notice. He had thrown himself into his new role too wholeheartedly to be bothered by anything so trivial as a few basic facts about his recent life. It was as though he were selling himself to some total stranger.

"I could see the future all too clearly and, let me tell you, it looked disastrous." Tony took a cigarette from his gold case, fitted it into a stubby, gold-banded Dunhill holder, and flicked at it with a gold lighter. "There was poor little Posy all but climbing the walls with boredom. You know, this New York social grind can be pretty wearing. The same old routine—living somewhere between Fifth and the East River, north of Forty-ninth Street and south of Ninety-sixth; going to one of a dozen decent schools; dancing class; boarding school; the Junior Assemblies, coming out; parties, parties, parties; engagement; a big society wedding; the honeymoon in Europe . . ."

"Where are you and Posy going?"

"Europe. The little apartment in the same old compound; babies; then the same old routine all over again for the next generation. A girl with Posy's potential certainly deserves something different."

"Well, that's you."

"Right. So I simply took over."

"You mean you broke up the engagement? Asked her to marry you?"

"Not just then. But I realized that Posy was too good to throw herself away on that stagnant sort of existence. I said to her, 'Posy, you're still young. You can get married any time you want. But why not live a little first? Get a job. Do something new and different. Meet interesting people.' So she broke off with Wyckoff, came back to New York, and got a job modeling at Bonwit's."

"That must have been a challenge."

"It was a beginning. Well, I came into some money about then. . . ."

"Sure. Tatham Purdom's. I read all about it. It even made the airmail edition of the New York Times. I'm sure the Mirror gave the story a much jazzier treatment. They're awfully good with contested wills—undue influence, unnatural relationships, and all the rest of it. Tell me, what did Miz Purdom wear to the trial?"

He ignored me. "Well, it occurred to me that New York was ready for a new kind of magazine. I mean The New Yorker really is 'for the little old lady in Dubuque' by now—and for the birds. You can hop on a plane today and before you know it you're in London, Paris, Rome—anywhere you want to be. Society is on the move and up till now there's been no magazine to keep track of it."

"Does anybody care that much?"

"Well, you just bet they do and I'm the one to tell them about it."

Posy Perry was forgotten. From then on the talk was exclusively concerned with East of Fifth (which, I learned, meant all the way east as far as the Iron Curtain) and what a tremendous gazette of the high life and high times it was going to be. Yes, going to be. From one of the room's many hidden recesses Tony produced a stack of dummy copies of his revolutionary chronicle. It looked like the kind of magazine that comes free with a hotel room: little squibs about local restaurants, plays, parties, and photographs of people eating. As a bow to the beau monde at large, it contained the startling information that Claridge's Hotel was in London, a dressmaker named Dior was in Paris, and the Pope in Rome. Although Elsa Maxwell, Cleveland Amory, Lucius Beebe, Jerome Zerbe, and a lot of other names were mentioned by Tony as regular contributors, the only article was an inaccurate panegyric to the old Ritz-Carlton filled with terms like "milady," "residence," "drapes," and every other taboo of the glossy magazine trade. Its author was Posy Perry.

149

"How much did Posy invest in *East of Fifth?*" I asked.

Too wrapped up in himself to grasp my meaning, Tony said, "Not much. Only ten thousand. But to get this thing really off the ground I'll need at least a million." The names of such prominent magazine sponsors as Henry Luce, Gardiner Cowles, and Marshall Field—"Hank," "Mike," and "Marsh"—were all mentioned as being "very interested." With a lot of specific questioning, the actual backers of *East of Fifth* boiled down to Posy, her mother, and Tony's mother, Mrs. Willingham. "I don't suppose you'd be interested in sinking any of your movie money into a sure thing?"

"Correct. Now get back to Posy, please."

Reluctantly Tony shifted gears, reassumed the misty-eyed look, and was once more the young man in love. "We're just perfect for each other. Really we are."

"I'm sure of it."

"What a life it's going to be! And to share it with someone like Posy—a girl with background, breeding, beauty, and brains."

The door opened and there stood background, breeding, beauty, and brains in the flesh. Posy, apparently, carried a key to Tony's apartment and for all of her background, breeding, beauty, and brains didn't bother to ring the bell. Their embrace was epic—so steamy that I wanted to look away, although there was no other place to look. I grasped immediately what Posy saw in Tony. It is almost impossible to sense sex appeal in someone of your own gender, but I had always been fairly certain that Tony must have had lots of it, even though to me he would forever be the raffish youngster who had bowled me over with his line of malarkey on our first day at school. Posy, a bit wobbly, finally broke away from Tony and held out her limp hand to greet me. "How nice to see you again," she said. For all the changes Tony claimed to have wrought, once out of his arms Posy seemed to be the same stupid girl I had taken to dinner more than three years ago.

"I can't tell you how I adored your book," she said. "We both did. Didn't we, darling?"

"It was terrific," Tony said. "I read it in one sitting, didn't I, darling?"

"Did you?" Posy asked blankly, stunned at such an achievement.

"Here, you've got to sign it for us," Tony said, handing me a copy of my book. From the noise the binding made as I turned to the flyleaf, I knew that the book had never been opened before. It seemed wiser not to question either of them too closely as to plot and character delineation, so I asked them instead about their own immediate plans.

"Well, naturally we're getting married in the country next week. It'll be really the first wedding of the Southampton season," Posy said. "I mean everybody'll be there by then. And Europe for a honeymoon and then we'll be settling into our apartment. It's a divine apartment."

"A duplex," Tony said.

"It's awfully big for just two people, but Mummy said if I get pregnant right away I won't feel like hunting around for a larger place and moving."

"Are you planning on a large family?" I asked. The thought was appalling.

"Well . . ."

"You bet we are! I love kids. Boys to enter in our old school. Little girls to bring up and bring out." Tony and Posy gushed on and from their fulsome descriptions of good addresses, good clubs, good nannies and good schools for their unborn brood, I didn't see how Posy's future under Tony's tutelage was to differ radically from the stereotyped existence she would have faced with Morgan Wyckoff except possibly in bed. The life Tony had so deplored was exactly the life he intended to lead and it was also the life Posy really wanted to continue leading, assuming that she could share it with someone who aroused her. At that point Tony started arousing her again. I excused myself and went into the bathroom. From the supplies in the medicine chest I gathered that Tony had been arousing Posy for some time and that there would be little danger of an unexpected pregnancy.

I used the toilet, washed my hands, brushed my teeth, and gargled. After a great deal of rattling the knob, I opened the door, hoping against hope not to interrupt them in the midst of copulation. In my absence the party had been joined by a girl named Tracy Something, who was to be Posy's maid of honor. Most of Posy's friends suffered from epicene names such as Tracy, Whitney, Leslie, or Courtney, and during the week of the wedding festivities they whined, to a woman, "It's too maddening. Half my mail comes addressed to 'Mister.' " Tracy could have been Posy in a dark wig for all of the individuality either of them possessed. However Tracy did comprise an audience—an unknown quantity for Tony to impress—and the new Tony stepped on stage.

The new Tony was the natural culmination of Madcap Tony, the Gilded Youth; Dashing Tony, the Debutantes' Delight; Pukka Sahib Tony, Menace of the Middle East; and Chi-chi Tony of the Gay Set. The new Tony was altogether Smart New York, vintage of 1949. He was known and knowing and not at all the sort to rush to the Stork Club, Brooks Brothers, Tiffany's, or Twenty-one simply because they were highly touted places where "everyone" went. Oh yes, he knew them well and would attend them now and again because they were standards in their field, classics so to speak, but he would enter such places rarely and, when he honored them with his presence, he would do so with an air of amused detachment, watching the yokels being impressed by what was, really, terribly old hat. The new Tony haunted the small, chic, inside places that had sprung up in the East Fifties and Sixties since the war.

Tony took us to dinner, but not to an obvious place like the Colony or Voisin, although they were, as he said, "quite nice enough in their way." We dined in a brocade cave run by a ruined Sicilian princess where the chandeliers and drinking

152

glasses were Baccarat, where no prices appeared on the menu, and where no money was ever seen changing hands. Tracy thought it was divine and Posy said, "Tony knows the most fantastic places. Don't you, darling?"

The evening's entertainment was not El Morocco ("Elmer's used to be fun," Tony said), but yet another basement, pitch black inside, where no one spoke above a whisper and at midnight a former leader of the Yugoslav resistance movement sang in Serbo-Croatian.

Posy's glittering engagement ring had not come from Cartier's or even Van Cleef & Arpels, but from the very newest smart jeweler—a Bulgarian known to only the very few. Even Tony's trousseau—for it amounted to that—had been ordered from an almost secret tailor with an unpronounceable Italian name. Under the guidance of the new Tony, New York became as foreign to me as Belgrade or Saigon and I was happy to get out of it.

The wedding, from the very outset, had had all the earmarks of the supercolossal production, and watching the machinery begin to turn in Southampton, I felt thankful that love had passed me by. With the aid of a Mrs. Edgecomb, a decayed gentlewoman adept at bullying caterers, ticking names off lists, and recording gifts, Mrs. Perry (the Mrs. Mallory of my day had since shucked both Mr. Mallory and Mr. Thaxter and had remarried Mr. Perry if, for no other reason, only to simplify the problems of engraving, press releases, and giving the bride away) was in her element. One would have thought that a woman with so much firsthand matrimonial experience could have handled every detail with her eyes closed, but Posy's was to be no run-of-the-mill wedding. "Poor little thing had such a pokey coming-out party, with the war and all, that I simply had to make it up to her somehow." Mrs. Perry spoke of a world holocaust as though it had been an annoying inconvenience along the lines of a flu epidemic or unseasonable rains.

Perry-go-Round, the family seat in Southampton, although its style was Mediterranean and its furnishings a professionally assembled Franco-Italo-Hispanic mélange, managed to look exactly like the apartment on Fifth Avenue. The main hall was hung with the old Augustus John painting of Mrs. Perry, joined familially by portraits of Posy in her debut dress, Mr. Perry in hunting pinks, Greer in uniform, and Greer's Brazilian wife in emeralds. I could never pass through it to the quarters which I shared with Tony without being reminded of a very minor gallery in the Prado.

The celebrations were endless as ushers, bridesmaids, and relatives poured in. The Whitneys and Tracys and Leslies and Courtneys, who were to function as Posy's handmaidens, didn't seem to like her, each other, or the whole idea of the wedding very much, although they twittered brightly over Tony. They complained about the color, cut, and cost of their dresses (a rather trying shade of green), the hardship of traveling to Southampton for the wedding, and the ushers with whom they would be paired. Tony's ushers were all somewhat younger and so alike that I never quite sorted them out. The only ones known to me were Lady ffynche's dreary grandson and Greer Perry. Greer arrived from Rio de Janeiro complete with child, governess, and Maria Luisa his wife, a tiny beauty who looked like a soignée midget. She had a mechanical charm, spoke Portuguese, Spanish, French, and English interchangeably but with such a strong accent that it was impossible for me to decide which language she had just turned on or off. Maria Luisa wore Paris dresses and—a failing of all South American women—too much jewelry, all of it real. What, or if, she thought about anything was impossible to guess, but I got the feeling that she loathed all of the Perry family—especially Greer.

So did I, and nothing that had happened to Greer over the past decade had made him any more attractive. He had gained at least fifty pounds. For all the tars and oils and lotions he had rubbed into his scalp, his hair had nearly given up the ghost. He was, in 1949, what you'd call a hairy bald man, the few locks

154

remaining to him grown shoulder length and combed across his skull in a dozen strands which probably appeared to him—face to face in his mirror—as a fine, full head of hair, but to all others looked like the dregs of a macaroni casserole. His skin was smooth at last, but where acne had left off, alcohol took over. His face was bloated and florid, the tracery of hundreds of tiny broken blood vessels marking his nose and cheeks. His small blue eyes, seeming even smaller now in the blubber, were perpetually glazed. I wondered if I looked as old to Greer as he did to me. Without caring very much, I asked what he was doing and learned that he had left the Foreign Service—a body blow to American diplomacy—and using the bottomless resources of Maria Luisa's father (one of the ten richest men in Brazil, as I was told often by Tony and all the Perrys) and what Greer called a "dummy Brazilian," was involved in some sort of business that sounded faintly crooked. "Perfectly legal. Completely. With a good lawyer and a decent despajado to grease the right palms, you can accomplish quite a lot down there. Congratulations on your book, by the way. I haven't read it," he said with some pride.

Greer's remark was the keynote for the whole week of parties. Although the proud bridegroom introduced me to everyone as "The author," my star billing created little stir beyond a vague "Oh, yes," or a blank stare. If Tony wanted a real name for best man, he never should have settled for a writer—not with the people in the Perry Set. Say what you will about New York's Old Guard—and ignorance certainly flourishes within its ranks—they cannot spend as much time as they do in their subscription seats at the opera and the Philharmonic, in their discussion clubs and cercles françaises, without a little culture rubbing off. And they do read—even if only as an escape from boredom. As for the Perry crowd, they could never spare the time from the work they called play to read a book, or even its jacket blurb. Since they could glance at a picture or a piece of statuary, pronounce it "Interesting," and move on to something else in less than a second, the intellectual gods who adorned their dinner tables and cocktail parties were invariably the more presentable painters and sculptors. Forming a considered opinion of a couple of hundred pages of type simply took too long.

But I was not without my champion. It was Tony's mother, Rose, the new Mrs. Willingham. As befitted the wife of a railway president, she arrived at Southampton in a private railway car called simply "Rose"—a nightmare of rosewood paneling and rose silk upholstery—and set up housekeeping on a siding. It had been some years since anything like *that* had happened—even in Southampton. Poor, Rose had been glorious. Rich, she was ten times more so. Some people should simply *have* money and lots of it—provided, if necessary, by an act of Congress. Rose was just such a person. She reveled in Mr. Willingham's millions, man-handling them like a child with a puppy. Married to an unsuccessful Chicago dentist, Rose's appearance at Perry-go-Round would have been a disaster. If she had not been mistaken for a door-to-door saleswoman and turned away by the butler, she would have been given less than fifteen minutes of Mrs. Perry's smirking patronage. A transparent excuse involving a prior engagement would have been invented, a taxi summoned, and Rose would not have been halfway down the blue gravel drive before Mrs. Perry could be found pleading with Posy—pointing out the lunacy of marriage to the spawn of such a hopeless vulgarian.

As Mrs. Willingham, Rose outdid the Perrys at their own game without even trying. Mr. Willingham was a known quantity, a captain of industry and an old boy at school, who had been in the same class with Mr. Perry. Plenty of gray hair, gray suits, gray matter, and no surprises whatsoever. Not Rose. She burst upon the scene like an aerial bomb, her raucous voice, her booming laugh, her "honeys" and "dearies" and "sweeties" and "kids" setting the window panes of Perry-go-Round to rattling. Mrs. Perry, who had to be at least fifty, was dressed in the teenage fashions of that summer—bare shoulders, cinched waist, whirly girly skirt over myriad petticoats—her hair determinedly ash blond and arranged in a girlish fluff. Rose, who stood nearly six feet tall in her heels, was given to stylish stouts in solid silks, large hats, long gloves, and gigantic handbags in genuine leather. She owned at least one garment in every known mutation of mink and was never—not even on the hottest day—non-fur-bearing. Her jewels—pearls the size of ping-pong balls, full parures of rubies, sapphires or emeralds set in diamonds—were as outrageous as Maria Luisa Perry's, the difference being that Rose was large enough to look as though she were wearing the jewelry and not the other way round. She was only too happy to tell you the source and price—wholesale and/or retail—of any item in her amazing wardrobe. Side by side, the two women made an odd picture—the Junoesque leading lady next to the kid from the chorus; the bird of paradise beside the Easter chick. Rich, Rose set Southampton on its collective ear. Her earthy vulgarity was defined as "refreshing frankness" and, therefore, charming. "I simply adore your mother," Mrs. Perry said to Tony, who looked as though he were being crucified. "She's such a *real person.*" Not being one herself, Mrs. Perry had no way of knowing that Rose had talked to the milkmen, the cleaning women, the bus drivers and soda jerkers of her past exactly the way she talked to the trash collected at Perry-go-Round.

The only person who wasn't bowled over by Rose was Greer Perry, although he probably would have been had she been anyone else's mother.

"Big, vulgar cow," Greer muttered to me at one of the prenuptial cocktail parties held on one or another Southampton lawn. "I suppose you know that she was sleeping with old Willingham for years before he married her."

"No, I don't know."

"Well, I do. And to think that *my sister* could go and get mixed up with riffraff like that." I said nothing. "And it's no secret that Posy comes into a million dollars on her twenty-fifth birthday—just a month from now. Very convenient for your friend Phony."

"Is it a secret that Maria Luisa will inherit ten million dollars on her next birthday? How much is that in Brazilian cruzeiros, Greer?"

"I don't see what that's got to do with . . ."

We were interrupted by Rose herself, her creamy bosom heaving under a load of canary diamonds. "Honey! I been dying to get you alone and tell you how ca-razy I am about that book of yours. I already read it twice—once to myself and once aloud to Will. (Will can't even read a business letter. Honest to Gawd, I don't know what they teach kids at that fancy school you all went to.)" Her remark—almost blasphemy around anyone in the Perry family—put Greer to flight. "He's kind of a stuffed shirt, isn't he? Drinks too much, too. Will says Gregory Peck but I still say Clark Gable."

"You say *what?*"

"To be in the movie of your book, sweetie. Boy, there's one picture I can't wait to see. I'll prob'ly bust out bawling when they flash your name on the screen. Time sure flies. It don't seem possible that so many years have gone by since I was putting you and Jackie on the train for school and now you're a famous author and he's getting married! Well, you been a real friend to him, I'll tell the cockeyed world! I only hope Jackie'll be happy with her, but I can't help thinking he'd be better off with a girl of his own kind. Well, I bet a lotta people say that about Will and I. Confidentially . . ." Her confidence was never shared. Rose, whose taste in painting ran to *Pinky* and the *Blue Boy*, was led off by Mrs. Perry to meet Jackson Pollock.

Somehow the interminable week of merrymaking drew to a close. There had been some sort of party given at every possible meal. There had been parties in evening dress, parties in Bermuda shorts, parties in dungarees, and parties in bathing suits. Only the clothes were different. The people, the food, the drink, the conversation, the houses and clubs had been undistinguishable one from another. Tony's bachelor dinner stands out from the massed bacchanalia—probably because it was the most clinical.

The evening was unique from the outset in that it was held in the Willinghams' railway car and that Rose had elected to be present. She received in the vestibule, splendid in chiffon and rubies, a Pullman porter's cap set jauntily on her head.

Greer arrived last, so drunk that he could barely stand. "What are you doing here?" he said to his hostess. "Going to come out of the cake and dance down the table?"

"You're a scream," Rose said genially. Strictly speaking, Rose's presence at an all-male dinner was a gaffe, of sorts, but since she was more attractive than any of the other guests, I was glad she was there.

Everything was done with the most lavish of hands. After too many cocktails and too much caviar there was too much food with three wines and jeroboams of champagne. But it didn't make the evening any less awful. Tony, pent up, I suppose, from spending his nights in a room with me away from the more pneumatic company of Posy, was maddeningly brittle and grand. Mr. Willingham and Mr. Perry were busily being as youthful as possible. Greer was nearly unconscious, spilling large amounts of food down his shirt front and knocking over wineglasses. Champagne flowed, toasts were proposed, crystal shattered. Finally Greer struggled to a more or less upright position and, wine sloshing in his glass, began a long, rambling, incoherent speech in which the terms "phony," "kike," and "social climber" could just barely be understood.

Mr. Willingham could be heard growling. Rose stood up and said, "I don't happen to think that kinda talk is very funny."

Greer turned on her with glazed, unfocused eyes.

"Greer!" Mr. Perry snapped. "Sit down!" Greer did even better: He collapsed into the centerpiece.

"Jesus," Mr. Perry moaned.

"Here," Rose said. "Gimme a hand, honey. We'll get the poor kid off of his feet."

I helped Rose carry Greer into the amazing compartment that was her rolling bedchamber and deposit him on the satin and lace confection of her bedspread. "The way these society fellahs guzzle at a big wedding! Like I said to Jackie, it's a lot better to go to city hall like I done with Will—and also with Doctor. You loosen his shirt and tie, I'll take off his shoes." The competence with which she set about her task made me think of a wonderfully efficient undertaker's assistant. She rang for the porter and ordered ice and cold towels, Fernet Branca and black coffee. "Suppose he'd think I was tryin' something funny if I undid his pants? They're awful tight. One thing I'll say for my own kid—and you, too—you've kept your figures. There. Now let's leave him lay. Sleep it off."

There was much hearty laughter upon our return, oblivion being considered essential to the merriment of an all-male gathering, but the manly chuckles died when Greer suddenly reappeared, trousers falling around his knees, to throw up eloquently all over the petitpoint upholstery of the private car. For all practical purposes the party was over.

One of my duties as best man seemed to be caring for neglected bridesmaids and drunken ushers. At least everyone else got out in a hurry, leaving Greer with me. With the aid of a porter I got him down to the gravel of the siding.

"A woman at a bachelor dinner," he muttered as he relieved himself against one of the wheels. "I've never seen such a breach of etiquette!"

"Christ but Greer's a shit," Tony said, in one of his rare honest moments, as we got ready to go to bed. "I hate his guts and I always have."

"Well, why did you ask him to be an usher?"

"Because he's Posy's brother. I didn't think he'd accept. I thought he'd stay down in Rio with Senhora Moneybags—who's not at all bad, by the way."

"I hadn't noticed. Well, two more days and you and Posy will be off on your own. A long, idyllic honeymoon."

"Yes. I'm anxious to get to London. The Season is still on and I have a letter of introduction to Lord Beaverbrook. I mean if I could sell him on *East of Fifth* . . ."

"Good night, Tony."

On the eve of the wedding the rehearsal took place, followed by a dinner dance at a club Tony assured me was terribly exclusive. Nothing went well. Posy, Mrs. Perry, Mrs. Edgecomb, wedding expert, and the clergyman aired serious differences of opinion as to the grouping around the altar. Something had gone wrong with the place cards at dinner so that Mrs. Perry was querulous and Posy petulant, and a good deal more than mere seating arrangements went wrong at dinner itself. Greer got sensationally drunk again and his vicious asides could be heard over the repeated toasts to health, wealth, and happiness. He got into a violent quarrel with Maria Luisa in several languages and, I guess, insulted Rose, as he was given a public chewing-out by his father and Mr. Willingham. I was ready to commit hara-kiri by the time the evening ended. There was great confusion as to who was to ride with whom, names and directions being bleated out in the darkness for what felt like hours. Tony was nowhere to be found. Neither were Greer and Maria Luisa. In desperation I fell into a car with Posy and her parents. Posy was sniveling about something or other and her mother was scanning the heavens and prophesying rain.

Tony was not in our bedroom and I felt humbly grateful for the solitude. At least I would have to make no further conversation. Wondering why I had ever left a peaceful place like Mexico for the battlefields of Southampton, I fell into bed and, instead of counting sheep, counted the hours until I could make my departure. I was just dropping off to sleep when the door burst open. I switched on the bedside lamp and there stood Greer. He was drunker than ever, his sparse hair hanging like Spanish moss to one shoulder. He wore a Charvet dressing gown crazily

161

knotted so that an unappetizing expanse of hirsute, bulging belly was exposed.

"You're in the wrong room, Greer," I said. "Yours is down the hall."

"Wanna talk to Tony."

"Well, obviously you can't."

"Why not?"

"Because he isn't here, as you see. If you can see at all."

"Where is he?"

"I don't know. Now run along to bed. Tomorrow's a big . . ."

"Got a cigarette?"

"Yes and so have you. There are boxes of them in all the rooms."

"I'm not sleeping in my room tonight. Damn Portuguese bitch locked me out. She's part nigger, you know. They all are."

"That's nice. God's own children. Always singing, laughing, dancing. Real sense of rhythm. Good night."

"Gimme cigarette."

"Here," I said, thrusting a whole pack toward him. "Take these and go. I'm half dead."

With a supreme effort he put a cigarette between his lips and got it lighted. Then he sank to my bed. "Where's Tony?"

"I don't know where Tony is. I don't care. It's late, Greer."

"Can I sleep here tonight?"

"Not unless you want to share Tony's bed and I hardly think . . ."

"Tony!" Greer spat out the name and the fumes on his breath nearly knocked me flat. "Cheap little Middle Western upstart. What the hell has he got?"

"Your sister for one thing."

"Sweet, innocent little kid. You suppose that louse is screwing her?"

"Not being a voyeur . . ."

"Echhhhh! The thought of it makes me sick." He went into

such a piteous coughing fit that I was afraid he might throw up again right on my bed.

"Apparently the thought of it doesn't make Posy sick or she wouldn't be marrying him. Now why don't you try to get a little sleep and . . ."

"Posy's a Perry and she's going to be a rich girl soon. Why else do you suppose he's marrying her?"

"I couldn't tell you. Why did you marry Maria Luisa?"

"My wife's a Bragança," he said loftily. "Her father is one of the ten richest men in Brazil."

"Then I should think you'd have no difficulty in understanding Tony's motives. They must be about the same as yours."

"What are you trying to say?"

"I'm trying to say good night. Now I'm saying it. Good night, Greer."

He got to his feet and stumbled out of the room. I turned off the lamp, thumped my pillow, and buried my head in it. My lids had barely closed when they shot open again. From somewhere down the corridor I could hear Greer's drunken roar, a dull thud, the splintering of wood, and a shrill scream. I leapt out of bed and struggled into my robe.

I was not the first on the scene. Mr. and Mrs. Perry, Posy and Mrs. Edgecomb, who was so good with weddings, had all arrived before me. But it was some scene and I got there in time to see Tony trying to cover his nakedness in one of Greer's many dressing gowns.

"God damn you, that's not only my wife, it's my robe!"

"See here, young man, if you think you're going to marry my daughter . . ."

"Posy, darling, don't look! That beast and that awful mulatto slut . . ."

"Que maçado!"

"Tony! How could you? With my own brother's wife . . ."

"Dad, if you permit this wedding to take place tomorrow
. . ."

"Shut up, Gig. You're drunk!"

"As usual. If he hadn't come busting into this room like a . . ."

"Really, Mrs. Perry, I've handled all sorts of weddings, but this is most . . ."

"Now, Mrs. Edgecomb, I know this looks unusual . . ."

"Looks unusual! Mummy, my own fiancé on the very eve of . . ."

"Mrs. Perry, I really think . . ."

"Are you paying her to address invitations or to think?"

"As for you, Maria Luisa, there's going to be a divorce action that will rock your old coon of a father . . ."

"*Olhe que giro!* After you with the maids, with Senhora de Pombal, with my cousin Sidónia, with any girl in Rio? *Sinto-me mal disposto! Qual o número da sua Embaixada Brasiliana?*"

"Now, Maria Luisa, you've made a mistake, but this can be ironed out—can't it, darling?—we don't want a lot of reporters . . ."

"*She* made a mistake? What about me when I married her? You're witnesses—every damned one of you. . . ."

"Darling, you've got to stop him. We'll be the laughing stock . . ."

"Doesn't anybody care about *me*? I'm supposed to marry Tony tomorrow. Well, I wouldn't marry him if he were the last man . . ."

"Posy Perry! Do you realize that we have nearly a thousand guests coming to the reception alone and . . ."

"Posy, as your father I forbid you to get tied up with this . . ."

"As her *father*? Well, a lot you ever did about bringing up the children! A young man's supposed to sow his wild oats before . . ."

"If you had the sense God gave a goose . . ."

"Oh, shut up, you . . . you . . ."

It did not take clairvoyance to see that all three Perry marriages were on quicksand. Unnoticed I tiptoed out of the room, dressed, threw my belongings into a suitcase, and walked to the station.

The plane to Mexico was delayed. There was nearly an hour to kill and I decided to do it in the Kitty Hawk Bar on top of LaGuardia Airport. There was only one vacant stool. I took it. Seated next to me, dapper in a sparely cut Italian suit, was Tony.

"That was a cute stunt you pulled last night," he said.

"I pulled?"

"Walking out with never so much as a word. What do you suppose the people in Southampton are saying?"

"Plenty. But not about me. I gather that the wedding did not come off?"

Tony took his frayed old ermine-tail good-luck piece from one of the many oddly placed pockets of his suit. "It was a narrow escape, but I guess this pulled me through."

"I didn't notice it in Maria Luisa's bedroom last night. Of course you didn't have any pockets . . ."

"She's a sweet girl. Intelligent. Imagine being stuck with a clot like Greer Perry—any of the Perrys for that matter."

"I got the distinct impression that she won't be for much longer."

"Right. I just put her and the baby on a plane for Rio."

"Oh, is that what you're doing here?"

"And then I'm off to Europe as soon as I finish this drink. I mean since I had the seats anyway . . . Say, you wouldn't like to come along on Posy's ticket, would you? We could have a ball."

"No thank you. I've had ball enough to last for some time. You seem to have wriggled out of your 'blanket of love' fairly fast. Or is this trip some sort of therapy for a broken heart?"

"You may not believe this, but I was pretty badly cut up about what . . . what happened last night."

"Correct. I don't believe it."

"I mean when a man's in love—*really* in love—for the first time and then the whole thing blows up in his face . . ."

"And naturally you had nothing to do with that explosion?"

"All right, I was weak. I'm not perfect, you know."

"Oh, I know."

"I was attracted to Maria Luisa. I felt sorry for her, tied down to that lush. He only married her for money—and her position in Brazil. She's a damned attractive woman. As for Posy, well she's very pretty and I wish her nothing but the best, but, after all, she's just a child. . . ."

"Of almost twenty-five."

"While Maria Luisa is a mature woman. . . ."

"Of twenty-two."

"Age has nothing to do with it. Maria Luisa is worldly, sophisticated, a true cosmopolitan. . . ."

"And a better lay than Posy?"

"Really! I thought you were a gentleman! After all, Maria Luisa is a Bragança and her father . . ."

"Is one of the ten richest men in Brazil," I finished for him. It was something I had learned by heart like The Lord's Prayer or our National Anthem. "Do your travel plans include Rio?"

"Well, Maria Luisa said something about it. Of course things are rather up in the air just now."

"Perhaps you could publish *East of Fifth* in Portuguese. Call it *North of Copa Cabana*—something like that. With all the Brazilian money . . ."

"Don't kid, please. I'm too upset to worry about the magazine just now. In the long run I suspect it's too far ahead of its time to really go over. What I need right now is to get away from this rat race—shit-house aristocracy like the Perry family—and take a good, long look at my life up till now."

"That should be some picture."

"Don't think this big bust-up hasn't created a lot of problems."

"I'm sure it has. A big, dirty divorce case. A thousand wedding guests waiting at the church . . ."

"I mean for me. I've got a lot of unpaid bills. There's my little apartment on Park and the duplex on . . . Say, I don't suppose you'd be interested in taking over one of them?"

"Right as rain. I would not."

"And then Mom's terribly cut up about the whole thing. She was crying when I left. As for old Willingham . . . Promise me you'll do one thing: Look after Mom. She's always had a soft spot for you and . . ."

"You want *me* to look after your mother?"

"Well, I'll be abroad, you see, for I-don't-know-how-long, and . . ." The public address system sputtered something about the TWA sleeper flight for Paris. "Hey, there's my plane. Gotta shove off. If you want to reach me . . ."

"Don't worry. I won't."

"It's been a pretty grim ordeal—for everybody. But I guess I'll be all right."

"I'm sure of it."

"Well, so long."

"Good-by."

Tony got down from the bar stool, gave his Italian suit a shake and a pat, squared his shoulders, and marched away—the man of mystery, the world traveler and international citizen.

"Hey!" the bartender called just as the doors swung shut behind Tony. "Hey, yer check! That bastard had three gin and tonics and walks outta here without even . . ."

"I'll pay for him," I said. "I expected to."

VII

TONY

in suburbia

Authors, when they are not writing, are generally talking. Especially if they're paid for it. This trait—perhaps an unfortunate one—has been put down to the creative urge and the constant need to communicate. In my own case it stemmed from need and greed. With the publication of my second novel I moved back to New York, soon grew weary of it, and set forth on the lecture circuit. After my initial stage fright at facing an auditorium full of mink stoles and flower hats, I discovered that I rather liked it. Lecturing was pleasant, profitable, and often interesting. Over the next five years I worked up three separate talks—one for afternoons at women's clubs, another for colleges, and a racier one for the occasional evening appearance to which husbands had been lured. It was at one of these mixed sessions held at the opulent country club of an expensive suburban community that I gazed over the lectern and into the upturned grinning face of Tony.

The affluent brokers and bankers who dominate the census rolls of Chisholm's Crossing, Connecticut, will be outraged to hear their carefully zoned hamlet described as a suburb. They call it The Country. Yet its fertile soil produces nothing beyond hardy perennials and, in the gardens of the more ambitious, some radishes and a few heads of lettuce. Save for an overpriced inn-cum-gift shop on the banks of the Housatonic River, all business is banned or, rather, shunted off to a carefully landscaped shopping center of colonial persuasion adjoining the less fashionable neighboring village. The detractors of Chisholm's Crossing (those who don't live there) speak of it as "a snob's bedroom." Actually it is more. It is an autonomous monarchy where the surveyor is king, the architect crown prince, and the board of admissions court chamberlain. The country club is its palace, its axis, its throbbing heart. The houses radiating from the club to the very borders of Chisholm's Crossing are set on plots of not less than five acres. The buildings themselves meet specific requirements of price and style. They are constructed, like the few genuinely old houses still extant, of fieldstone or white clapboard or pink brick or not at all. All phases of public life are governed by committees and, like the Soviet, a better-known totalitarianism, everything is done to keep the citizens inside Chisholm's Crossing and the aliens out. Having tortured its applicants with every known form of interrogation, investigation, and assessment, the Country Club of Chisholm's Crossing, once having accepted them into the fold, coddles its membership with golf, tennis, riding, boating, swimming, and dancing by summer and with squash, billiards, bowling, shooting, skating, and dancing by winter. To keep the flame of intellect burning bright, there are also a foreign affairs discussion circle, a choral society, a little theater group, and a fortnightly "series of distinguished speakers." (I had been preceded by Van Wyck Brooks and would be followed by Ruth Draper.)

On that Friday in February, 1955, I had been met at the station in New Haven by Mr. and Mrs. President-of-the-Club, bundled into the largest kind of Mercedes Benz, and taken back to their house to dine with Mr. and Mrs. Chairman-of-the-Entertainment-Committee—two martinis made with English gin, sorrel soup, vol au vent of seafood (in case I happened to be a Catholic), field salad with ham cornets (in case I happened not to be a Catholic), Pouilly Fuissé, and a crème brulée that hadn't quite come off. We discussed the beauties of Chisholm's Crossing during each of the four seasons, the advantages of country-club membership, the difficulty of obtaining and keeping good help, Mrs. President's Worcester china and whether or not it felt like snow. A little after eight I was driven to the club in Mr. and Mrs. Entertainment Committee's Jaguar, installed in a dainty dressing room off the stage in the ballroom, and told to relax. I waited in the wings while Mrs. Entertainment Committee announced that Cornelia Otis Skinner would not be able to appear in March (loud groans) but that she had been replaced by Vilhjalmur Stefansson (loud applause); that play-offs for the ladies' bowling championship would be held the following afternoon at three o'clock sharp; that tryouts for the little theater group's last play of the season, Blithe Spirit, would be held on Monday evening; that only a few tables remained for the Valentine's Day Dinner Dance; that children under sixteen were not to use the adults' skating rink unless accompanied by at least one parent; and that Mrs. Guy Griffith reported the loss of a gold circle pin set with three baguette diamonds—"a suitable reward is offered and no questions asked" (loud laughter). It occurred to me what a wonderful place Chisholm's Crossing would be to live and that I would cut my throat if I had to do it. After an effusive description of me and my work I was on.

Halfway through my speech I spotted Tony, seated in the first row with two women who looked like sisters and a red-faced older man who laughed too heartily at everything that was even vaguely intended to be amusing.

Having made the same speech a couple of dozen times in the last few months I knew every pause and nuance by heart. I gave up thinking about what I was saying and, flying on instruments, started wondering just what in Tophet someone like Tony was doing at a place like this. Since the day of his departure for Europe I had heard from him only through my mother who from time to time had enclosed in her letters snippets from *The Tatler*—photographs of Tony at Royal Ascot, at various charity balls, the openings of art exhibits, and the things that were the easiest for an outsider to get into, as my mother pointed out. But whatever they were, they were a far cry from Chisholm's Crossing and its country club. Yet here he sat, not ten feet away, the tweedy American boy-man.

My speech ended on schedule just seventy-five minutes after it had begun. Mrs. Entertainment Chairman announced that I had been most enjoyable and illuminating; that sandwiches and coffee "or something stronger for those who wish it" would be served in the lounge; and that Mrs. Guy Griffith's pin had been found in the cloakroom. As a rule I made it a point never to hang around once I had spoken my piece and collected my check. From watching the fancy footwork of more celebrated public figures, I had learned just how to leave a place while giving the impression of staying. The secret was to aim for the door and to keep moving. Talk, smile, shake hands, answer questions, sign books, but don't stand still for a second. Never get stuck. But on that particular night I *wanted* to get stuck, if only long enough to find out what Tony was doing there. Until I did, wild horses couldn't drag me out of Chisholm's Crossing.

For just one brief moment panic set in. Tony had been out of my life for the past five years and more. Suppose that he had no wish to see me again, had put forth new roots and wanted no reminders of his checkered past? I need not have worried. In Chisholm's Crossing for that one night, I was a lion and wherever there was a lion Tony would be on hand to claim him and tame him. I had barely crossed the threshold of the lounge when he was all over me, subtly edging out the Chairman of the Entertainment Committee to take over the speaker of the evening as his own prize. He was perhaps not interested enough in *me* to have called or written, but he was quite interested enough in the figure he cut among the gentry of Chisholm's Crossing to put on the most violent show of friendship. I was embraced, my hand wrung and my back slapped. It was like a meeting of long lost brothers who had suddenly come face to face in the Sahara. His greeting was effusive enough to attract a small circle of interested spectators.

"First of all," Tony said, "I want you to meet my wife, Muffie."

"*Who?*"

"Muffie. You must remember Muffie Murray. That's who she was before she settled down to being a wife and mother."

The name oozed upward through a couple of hundred back issues of *Life*. Muffie Murray had been on its cover, billed as a "society actress"—a term used loosely enough to describe any girl who had not actually been scrubbing floors or walking the streets before being claimed by the theater. Muffie Murray, while perhaps not as social as Jane Wyatt or Diana Barrymore, had been *the* flash in the pan of 1951—a pretty girl from a well-to-do family who had gone, via Rosemary Hall and Finch Junior College, onto the stage in the ingenue role of a popular light farce. There had been talk of Hollywood and television but that was all. Muffie Murray's career ended with the play's closing. For a time people wondered when that adorable girl would be heard from again. Then they forgot about her. In a place like Chisholm's Crossing, however, where she had grown up, Muffie Murray was the equivalent of Mrs. Siddons—"a real pro," as they said, and a guiding light of the little theater movement. Failing a marriage to Henry Irving or John Drew, Tony was the ideal choice of mates. Among his neighbors and fellow club members, who had all enjoyed the privileges of good schools, Ivy League colleges, and the better dances, Tony still had prestige. His mother was Mrs. Willingham, his press coverage had been considerable on both sides of the Atlantic, and he had met Princess Margaret. Even in a community where per capita incomes were dazzling, where the citizenry appeared constantly on the business and society pages, where junior years abroad were customary, Tony was impressive. "But such a great guy with it all," several people said to me. In Chisholm's Crossing Muffie and Tony were royalty.

In a moment Muffie was at Tony's side, looking just as Junior Miss as she had in the cutesy little play that brought her to the attention of the world at large some years before. Her hair fell from a broad ribbon in the style of Alice in Wonderland and hung halfway down the back of her little pink wool dress. (No matter what color Muffie wore it always gave the impression of being either pink or blue.) She clung to Tony like a child being led off to its first day at kindergarten, toed-in demurely and laughed a lot, throwing her slightly shiny retroussé nose into the air and tossing her curls. I almost expected her to curtsy when we were introduced. Like her nickname (she had actually been christened something very straightforward—Edith, if memory serves), everything else about her should have been abandoned at puberty. Her inexhaustible girlishness had even affected Tony. Although he was past thirty-five, his clothes, his slang, his boyish grin were all out of a campus musical.

Before I could quite prevent it I found myself squeezed into Tony's white Thunderbird, being driven along the twisting lanes of Chisholm's Crossing toward "a real drink," with Muffie's parents—as in all things—just behind.

Mamma and Pappa—for that is what Muffie and Tony called them—lived in an old grist mill, expensively fitted out with such non-period refinements as pastel bathrooms and an electric kitchen. The Children—for that is what Mamma and Pappa called Muffie and Tony—occupied a converted stable connected by an umbilical breezeway to the main house. Togetherness was rampant and that seemed to be exactly as Mamma and Pappa wanted it.

Mrs. Murray was a cute trick of about fifty who said more than once that she and Muffie were inseparable—"like sisters instead of mother and daughter." As far as their attitudes went she was perfectly correct. Mrs. Murray's only concession to advancing age was a "grandmother's bracelet" with two gold discs bobbing from it. "Imagine! *Me! A* grandmother! Twins. The first we've ever had in the family. Such a surprise."

It didn't surprise me at all. In a family as determinedly darling as this one, twins were essential. Twice as cunning as just one baby.

"Twins! Really? I had no idea," I said. "What are their names?"

"Flopsy and Mopsy," Muffie giggled.

I had to be excused.

Pappa Murray looked like Harry S Truman, whom he abhorred, his favorite personage, next to General MacArthur, being General Eisenhower. Mr. Murray was, I had been told twice at dinner, the richest man in Chisholm's Crossing, unique in that he commuted neither to Wall Street nor Madison Avenue but was the founder, president, and chairman of the board of Murray Manufacturing—a local enterprise that turned out something very small like locks or transistor parts or timing mechanisms or one of the tiny products indigenous to Connecticut manufacturing. It had started out as a cottage industry but the war had made it big and its owner even bigger. Mr. Murray was one of those retiring, semisecret millionaires whose exact holdings are guessed at only by friends, neighbors, and fellow members of the National Association of Manufacturers. A harder-bitten man might have chosen to go onward and upward, controlling local politics, invading Washington to see that things were run his way, hiring the services of a public relations firm, or establishing some ingenious tax-dodge under the guise of a non-profit foundation. Not Mr. Murray. He was loudly self-effacing. The factory outside Waterbury, "a little place" in Chisholm's Crossing, membership in its country club, a devoted son-in-law, and two precious grandchildren having been acquired, Mr. Murray was more than satisfied—or so he said, his carefully cultivated colloquialisms contradicting the three diplomas hanging conspicuously on the wall.

"I don't put on a lot of side," Mr. Murray was saying over his third drink. "There ain't a man who works for Murray Manufacturing from Tony here right down to a stock boy who can't come inta my office and say, 'Fred . . .'"

"Heavens, Daddy, is that snow I see?" Mrs. Murray said.

Snow it was and flying fast and thick. There was no question of my getting to New Haven and catching the New York train. "Frankly, I'm glad," Tony said, clutching my arm as we hurried along the breezeway. "Now I've got you here—practically a prisoner—and we've got a chance to really talk. In fact, I hope we get snowed in."

"Oh, wouldn't that be *exciting!*" Muffie squealed.

Tony's and Muffie's stable—a wedding present from the Murrays and one that would keep them under the parental eye—was as picturesque as the grist mill and even larger. "I'm supposed to keep Muffie in foal until every stall is filled," Tony said. Muffie giggled immoderately. Away from her parents she was permitted certain liberties such as hearing grown-up talk and allusions to sex—almost like a child being allowed watered wine and a sugary demitasse when taken to a restaurant by a doting uncle.

I was shown first to a large guest room up in what had once been a hay mow, given a robe, slippers, and pajamas of Tony's and told to put them on. "Isn't this fun!" Muffie said, just as though we were children dressing up. In costume we tiptoed into the room occupied by the twins. Muffie, whispering, showed them off in their cribs like a little girl with her dolls. Then we went downstairs. The house, while large, had a cloying air of the

175

quaint, the cozy, the whimsical, yes, the *cute* about it. Too many heart-shaped objects, perhaps.

Tony poured out two drinks and a Coca-Cola for Muffie. Muffie did not touch alcohol. "I don't object to drinking. I just hate the taste of it."

"Tastes like nassy ole meddie, doesn't it?" Tony said. I was aghast.

We retired to Tony's den—paneling, horse brasses, and café curtains—where we invented conversation until Muffie was told that she was tired. Dutifully she got up, twirled in her little white flannel nightie with blue ribbons, kissed Tony good night, very nearly curtsied again, and went off to bed. "Nighty-night," she said, blowing a kiss from halfway up the stairs.

"Well," Tony said.

"Well," I said, almost gasping.

"I'll bet you were surprised to find me out here in Chisholm's Crossing, eh, chum?"

"Surprised hardly begins to express it, Tony."

"I always knew I'd land on my feet."

"So did I—but not here."

"Muffie's a doll, isn't she?"

"Yes. She is. Exactly. But what I wonder is how you two ever met."

"Regular stage-door-Johnny stuff. I came back from England, went to the theater to see Muffie's play—naturally I'd read all that crap about her in *Life*: 'millionaire's daughter invades show biz . . .'"

"Naturally."

"Did you happen to see the show?"

"The first act of it."

"How come you didn't stay?"

"I was ill."

"It was a cute little play."

"It certainly was."

"The sheltered girl almost falling into the clutches of the slick adventurer . . . Funny as hell. So I sent a mass of flowers backstage with my card. . . ."

"Life imitates art."

"Then one thing led to another and the next thing I knew I was asking Fred for Muffie's hand. Wedding at the club. This house. Twins on the way. It's really the life. You oughta try it."

"Not just yet, thanks. I take it that you work for Muffie's father?"

"Vice-President in charge of Advertising, Publicity, and Promotion. Funny thing. Until I came along Fred never spent a nickel on plugging his product. Here he's got a little gold mine over there in Waterbury and yet he keeps it a secret—like he was running a cat house."

"But of course you've changed all that."

"Oh, sure. Fred won't give me the budget I want, but I've begun breaking him down. We'll be starting a big ad campaign to familiarize the public with the name of Murray. And I hope to get a television show on. But it's not easy. My father-in-law is a very modest man."

"So he told me."

"He's perfectly content with Chisholm's Crossing, the club, his little family all living together on the place . . ."

"Yes, he told me that, too. But are you?"

"Am I what?"

"Are you content with Chisholm's Crossing?"

"Am I what? Am I *content*? Well, let me tell you here and now, boy, you're looking at a man who's more than content. This is the life for me. The *only* life. You can have your name splashed all over the front pages . . ."

"I don't," I said.

But he was performing again—playing and living a new part. "I've got everything any man could ever ask for—a beautiful little wife, the twins, a lovely place in one of the best all-round communities in America. No knocking myself out in that New

York rat race. I'm vice-president of a great little company and I'm my own boss—except for Fred."

"And he can't last forever, can he?"

Like an actor ignoring a cough in the audience, Tony raced on. He hadn't even heard me. "I've learned a lot since the last time you saw me. It's been five years. Five long years, and I can admit—*now*—that when you saw me, I was pretty low." He sounded like someone who had recently seen The Light through the intercession of Billy Graham or A.A.

"That's right, Tony."

"Yes. Being thrown over by Posy was an awful blow. It nearly killed me. I tried to run away from it. London, Paris, Rome, the Côte d'Azur. But when I stopped to catch my breath and take a good look at myself I saw that I wasn't running from anything. I was on a treadmill"—now from what third-rate play had he picked up that line? "Instead of getting away from the terrible, artificial life that Posy would have dragged me into, I was racing headlong into its jaws. Then I got hold of myself, came home, met Muffie, married, and settled down here. I can't tell you what a difference there is between the life—the people—out here in Chisholm's Crossing . . ."

"Bucolic?"

"The difference between life out here in Chisholm's Crossing and that chi-chi existence of the Posy Perry crowd. I just can't tell you."

I could have told him after two minutes in Chisholm's Crossing. The life was just the same only less so. In Chisholm's Crossing you could run the race in second gear and still come out ahead. I could also have told Tony that if it *hadn't* been for Posy Perry—who, under her own lethargic head of steam, could hardly have dragged anyone into anything more depraved than a Junior League Ball—and London and Paris and Rome and the Côte d'Azur, he would have cut about as much ice at the country club as a junior accountant with a C.C.N.Y. night school degree. Outsiders had to have glamour to flourish in Chisholm's Crossing. Tony had it. He thrived on being different. Not exactly different—just more so. Further, I could have reminded him that I had been on hand to watch the whole Perry fiasco and that he wasn't fooling me one little bit. But it would have been pointless. No matter how good Tony was at deceiving others, he was even better at deceiving himself.

What gave Tony his perpetual freshness was that he regarded me as a perpetually fresh audience. Whenever we met it was opening night. Tony was the consummate ham and I was the fan club. It made no difference that I had seen him in every other role, knew his vital statistics, had even visited backstage and seen with my own eyes that the palace was painted canvas, that the ermine was rabbit and the diamonds glass. As he read each new role I was expected to forget that only last season I had seen Benedict as Romeo and in seasons before that as Shylock, Hamlet, and Caesar. The play was the thing.

"Next week *King Lear*," I said.

"What?"

"I said I'm tired. I ought to turn in."

"Let's just have a nightcap."

"I've had plenty, Tony. More than enough." I had. But for my every drink, Tony had downed two. Was the liquor just a sort of stage prop to round out the perfect picture of hard-drinking suburbia, or had our leading man reached the point where a bottle on the dressing table was essential to every performance?

"I'm really going up to bed. Oh, and Tony?"

"Yes?" He was already at the bar.

"I'm glad you're so happy out here."

I awoke the next morning smothered in the pervasive silence of the countryside under snow. The actual storm had stopped but the drifts were deep. No cars were on the road. I realized, with a sinking feeling, that I was snowed in—"practically a prisoner," as Tony had said. But the silence was out of doors only. The rafters rang with the cries of Tony's twin daughters and, even louder, Muffie as the Little Mother. Shuddering, I went downstairs. Tony looked rumpled and grim until he was conscious of my presence. Then he became the Tousled Daddy of the Lord & Taylor ads. Muffie, her hair in pigtails, was very much the little girl with a new sled. "Isn't this fun!" Muffie screamed. "Snow! Right up to the window sills. Now you'll *have* to stay."

Flopsy and Mopsy (like their mother, they too had perfectly decent names that would never be used) were perfectly loathsome. I suppose it's unreasonable to accuse two-year-olds of being childish, but these kids were. They were pretty, willful, spoiled, and, except from their nurse—an elderly Scotswoman who had also been Muffie's nurse—they had never heard the word No.

"I'll take them now, Miss Muffie," the nurse said. In this never-never land Muffie would grow just to the point of being *Miss* Muffie, but she would never be called Mrs. Vandenberg—or, as it was now spelled, van den Burg.

"Oh, must you, Nanny?" Muffie pouted prettily.

"Yes. The toidy."

"Oh, Mummy's dunna miss her liddle dirls. Oooooh, Mummy could dus eat 'em up."

"Well, pal, it looks like you're here for an extended engagement," Tony said. He, too, was in costume—ski pants and a bulky sweater with a lot of elks on it. "Snowed in tight. No telling when the county will get the roads cleared. They hate Chisholm's Crossing like poison."

"I'll bet they do."

"It isn't fair!" Muffie said, all but stamping her foot. "We pay about a million times the taxes of any other town around here and we're always the last to have our roads or anything else looked after."

"But it won't be so bad. We've got a gang coming in for dinner tonight and Mamma and Pappa—I mean the Murrays— are having a sort of company luncheon tomorrow and . . ."

"Well, if people can get here, I should think I could get to the station." The statement seemed reasonable enough to me.

"Oh, never! You should see the way some of them come to parties—sleighs, skis, snowshoes, one guy—Bill Putnam—has this sort of Army surplus tank . . ."

"Oh, it's such fun!" Muffie cried, doing an impromptu dance step in her little blue snowsuit. No one had been out of doors, but the costumes suggested Antarctica.

"Ooo-hoo!" Mr. and Mrs. Murray, also dressed for the next ice age, had mushed their way through the bone-dry breezeway and burst through the front door. Muffie flung herself upon them as though they had been separated for some years, then everyone talked about the snow and what fun it was. It was only ten o'clock but Tony started making hot buttered rums at the fireplace while Mr. Murray told him a better way to do it. Mr. Murray also told Mrs. Murray where to sit and Muffie what station to get on the radio so that we could hear officially that it had snowed. As he had no immediate orders for me to carry out, he satisfied himself by telling me again what a simple man he was and, to prove it, snapped his red fireman's braces and lighted a corncob pipe. I suppose that this self-styled old character fancied himself as a sort of upper-crust Will Rogers. He went out of his way to be rustic, to quote *The Old Farmer's Almanack*, and to misuse the English language. I saw him as a primitive God figure surrounded by fools and children who, whether they grasped his infinite wisdom or not, had better be quick to carry out his bidding. The twins, alas, returned, lisping vivid descriptions of their defecations, and "Gompa," as Mr. Murray was called, now had a full army to obey his instructions. Eventually he even found something for me to do: I was to go upstairs and "put on something sensible." In this case, fleece-lined dungarees, a turtle-necked sweater, and a Norfolk jacket from Tony's inexhaustible supply of country clothes. While I was changing I decided to call Maggie Faye in New York to tell her where I was and why and not to worry. I picked up the receiver only to hear

Tony's voice coming from another extension: ". . . oldest and dearest friend. You heard him talk at the club last night. Anyhow, Muffie and I are having a little get-together for him tonight and we hope you can come. . . . Of course you can get here. The roads are perfectly clear. . . ."

Downstairs once again I was greeted by Muffie's squeals of appreciation of my outfit. Photographs had to be taken of me, of me with the twins, of me with the Murrays, of me with Muffie, of me with Tony, of me with Muffie and Tony, and finally a masterpiece of technology in which the camera was set by Tony who rushed back in time to pose for a whole group picture. An argument ensued about lunch. Would we have it at the Murrays' or the van den Burgs'? As in all serious matters, Mr. Murray finally handed down his considered decision. The Murrays would bring the food to the van den Burgs and it would be eaten, picnic style, in the living room. To emphasize his country character, he announced that he would pour his special brand of cider from the Danbury Fair in its special stone jug. There was more talk about the snow and about our going out to play in it, but no one ventured as far as the doorsill. I got through the afternoon only by excusing myself to take a nap.

It was dark when I awakened and I could hear voices from the next room in a conversation that sorely lacked the established tone of rural geniality. "Of all the ridiculous dude outfits I've ever seen . . ."

"If you don't like what I'm wearing, Fred, you don't have to look. I didn't ask you up to my bedroom to talk about clothes."

"Your bedroom. I'd like ta know whose property this is anyways."

"All right, Fred, we live here because you and Ethel wanted Muffie close at hand."

"Damn tootin' we do. I didn't work like a dog to make all this money for my little girl and then have her all over the . . ."

"Okay, Fred, okay. Money. Now that brings us back to what

we came up here to talk about in the first place: A, my salary and B, my budget."

"Your budget? That's a queer way to put it. From what I can figure you want me to shell out close to a million dollars a year so you can have your television program with your name on it."

"With your name on it, Fred. The purpose of the show would be to familiarize the public with Murray Manufacturing and . . ." Tony's tone was velvety now, persuasive.

"Public don't buy our stuff. The govermunt does. We got more orders 'n we can handle and now you wanta . . ."

"Fred. The program would serve as institutional advertising so that the name of Murray . . ."

"Ain't a businessman in the country don't know the name of Murray. Now the name John Anthony van den Burg might . . ."

"Fred, just because you're big in Chisholm's Crossing . . ."

"Damn right I am. And that's the reason you're big."

I went out of my way to make as much noise as possible. "Shhhhh. He's awake," Tony said. In a moment there was a tap at my door and they were both in my room, armed with further eccentric clothing for me to wear. Tony was resplendent in tartan trews, pumps, and a scarlet dinner jacket. Mr. Murray was got up to resemble Fred Stone in *Lightnin'*. Politely but firmly I refused their offers of corduroys, leather-patched shooting jackets, alpaca sweaters, and mukluks in favor of my dark suit. "You won't look like any of the rest of the crowd," Mr. Murray said.

"Good."

Downstairs Muffie in a dirndl, a demure apron, and a pony tail (Muffie could arrange her hair in a number of ways, none of which was suitable for a girl past the age of twelve) twittered around the buffet table. In honor of the weather it had been shrouded in white with a little Swiss village set up around a giant snowman made of absorbent cotton. Her mother, as though the two were joined at the hip, was right at her side. The whole atmosphere was so much that of a children's party that I almost expected to find little favors tucked away in easy hiding places.

An hour after they had been invited, the guests began piling in. Although every last one of them had arrived by heated automobile, a Jeep station wagon being the most rugged mode of conveyance, they were dressed in old raccoon coats, boots, parkas, and fur hats as though they had caught the last dog sled from Nome. The women talked about the snow, the men about means of removing it—blowers versus plows and so on. Moving among them I felt very elderly although they were all my age and more. Great deference was paid to Mr. Murray, not because of politeness or respect for his years, but because most of the men were in some way connected with Murray Manufacturing. True, they all called him Fred, but I felt it was because they had been told to and not because they liked him. Nor did they seem genuinely fond of Tony. I got the impression that their cordiality was tempered by fear. Tony was, after all, the heir apparent and unless the courtiers could manage an assassination, he would someday rule over them as his father-in-law did.

Muffie struck me as truly pathetic. For a time I had accused her, unjustly, of putting on an act. After all, she had been, however briefly, on the stage. But as the liquor caught hold of the party, I began to sense Muffie's plight. She, who was sober, had every right to be bored with her guests. For they were, at best, aggressively, noisily, heartily boring. Yet she kept striving to enter into conversations that were beyond her, laughing at jokes she didn't quite grasp. Far from being the clever actress who had played the little girl, Muffie had been the clever little girl playing the actress. Luck, Fate, Kismet, Sun Spots, the Conjunction of Planets, not talent—and surely not bedding down with the producer—must have been responsible for putting her into the theater. She had simply played Muffie Murray and the reason she had not progressed onward and upward was that no new play had come along requiring the services of a baby in her twenties. Muffie was a true case of arrested development. She had had her day in the sun—probably two days in the sun, for as a vivacious teen-ager she must surely have been the heart and soul of the

Chisholm's Crossing younger set. Now her contemporaries had husbands, children, and the beginnings of double chins. So had Muffie, but there all similarity ceased. She was now just Tony's wife and, more importantly, Fred Murray's daughter—the little girl who was allowed to stay up late and pass canapés at the grown-ups' party.

Although everyone there assured me that Chisholm's Crossing was unique and unlike any other suburban or exurban community, I found the people in no way different from their counterparts in any of a dozen places named Highland Park. Even so, it could have been a pleasant enough evening. It was not. Mr. Murray, secure in his role of president, chairman of the board, and founding father, took over the floor at the beginning of the party and did not relinquish it. His style of comedy—if it can be called that—was pure cracker-barrel bumpkin with heavy emphasis on ignorance and arrogance. Nor was his humor good-natured as such rural jollity traditionally is. Being largely parochial, most of what he had to say was lost on me, but the little I got seemed to be both barbed and personal and directed at people in the room. The old man was a boor and a bore who had never learned that brevity is the soul of wit. In a hick-town tent show he would have been booed off the stage. In this expensive living room his every heavy sally was greeted by loud, hastily manufactured laughter. I had never disliked anyone quite so thoroughly so quickly and with so little personal reason.

Dinner was served when Mr. Murray told Muffie he was ready to eat it, a good two hours after everyone else was. I believe that it would have been delicious dished up hot and on time. After dinner the men of the party were herded into Tony's study by Mr. Murray. The door was closed and I had the sinking feeling that we were about to be regaled with witticisms considered unfit for female ears. Even worse, Mr. Murray began to hold a full-scale business meeting. I had drunk more than I should have but under the circumstances it didn't seem nearly enough.

"All right, fellahs," Mr. Murray said, "now that we're all here tagether, there's a few little business matters need discussin'."

"Are you paid overtime for this sort of thing?" I asked the man next to me. He looked horrified and edged his chair away from mine.

Mr. Murray, who had overheard my remark just as I intended him to, shot me a malevolent glance and went on. "Old Tony here is convinced that we should shell out a lot of money here spreadin' me all over the papers and on the idiot box. (That's what I call tellyvision.)"

"That's a good one, Fred!" some toady barked appreciatively.

"Thanks. Now I say what's the sense of monkeyin' with success? We're doin' real good just as we are. Ain't a company in Connecticut that don't know and envy Murray Manafacturin'."

"Connecticut isn't the world, Fred," Tony said suavely. "My plan is to build the public image of . . ."

"Don't interrupt, son. Now all I know about this-here television is I can't stand to look at it. But all you fellahs are a lot smarter'n me, so I'm gonna lay it right out on the floor here and let you kick it around."

"Any day," I said louder than I had meant to.

The meeting began, with every man present anxious to say something—but not too much. It was not surprising that every ensuing comment was carefully edited to flatter Mr. Murray and yet not to antagonize Tony. "On one hand, Fred, I'm with you, but on the other hand old Tony has a good point. . . ."

I watched and listened with growing disgust. Disgust with Mr. Murray for his wily provincialism, his unashamed showing off, his loaded questions, and his obvious, corny witticisms; disgust with the other men for their whorish kowtowing to the old tyrant; disgust with Tony for his glibness, his over-exquisite tact, his exaggerated patience; and disgust with myself for being there.

After several hours of unadulterated hot air, Mr. Murray turned to me. "Now let's hear from this-here writer fellah. Yer the only one hasn't said his piece yet."

"I have no piece to say, Mr. Murray. . . ."

"I thought I tolja ta call me Fred."

"You don't *tell* me to do anything, Mr. Murray."

"Fred," Tony said hastily, placatingly, "what he means is . . ."

"What I mean is that none of this concerns me or interests me in the least," I said.

"Oh, it don't?"

"No, it *doesn't*."

"Well now, sir, that's mighty fancy talk from a fellah that's tryin' to sell us this expensive tellyvision program. Mighty fancy. Arrogant."

"*I'm* trying to sell? I'm trying to sell you *what?*"

"Uh, I didn't want to bother you with it until our plans were, uh, finalized," Tony said. The tone was smooth, but he looked tense. "You see, I was planning to base the series on your last book and . . ."

"My last book isn't for sale, Tony. It's already sold, or at least optioned. It's going on the stage next fall."

"You didn't tell me that," Tony said. He sounded hurt, as though I had been holding something back.

"You didn't ask."

"Fer the stage, huh? Well, that's pretty small potatoes. If Murray Manafacturin' wanted it—mind you, I say *if*—I reckon you could always option it back?"

"Yes, I suppose I could, if—mind you, I say *if*—I wanted to. I don't. The playwright, the producer, all the people concerned have put too much into it to have the whole thing yanked out from under them. I don't do business that way."

"That's admirable, ain't it, fellahs? Admirable. But I reckon if you was to get a big fat check from Murray Manafacturin' you might sing a diffrunt tune."

"I don't sing for money, Mr. Murray. The book isn't for sale. It can't make very much difference anyhow, as you don't want a television program."

"I didn't say that. That's why we're havin' this informal meeting. The way I run Murray Manafacturin' every man-jack in the whole outfit has his say. That's democracy. Why, there ain't a man in the whole company from these fellahs shootin' the breeze around here down to a stock boy can't come inta my office and say . . ."

"Yes, I know, Mr. Murray. You've told me. But I suggest that you discuss your problems with your employees and not with me. I never heard of you or of Murray Manufacturing before. Now if I may be excused . . ."

Mr. Murray looked as though he'd been struck and so did the rest of the men in the room. As I opened the door Tony was saying, "See, Fred. That's what I mean. No public image. Here's a famous author who's never even heard of you or . . ."

"Shut up!" Murray roared.

Once out of the room I kept on going straight to the telephone. I called for a taxi and was on my way to New York before the Star Chamber in Tony's study had been adjourned.

My telephone was ringing when I let myself into my apartment. It was Tony.

"Hey! What happened to you? What do you mean slipping away without a word?"

"I said all the words I should have. Probably more."

"You were terrific, pal. Really Sensational. Nobody ever talked that way to Fred before."

"Somebody should have."

"You really hit him right between the eyes. He likes you. Really he does. Respects you."

"Well, that's more than I can say for him."

"But don't you realize what you've done? You got the old bastard right where he lives. He was so stunned to find out that you'd never heard of him—or anybody else outside Connecticut for that matter—that Fred's going right on with my television show, over all the opposition."

"What opposition?"

"That act you put on really impressed him."

"That was no act."

"Now listen, here's my plan: I'm coming into New York Monday to set up an office—just to be on the T.V. scene. We'll have lunch together and then you can start getting your book back from whatever producer optioned it. That is, if you really *did* sell it. We could offer him a small profit on the whole package and have it free and . . ." Tony was still talking as I hung up the receiver.

VIII

TONY

in town

After my enforced stay at Chisholm's Crossing my telephone wires were kept hot by John Anthony van den Burg, television producer. He was truly crushed that I refused to renege on my original commitment and turn my last book over to him, "for the sake of our friendship, not to mention the enormous sum of money I'm willing to offer."

Tony, from his Knoll Associates office in a big, green glass box on Madison Avenue, would not take No for an answer. Like a child, having told Santa Claus what he wanted for Christmas, Tony waited in noisy anticipation for his wish to come true. Valid excuses of prior commitments, contractual obligations, and complete lack of interest were lost on him. He simply would not believe that I had no intention of furthering his career in communications. He telephoned daily, was full of more improbable stories than a plot wheel, and I listened with admiration to his transparent lies, his ploys and ruses, his infantile wheedling.

"Listen," he would say, "I was just lunching with Papa at the Sherry Netherland . . ."

"Mr. Murray?"

"No! Ernest Hemingway."

"Sorry, Tony, I don't believe I know him."

"Oh, come off it. Anyway, Papa came up with this socko idea for the comedy series. There are these two nuns, see. . . ."

"That's killing, Tony. A scream. I can't wait to see it. You might call it *For Whom the Bell Tolls*. Well, I knew if you shopped around long enough for a decent writer you'd find one."

"But *he* doesn't want to write it. He wants you to. He said to me not ten minutes ago that you were the ideal . . ."

"You certainly got back from Cuba in a hurry, Tony."

"What?"

"If you'll look on page twenty of this morning's *Times* you'll see that Hemingway flew back to Havana last night."

"He missed the plane."

"So did you, Tony. But best of luck with the series."

Another time my work was interrupted by a Southern accent so broad that it could have come only from a minstrel show. "Ah hay-uve a pusson-ta-pusson cawl fo' you-all fum Oxfud, Mizz-sippi. Mistah van den Bug." There was a slight giggle and then Tony was on. "Hi! Can you hear me?"

"Yes, more's the pity."

"Listen, I'm down here in Oxford with Bill."

"Bill who?"

"Bill Faulkner. We've been kicking this story idea around." The rest of the conversation was pure science fiction. Tony's dear friend William Faulkner was to supply the basic idea for a television series and Tony's even dearer friend Eleanor Roosevelt was to narrate. All I had to do was write it. "I'll think it over, Tony, and let you know. When are you coming back to New York?"

"Bill's driving me out to the airport. I'll be in the office tomorrow and I'll call you. This is great news, kiddo, you and Bill and Eleanor. What a combo!"

On pure hunch I dialed Tony's office immediately. "Murray Manufacturing, New York," a voice said. The accent was pure Bronx but the timbre of the voice was the same as the Oxford, Mississippi operator's.

"Mr. van den Burg, please."

"May I know who's callingue?"

"I reckon you didn't get the name, sister. It's Fred Murray."

"Just a moment, Mr. Murray. I'll ringue Mr. van den Burg."

"Yes, Fred?" Tony said, all eagerness.

"Turn in your Equity card, Tony, you're through," I said and hung up.

On a more realistic level, Tony continued to woo me, as though I were the only author alive. There were little dinners with Muffie at quasi-show-business restaurants such as Sardi's, Toots Shor's, and the Algonquin (having conquered the East Side, Tony had now very decidedly crossed Fifth Avenue and entered the world of the Arts). There were invitations to inspect the newly acquired Manhattan offices of Murray Manufacturing—two starkly modern rooms and a large couch for Tony and the tart of the bogus Southern accent. "I get a lot of ideas on that couch," Tony said.

"I'll bet you do. And carry them out as well. Can that tramp type?"

"Miss La Verne is a very nice girl. She wants to go on television."

"She's got the cleavage for it, if nothing else."

When I was still able to resist the blandishments of Murray Manufacturing, Tony took to dropping in on me, sometimes alone, sometimes with Miss La Verne, and finally with the bland young man from Chisholm's Crossing who worked for whichever advertising agency handled the Murray account. One drink always led to another and another and another, and thence to the real reason for Tony's visit: When was I going to stop being so silly and start turning out a history-making television series for Murray Manufacturing?

After a few weeks of Tony's ceaseless importuning I got bored. "Tony," I said, "you're wasting your time and mine. I've never written for television. I don't want to write for television. I don't even watch it."

"That's just what I keep telling Tony," the agency man said. "A writer as well known as you . . ."

"There are hundreds of authors—a lot of them *really* famous and all of them perfectly competent—who would give their eye teeth to do a series. . . ."

"Isn't that funny, that's just what I was saying to Tony on the way over," the agency man said. He probably had a dozen unsold television shows on his hands and was dying to unload one of them. "I said, 'Tony, if a man doesn't *want* to write for the tube . . .'"

"Well, I don't and even if I did, I wouldn't want to work for your father-in-law."

"Why not?" Tony asked.

"Because I hate the old bastard's guts. And so do you. And so," I said, fixing the agency man with a glare, "probably do you." The agency man looked as though he'd been stabbed. He leapt to his feet, said something about not wanting to miss his train, and vanished. Tony and I were left alone together.

"Nice apartment," he said.

"I like it." I did, too. It occupied the top two floors of a converted brownstone in the East Seventies. It was large, quiet, comfortable, and fairly inexpensive.

"I wish I had a little place of my own," Tony said.

"You've got a little place of your own out in Chisholm's Crossing."

"It's not my own. It's Fred's. I'm under his thumb twenty-four hours a day. I wouldn't admit this to anyone else in the world, but you're right about Fred and me. I can't stand the sight of him and vice versa. He'll never forgive me for marrying his baby. That's why I want to get going in television—so I can tell the old fart where to shove it."

With the inconsistency of people who have drunk too much, he switched the conversation back to my apartment. "Yes, you've really got it made here. Peace and privacy. Your own entrance. No doormen or elevator boys to stick their noses into your business. I don't suppose you'd ever like to lend it to me when you're out of town?"

"I'm not out of town that much. I'm working on a new book. Why? Doesn't Miss La Verne have a place of her own?"

"She lives with her . . . For God's sake! What a filthy mind you have! But in case I ever did want to stay in town overnight . . ."

"My landlady wouldn't like it." I looked at my watch. "I hate to speed the parting guest, Tony, but I've got to get dressed. Dinner party."

"Oh, that's okay. Anyone I know?"

"Maggie Faye."

"Hey! You are moving in fancy circles. Who's going to be there?"

"Just the usual crowd—Mrs. Roosevelt, Faulkner, Hemingway . . ."

Tony tried to laugh good-naturedly. "Well, I'll just mix myself another and drop you off on my way to the station."

"Thanks, Tony, but it's just downstairs. Maggie's my landlady."

There can't be anyone past the age of thirty who does not remember Maggie Faye. Born plain—in every sense of the word —Mary Margaret Fahey in St. Louis, Missouri, she hit New York like lightning during the latish thirties when other girls of her age were wishing they were Brenda Frazier. A little more than a year after her arrival, her first book burst into print. Maggie Faye's merry memoir—the more or less true story of a nice, middle-class Irish Catholic convent girl's early days in New York; depression, jobs, Greenwich Village, the Communist Party, and all the rest of it—is an established classic and the basis of a play, a movie, a musical comedy, a Glorious Technicolor musical, and a television series. But Maggie was not content to stop with her first book or to write others that were merely pallid sequels. Maggie was hot and Maggie stayed hot. Maggie had the knack of being able to tell people what they already knew so refreshingly that they would accept any old saw as a new landmark in profundity. Her book of advice to career girls, her famous tips to teen-agers, her account of touring the European Theater of Operations with a U.S.O. troupe, her froth about wartime shortages, were snatched up by the eager public and quickly converted into gold.

One could reasonably expect a girl like Maggie, coming from nowhere, to return there, leaving a profligate's trail of ermine coats, flashy cars, and expensive ex-husbands in her wake. But Maggie, having known poverty as a child, decided never to meet up with it again. She invested her money shrewdly and carefully. At a time when property was plentiful, prices low, and contractors eager to please, Maggie bought a derelict roominghouse in a not-yet-fashionable block in the East Seventies, then another and another and another, until she owned five in a row, converted cheaply and charmingly into duplex apartments, bright with paint and trees and flowers. (In 1955 she refused an offer of one million dollars, cash, for what had cost her about a tenth of that amount. And she was wise to do so. The property was worth more. The neighborhood had become chic and Maggie had made it so.) "It would only go in taxes," Maggie said. "And, besides, where would I live? No, darling, it's the Irish love of the land. Anyhow, what would I do with a million dollars?"

"Something very crafty and clever and cagey, Maggie," I said. "Something that would at least double it."

Money was not the only thing Maggie was shrewd about. One

day she showed me a snapshot of a dark, dumpy, beetle-browed girl in a convent uniform squinting into the sunlight and smiling with gray, uneven teeth.

"Who's that," I asked, "one of the Dionnes?"

"That is Mary Margaret Fahey—me—taken just before I picked up my diploma and my suitcase and came to New York."

"But the figure. Those teeth. The hairline . . ."

"Losing the weight was easy on what a girl got paid in those days. The rest came a little higher. I took the advance on my first book and put it right in my mouth. My teeth were capped by the best theatrical dentist in town."

"And the hair?"

"I can thank Dr. Szilagy and his magic electric needle for the widow's peak—for having any forehead at all. As for the hair on my head, I saved that. Mother Superior didn't approve of the laity bobbing its hair. Anyhow, I had sort of a crush on those classic beauties like Dolores del Rio and Liz Whitney and Mrs. William Rhinelander Stewart. It's a lot easier to slick it back into a bun than to waste all that time and money with some hairdresser who hates women."

Maggie had been a public personality for a long time—but not quite from the very beginning. When her first book rocketed upward on the best-seller lists, everyone wanted to meet the amazing Maggie Faye. Miss Faye, however, was not ready to be met: not without a few further improvements. Diet, dentistry, and electrolysis had turned her into a beauty. Now someone or something would have to turn her into a lady. It wasn't a difficult job. Maggie—although her immediate background included a drunken unemployed day laborer for a father and a cramped two-family house filled with wet-bottomed brothers and sisters, bleeding hearts painted on velvet, and a bathtub in the kitchen for a setting—had taste and brains. At a reasonable fee, she put herself into the hands of a down-and-out refugee noblewoman and before long she was gabbling away in French, brandishing the European fork, and discussing art, music, and period furniture.

She sewed expertly ("It was the only thing the sisters taught that I really wanted to learn.") and she had mastered the art of dressing down instead of up. She could pick a dress or a suit off the rack on Fourteenth Street, snip off the cheap trimmings, alter it to fit flawlessly, finish it off with a string of Woolworth pearls, plain black pumps, and clean white gloves and look as though she had spent a fortune on the outfit. Before very long Maggie Faye was appearing on the best-dressed lists as well as the best-seller lists. Even with unlimited funds to spend, Maggie shopped carefully and did a lot of her own sewing. She dressed first as a woman, second as a lady, laying down rigid rules for herself such as never appearing on the street without gloves and a hat.

Maggie applied the same discipline to everything in her life. She rose at seven, discussed the management of her household with her maid, and then went to her desk where she worked all day. She napped from five until six and was dressed for a big evening every night at seven. Every Tuesday night was set aside for shampooing her hair, creaming her face, doing her nails, and mending. Every Wednesday she gave a dinner party. On Thursdays she was a panelist on a popular and faintly intellectual television program. On the seventh day she rested.

The casual reader probably thought of Maggie Faye as a witty, gregarious clothes horse whose considerable literary output was jotted down on the backs of dressmakers' bills between parties. Her comings and goings, her little dinners, her funny sayings, the magnificence of her clothes, her jewels, her furniture were all dutifully reported in the press. But there was nothing offhand or accidental about her. She would devote the same concentration to a new tree for her garden or an old chair for her living room as she would to the book she was writing or a report of her finances. When she looked especially pensive and I would ask, "What are you thinking about, Maggie?" the answer was just as likely to concern a dozen oyster plates she had seen at an antique shop as the contract she was negotiating with her publisher.

Inconsistent? Not at all. Maggie had no feminine inconsistencies. Her life was a well-run business in which the boss knew everything that was going on, and talking to Maggie about anything was like talking to a superbly intelligent businessman. If I make her sound cold, I have done her a great disservice. She was kind and generous, and for a woman whose life was as manufactured as her teeth or her brow, she was the most completely genuine person I have ever known. I had been her tenant for the past three years, her lover for the past two.

In many a high-styled husbandless household there is one omnipresent—and usually colorless—man who is the first to arrive, the last to leave. He knows the geography of the place by heart. It is he who sits at the head of the table, makes direct requests of the maid, mixes the drinks, stokes the embers in the fireplace. It does not require much in the way of instinct to realize that this man is madam's current favorite. People talk about the relationship, but they do so casually and knowingly. After all, poor old Mary or Jane or Betty is a normal, healthy woman and although that what's-his-name is a trifle dull, she might do worse—and he's not costing her anything.

If people talked about us, we were discussed only by that most exclusive company who were invited into Maggie's house for dinner. We rarely appeared together in public, not for any particular reason except that we preferred staying at home. Maggie had often pronounced herself "an old maid." She had even written a popular book on the joys of spinsterhood. Yet for the past twenty years her name had been linked with any number of beaux—writers, actors, painters, financiers, all of those mysterious cardboard characters who are touted from time to time as our most eligible bachelors. If I was jealous of the more dashing men who were seen out with Maggie—and of course I was—it did me little good. Maggie would only laugh and say, "Darling, he's old enough to be my father," or "Darling, he wouldn't look at a woman, he's only using me as a front," or "Darling, everybody knows he's been impotent for years." But as our relationship grew from my being "that nice man upstairs who might be free to fill in at dinner" to my sharing Maggie's bed, she went out less and less. She had, after all, been to so many hundreds of opening nights, dinner parties, and charity balls that staying at home was something of a novelty. Separately, and in our different ways, we were both lonely. Together we were not. We were like a long-married couple, but without benefit of matrimony.

After a time I began to object. In a way it was almost comical. I found myself in the distinctly female position of the seduced virgin who wants to be made an honest woman. I kept insisting on the security and respectability of marriage. Maggie, like the wary rake-hell, kept refusing. "Darling, I've got a reputation to maintain. I'm an old maid. I'm practically famous for it. Besides, I'm older than you."

"At our ages what difference could a couple of years make? Come on, Maggie, marry me."

"The only point in marriage is to have children. I can't—never could—so what's the sense of complicating our lives?"

"What does the priest say?"

"Plenty, but it's in Latin."

Finally I played my trump card. "Maggie, look at it this way: My income is about half what yours is. By marrying me we could file a joint income tax return and you'd save . . ."

"You sound like my accountant instead of my lover. The answer is No. Now come to bed before we're too old to enjoy it."

Although Tony had finally given up trying to enlist my services as a writer, he still kept stopping in, uninvited, unexpected, unannounced, and unwanted to drink too many drinks, to ask advice I couldn't possibly give on matters concerning his television empire, and to try to wheedle a key to the apartment. After three years as the smiling suburbanite, Tony was bored and all too anxious to stay in town. I gathered that he was spending a lot of nights someplace when Muffie took to telephoning at odd hours to ask if I had seen Tony. As Muffie understood matters, Tony was working day and night with me on the Murray Manufacturing television program. I was angry with Tony for involving me in this lie, but whenever Muffie called in her lost-little-girl voice, I hadn't the heart to set her straight.

Once Tony learned that the fabulous Maggie Faye lived below me and that we were friends—something warned me against telling him more—he was relentless in his attempts to meet her. "She's the sort of dame I could use for my show."

"She's no dame, Tony. And she's already on television—on it, in it, and of it. Two of her books are being dramatized every week and Maggie herself is on at nine o'clock Thursday nights. As the big T.V. mogul, you ought to know that."

"Sure, but if I could just get to meet her and talk her into doing a show for me."

"If you want the name of her agent . . ."

"What the hell do agents know about big-time T.V.? In my hands she could be famous overnight."

"She is famous. If she weren't you'd have no interest in meeting her."

Tony finally broke me down. Cocktails were arranged in Maggie's magnificent living room for the following day. The meeting was disastrous. Maggie, who was driving herself to finish a book on time, was tired and cross about missing her nap. Maggie drank nothing, Tony drank too much. Maggie said nothing, Tony talked too much. In his overeagerness to please and impress, he was positively gauche and more than a little vulgar. I was reminded of the adolescent Tony I had known back in school. The air was thick with big names and big prices. Tony's most impressive connections were dredged up and flung into the conversation. When, after overstaying by two hours, Tony excused himself to call Chisholm's Crossing—"We have a little place in Chisholm's Crossing, Miss Faye; or may I call you Maggie?"—Maggie gave me a withering look. "You got him in here, I'll give you just ten minutes to get him out. And speaking of out, that's where you're taking me to dinner tonight. Some-place very grand. It's to be my revenge."

When Tony came back, Maggie already had her hat on. "My watch must have stopped. I had no idea of the time. We're dining at Pavillon, Mr. van den Burg. We'll drop you."

In the end, Tony tagged along, made a great show of calling waiters by name, ordering dishes that were not on the menu, and waving at other diners, who stared back blankly. Finally, em-boldened by gin, wine, and cognac, he came right out and asked Maggie just what she had available for television adaptation. "Nothing, as far as I know," Maggie said sweetly. "You'd have to telephone my agent."

"I'd much rather telephone you, *Mag*. What's your number?"

"Have you a pencil, Mr. van den Burg? I'll write it down."

"I've had a lovely evening, but this wasn't it," Maggie said to me as we settled into a taxi together. "Would you tell me just one thing, darling? Where and how and when did a nice, upstanding, clean-living, hard-working Eagle Scout like you ever run across a windy little con man like Tony van den Burg?"

"Sorry, Maggie. I thought you'd be amused by him."

"You thought wrong."

"Most women think he's irresistible."

"I'm not most women. Oh, I'm sure that *somebody* must find him attractive in an obvious sort of way—glib charm, roving eye, big bulge in his trousers, which is either bad tailoring or bad taste or both. I see a long-suffering little wife out in Sneden's Landing or wherever he comes from and a big-bosomed secretary . . ."

I laughed and put an arm around Maggie.

The next day bad news arrived—a long letter from my mother. It was about my father. The lung thing that had plagued him since the first World War had finally caught up with him. It was cancer. Inoperable and terminal. He was being kept comfortable and he was given something between six weeks and six months to live. Would I come to Santa Fe immediately?

I was reading her letter a second time when Tony called. "Hey, I think this Maggie dame must have made some kind of mistake. Whenever Miss La Verne dials that number she gets the correct time."

"Tony, I'm afraid I can't talk to you right now. My father's dying and I've got to take off for Santa Fe."

"How long will you be gone?"

"Six weeks. Six months. Maybe longer, maybe shorter. I don't really know."

"But then you could let me have your apartment."

"Tony, I can't talk real estate just now." And then I realized that I could, that I would have to. With her usual English chinuppishness my mother had never mentioned money before. Now she was frank to say that they were ruined and matters would become worse before it was all over. They needed my help. "Tony, if you really want the apartment as is on a very indefinite arrangement and if you're willing to get out on a week's notice . . ."

"You bet, chum. A lot of big companies keep suites of rooms in town for their executives. It's all tax deductible. I'll have Fred tell the bookkeeper to . . ."

"Not so fast. I want to talk to Maggie first."

"I'll talk to her, chum. We're old friends."

"Tony, I'll call you back."

Maggie was everything I expected her to be—calm, kind, and sympathetic; there were encouraging little pats and kisses, offers of drinks, coffee, money, and the services of influential friends who were high up in travel agencies, airlines, and medicine.

"There isn't anything you can do, Maggie. I've got my plane reservations. I'll go around to the bank after lunch. There's nothing to do but pack, fly out there, and wait. Tony wants to sublet my apartment. . . ."

"Tony?"

"Not Tony himself. Murray Manufacturing. They'll take it furnished on a week-to-week basis."

"Darling, I wish you wouldn't. I'd really rather let the apartment stand vacant and not collect the rent while you're gone than . . ."

"I know you would, but I wouldn't. I'll need every penny I can scrape together."

"Darling, I've got loads of money. Just say whatever it is you want and . . ."

"That's sweet of you, Maggie, but I've managed to stay out of the kept-gentleman class so far and . . ."

"Don't you think that you and I are slightly different?"

"Not until we're married. And you needn't worry about Tony. He won't be here very much and even when he is you don't have to see him."

"Somehow I have a feeling that I will."

As a doctor my father knew that he was going to die. As a man he denied it. I sat with him every day, watching him fade away among the riotous blooms of my mother's English garden and listening to him talk. He spoke only of the past—our school and the wonderful times a boy could hardly avoid having there—and of the future—how he was going to march right into St. Vincent's Hospital and give them what-for. It was as though he were a Christian Scientist overcoming a slight head cold. The present was never mentioned at all.

Treated as an eccentric, an easy mark, someone whose free services were to be taken for granted during all of his years in Santa Fe, my father was suddenly overwhelmed by a popularity he was unable to appreciate. Wilting nosegays, hideous examples of Tesuque pottery, messes of inedible food, and elaborate greeting cards, mawkish with doves and flowers or gory with blood and crucifixions, arrived daily. The pièce de résistance was a huge color television set in limed oak, contributed by a long list of former patients who were alive only because of my father's ministrations. Maggie, who had never met my father, was splendid about sending things a sick man would like and could use. Every week a package arrived from her for my father, and every day for the first few weeks a letter came for me.

Tony had moved in, she wrote. He spent a good deal more time in my apartment than even Maggie had expected, and from the sounds of footsteps overhead, he was not spending it alone, unless he wore high heels. Tony was making rather a pest of himself and Maggie was busily discouraging any intimacy.

Still the letters kept coming. New York was blistering and everyone even vaguely amusing had left town. Out of desperation Maggie had had to ask Tony to her weekly dinner party. He hadn't been as awful as she had expected. She realized that he was only after something of hers for his wretched television show, but he simply could not be discouraged from dropping in for drinks every evening.

Maggie's letters began coming a little less often. She knew that I would understand how very busy she was. She had been dragooned into entertaining Tony, Muffie, the Murrays, and the man from the advertising agency, and the evening had been deadly. However, Tony had come up with an idea for a television program which wasn't half bad. Tony sent his regards.

In September Maggie wrote that she was so tied up with a dozen projects that a long, newsy letter once a week would have to do. She was sick to death of her old panel show and had refused to sign on for the next season. Maggie was really taken with Tony's idea and had agreed not only to write the Murray Manufacturing Hour but to act as hostess, just so that she could keep the whole thing under some kind of reasonable check. Tony was flourishing. The trampish Miss La Verne had been sacked and replaced by a competent older woman. Tony had meant to add a note, but he had to drive out to Chisholm's Crossing for some more clothes.

With the first cool days my father was confined to his bed under the constant supervision of a prissy male nurse who followed six daily soap operas on the big color television set. My father feigned an interest he could not possibly have felt in television, using it simply as an excuse for not talking. He lay almost comatose, pretending to watch while my mother twittered about the splendid educational programs available to the British public through the benign offices of B.B.C.

In October, with great fanfare, the Murray Manufacturing Hour had its premiere. The advance publicity made it sound bigger and more portentous than the Oberammergau Passion Play, except that great gaiety was promised. The Murray Manufacturing Company presented with great pride John Anthony van den Burg's production of *High Life*, a rollicking comedy series in living color conceived and written by Maggie Faye with an impressive cast of stars, costumes by Christian Dior, settings by Norman Bel Geddes, and music by the Murray Philharmonia. Lovely Maggie Faye, herself, would act as hostess.

My father's nurse, petulant about missing *December Bride*, tuned in the set and the show was on. "You friend Miss Faye looks . . . well, different from what I'd expected, de-ah," my mother said. "Harder." With that I realized that I had not even recognized Maggie—not until she spoke. Her legendary looks had vanished. She was heavily made up. Her long black hair had been cut short, curled and crimped and dyed an unearthly copper color. Her bosom was half in and half out of the sort of dress she would have damned as "pure Gabor" six months earlier and she was festooned with pounds of flashing junk jewelry. Her appearance was mercifully brief. What followed was even worse—a full hour of tired, pseudo-sophisticated comedy based loosely on the collected works of Noel Coward, Frederick Lonsdale, and Philip Barry. While my father bleated about turning the miserable thing off, I insisted on waiting to watch the crawl, to make sure that Maggie had actually written it. She had.

The critics, who had always treated anything Maggie had ever touched as scripture, tore the program apart. The Murray Manufacturing Hour was so elaborate, pretentious, costly, and terrible that newspapers were even rapping it on their editorial pages. I was sick with pity for Maggie. Her letters stopped abruptly. My telephone calls reached only a crisp, impersonal answering service. The sole contact I had with her was on the television screen each week. It was hardly the same thing. Nor was it the same Maggie. The Murray program grew worse instead of better each week. Maggie was trying too hard. Her hair and clothes grew more outlandish. She was beginning to go up in her lines and to ad lib badly. The cool, self-assured wit was gone.

In November my father finally died. His good works and selfless devotion to healing the poor were eulogized at a proper Church of England funeral. His ashes were scattered over the desert and that was the end of his unhappy life. My mother and I returned home alone.

"So many lovely things about your poor father in the *New Mexican*," my mother said crumpling her black bordered handkerchief into a ball. "And in the Albuquerque *Tribune*, too. Would you be a dear and clip them for my scrapbook? I think I'll lie down until time for tea."

I hadn't looked at a newspaper for days. The Southwestern press had treated my father, dead, with far greater reverence than they had shown him alive. His death was generously covered, but the big story, complete with photographs, was a wire service report of a sizzling New York divorce scandal.

BEST-SELLER NAMED CO-RESPONDENT

and

WRITER IS OTHER WOMAN IN SOCIETY DIVORCE SCANDAL

and . . .

But why go on? The unbelievable had happened. With the vindictive Miss La Verne furnishing both the information and the key, Muffie van den Burg, her father, two detectives, and a photographer had broken into my apartment to find Tony and Maggie together. The situation was classic—"Love Nest Raided," but with an all-star cast. The press, bored by the squalid shootings and stabbings of obscure sinners in Spanish Harlem, had all the ingredients for a full-scale orgy: Maggie Faye—that paragon among women—renowned for her writing, her television career, her clothes, her beauty, her wit, her wealth, her taste, her highly placed friends, was the ideal homewrecker; Tony van den Burg, rich, handsome, well publicized and married, made a superb villain; Muffie, the dewy-eyed ingenue who had forsaken her name in lights for love and marriage—also beautiful, also rich, and also visibly pregnant—was a perfect choice for the abandoned wife and mother; and Mr. Murray, "mystery million-aire manufacturer," as he was billed, provided exactly the correct picturesque touch as an off-beat father image. No one was spared. Miss La Verne, who had had the foresight to bring a flash camera along on the raid, did a booming business in amateur photography and was quoted as being against adultery and all in favor of the sanctity of marriage. Rose Willingham, in an exclusive interview, said that Tony was "a good boy" and that there must have been some mistake. I was briefly mentioned as an author and the rightful tenant of what was described as a "sybaritic bachelor apartment." Even my cleaning woman had her moment of fame when she was asked to air her views on Tony's way of life. They were not flattering. "East-side mansion," "luxurious showplace," "socialite"—every cliché beloved by the tabloid writer was brought into play.

Again there was no answer when I tried to telephone Maggie.

The Murray Manufacturing Hour appeared on television that evening, but without Maggie, without the cast of High Life, the splashy costumes and scenery. Instead the television audience was treated to no one but Mr. Murray, reading badly from a prepared script. "Folks, my name is Fred Murray, founder of the Murray Manufacturing Company of Waterbury, Connecticut. Yer prob'ly expectin' that fancy program of my son-in-law's called

High Life. Well, there ain't gonna be no *High Life*—not tonight or any other night. Instead, I'm gonna talk to you about another kinda life—the Good Life, the Decent Life. . . ." I stared numbly at the television set. The old charlatan was in his element.

"How can you sit there watching that vulgar television with your poor father not . . ."

"Please, Mother," I said, "I can't explain, but this is . . ." When I turned back to the set Fred Murray had disappeared and a usually suave announcer, looking flustered, was saying, "Owing to technical difficulties, the program scheduled at this time will not be heard."

The next day, however, the newspapers took great delight in reporting that Fred Murray had been shut off the air. He had thrown his script away and, before the technicians in the control booth could pull the switch, called Maggie a hack writer, a kept woman, and a notorious whore. If anything was needed to make a sizzling scandal hotter still, that was it.

There was a cluster of reporters stamping their feet on the cold pavement in front of Maggie's house when I returned to New York. I fought my way through them and let myself into Maggie's apartment. It looked the same, but different. The spick and span, everything-in-its-place quality had gone. It was not exactly dirty, but not exactly clean. It was also empty.

Big modern brass letters reading

VAN DEN BURG ASSOCIATES

had been attached to the door of my apartment. The place was a mess, full of half-finished drinks, overflowing ashtrays, and stale air. In my bedroom at the rear of the top floor I found Maggie. Under the circumstances I could hardly expect her to be looking her best, but nothing—not even her radically altered image on the television screen—had prepared me for the Maggie I saw huddled on my bed. Her hair, of course, was a disaster. Unkempt it was even worse. Even bald the old Maggie would have been beautiful. Now she was not. She was heavier, her face puffy and bloated. She wore a far from fresh housecoat with a series of spots and stains down the front.

"Maggie . . ."

She looked at me blankly with a glazed disinterest. I realized that there was something seriously wrong with her. "Maggie, what's happened to you?"

"You can read, can't you? How's your father?"

"He's dead."

"He's lucky. Are the gentlemen of the press still outside? I came up here to get away from the telephone and the doorbell. I hope you don't mind."

"Maggie, I . . ."

She held out a dirty glass in her trembling hand. "If you look on your desk you'll find the remains . . . the remains of a bottle of gin. All that's left, I'm afraid. Would you?"

I saw now what her trouble was. She was dead drunk—Maggie Faye, who had never in the years I had known her had more than one drink before dinner and a glass of wine at table. "Maggie, what the hell do you think you're doing? It's only nine o'clock in the morning and here you are . . ."

"Plastered? That's right, darling. High as a kite, boiled as an owl, drunk as a skunk."

"Maggie! Do you think this is making matters any better?"

"Immeasurably better, my dear. I wish I'd thought of it a long time ago. As Tony says . . ."

"Where is Tony?"

"Oh God, please don't say some tiresome thing about going after him with a horsewhip, like that psychotic father-in-law of his. You can't anyhow. Tony's gone."

"Gone where?"

"Last I heard he was planning to hide out in a motel in

Secaucus, New Jersey. 'The pig capital of the world,' I believe it's . . ."

"What are you talking about?"

"Tony's trying to avoid some papers they're going to serve on him. I don't quite understand. I don't understand any of this." She started to sing: "She's come a long way from St. Louis, but she's still got a long way to go. . . ."

"Maggie," I said, grabbing her by the shoulders and shaking her. "Stop this. I want to help you. Now pull yourself together and . . ." With that she started to cry. I had never seen Maggie cry before. Probably no one had.

"I haven't d-done anything like this . . . like this in y-years."

"Maybe it will help. Here, take my handkerchief. I'll make some coffee."

When Maggie was a little more lucid I said, "Now do you want to tell me about it?"

"What is there to tell? Surely you saw the photographs—Miss La Verne's, that is. The official ones taken by Muffie's detectives are much better—sharper, clearer, juicier."

"Maggie, don't try to be flip. All that tripe in the tabloids doesn't really matter. I just want to know how this . . . this mess ever got started."

"So do I."

"You hated Tony's guts when I left here."

"That was before I really knew him. Sorry, darling, but I'm helplessly in love with him. I think maybe I was from the very beginning. That's why I didn't want him here."

"But, Maggie, you're a mature, intelligent woman. . . ."

"So they say. At least they used to. Little Miss Sure Shot. Good old Maggie who could tell everyone else how to dress, how to live, how to love. And look at me now—a great gasping fool in love. A public spectacle with dyed hair and a roll around my middle."

"Just what did happen to your hair, Maggie?" It was a frivolous question, but I couldn't help wondering.

"Tony. He thought I'd better change my 'public image,' as they say in the advertising agencies. Well, I certainly did."

"And . . . and that television show?"

"*High Life* is what Tony wanted. I did it to please him."

"My God, what kind of power does he have over you women?"

"Power over *women?* He has none. Women have victimized him since the day he was born. Have you ever met his mother?"

"Rose? Many times."

"She's a dynamo. She's warped his whole life. And who was that great friend of his—the one who killed himself?"

"Tatham Purdom?"

"It was that evil-minded old mother—that Mrs. Purdom—who thought there was something fishy going on and appealed to Tony's better nature." I felt my jaw sag as Maggie raced on. "She was a powerful woman, too. Tony was weak. She had him right under her thumb where she wanted him. And that Perry girl . . ."

"Posy?"

"Yes. Spoiled, selfish, rich, and a hopeless nymphomaniac. Going to bed with some society stallion on the very eve of their wedding! Can you imagine how that must have hurt Tony?"

"Did Tony tell you that?"

"He didn't want to, but I wormed it out of him. And Muffie! That baby-faced clinging vine! Clinging? She nearly crushed the life out of him—tricking him into marrying her, dragging him out to Connecticut to invest every cent he had in her father's business. And now this—Tony's name and mine dragged into the gutter press just because that vicious little Muffie and her incestuous old father . . ."

"Maggie, have you gone right out of your mind?"

"Practically. But don't you see how awful it's been for poor Tony? No wonder he turned to other women. Now Muffie holds all the aces. She's got him right where she wants him. She's the wronged party. Now she can hold him up for a tremendous settlement. She doesn't want alimony, just a huge lump sum—so she can live happily ever after with that man she's been keeping on Tony's money. . . ."

"Maggie! Stop it! You've met Muffie—seen her with your own eyes?"

"Yes, and it's a type I know only too well, a power-driven little bitch who wouldn't say 'damn,' and a crafty little actress in the bargain. They're always the deadliest. It's always those man-killers who attract Tony."

"And you?"

"Me? I hope I'm not like the others. I love Tony. I understand him. I can help him."

"Listen to me, Maggie, the first person you've got to help is yourself. Don't worry about Tony. Worry about you. You've got to get out of here—out of this house, out of . . ."

"That's just what I'm going to do. I'm unloading these buildings so fast it'll make . . ."

"Maggie, wait! You don't have to do anything quite so drastic. I only meant . . ."

"Oh, but you see I do. The Murrays have bled Tony of every penny he inherited from his father and . . ."

"What's that got to do with selling your houses?"

"Why, to raise enough money for Muffie's settlement. Then Tony can marry me."

IX

TONY
at large

The scandal had hit the public with a far greater impact than any of the hundreds of other cases of adultery that are exposed daily—a matter of timing, I suppose, and of the luster attached to the people concerned. All the old jokes that had been told about King Carol and Magda Lupescu, Edward VIII and Mrs. Simpson, Roberto Rossellini and Ingrid Bergman were dragged out of the sewers where they had festered and revamped to fit Maggie and Tony. A very amateur lyricist somewhere had run up a new set of words to "Frankie and Johnny" which had been mimeographed and made available to music-lovers everywhere, and coy references to Maggie and Tony never failed to bring down the house on television.

Instead of withering away like a hothouse rose after a couple of mornings on the breakfast tables of the nation, the Maggie-Tony thing grew and grew. It smacked of dirty doings in high places—*and just before Christmas!*—which provided editorial writers and their readers with the sort of story they loved most.

The double standard being what it is, Tony did not suffer. Boys, after all, will be boys and through his philandering he acquired a public patina of sophistication and glamour. Like the names of Errol Flynn and Porfirio Rubirosa, the name of Tony van den Burg was mentioned with a smirk and snicker but also with a kind of grudging respect. Tony was officially sex on a stick, just as Muffie in her hair ribbons and maternity dresses, her plump little hands shielding her plump little face from the flash of the cameras, personified the Wronged Wife and Mother.

It remained then for Maggie to be Theda Bara. The public that had once embraced her now castigated her as a ruthless vampire who, from her silken lair on New York's "fashionable upper East Side" (with each succeeding edition Maggie's converted rooming house grew in size and splendor while Muffie's converted stable became so humble that one fully expected Mary and Joseph to seek shelter there before the month was out), broke up happy homes just for the hell of it.

Graffiti were scrawled on the facade of her house while her mailbox was glutted with crank letters, some containing used condoms, one enclosing a newspaper photograph of Maggie that had seen service as toilet paper and hundreds that, after employing every vile word of the gutter, were signed "A Good Christian."

Maggie neither knew nor cared what the public thought. She wanted only Tony and, failing that, oblivion. Tony could not be found, but oblivion was easily obtainable, even shut away in her house with me constantly standing watch. Bottles had a miraculous way of appearing from nowhere and with them barbiturates. I should have realized even then that there is no way to stop anyone who is bent on self-destruction, yet when you love someone as I loved Maggie, you keep trying. But the job of protecting her from the reporters, the public, the telephone, the doorbell, the mail, the newspapers, the liquor and the pills was too great a task and I failed. A week after my return I found Maggie in a coma with a tabloid at her side. Tony, from the Willinghams' suite in the Waldorf Towers, had graciously held a press conference. He loved his wife and children, he said. He and Miss Faye were just friends.

An hour later his friend Miss Faye, using my name, was admitted to a discreet private hospital in the East Sixties specializing in alcohol and addiction and I was on my way to the Waldorf Towers.

I had no idea as to how to get up to the Willingham apartment, but I needn't have worried. Rose, swathed in enough mink to make six coats, stepped down from her limousine just as I reached the door. "Honey!" she screamed. "Well, wouldn't I just of known! Jackie's oldest pal coming to see him when he needs a friend the most. And you're the only one bothered to do it, let me tell you." She propelled me past the flunkies hired to keep just such as I from harassing the tenants of the tower and into an elevator.

"Gee, was I ever sorry to hear about your dad," Rose said, squeezing my arm. "And him a doctor and all. 'Physician, take care of yourself,' like they say. Well, we all gotta go sometime. Oh, honey, will Jackie ever be surprised to see you!"

"I'm sure he will."

"It's been quite a time, let me tell you. Doesn't it just get your goat the way some old dame like that Maggie Faye will set her cap for a good-lookin' kid like Jackie and cause all this trouble? I used to think her books were kinda cute, but now I wouldn't read one, not if you paid me to. And as for that old Fred Murray . . . well, I never could stand him. Will neither. Will's lawyers have been with Jackie forever, it seems like. They told him just what to say."

"Well, I'm glad to hear that."

"I thought his interview was very dignified but the photos all . . ."

We got out of the elevator.

"Thanks, honey," Rose said to the elevator operator. "And don't you let *nobody* up here. I don't care who they say they are."

Rose let us into the apartment—very large, beige and Waldorfian.

"Ooo-hooo! Jackie?" she shouted. "Have I ever got a surprise for you!"

Had she ever! And yet I wondered just what I was doing here. Maggie was not my wife, my sister, my daughter, my charge. I was nothing but a cast-off lover with no legal rights whatever.

It would be nice to report that our meeting was dramatic. It would also be untrue. Tony acted just about as he had twenty years earlier when I had confronted him not at a palatial family seat, but in a small apartment above his father's dental parlors— *caught.*

"Isn't he ever a sight for sore eyes, Jackie?" Rose cried triumphantly, as though she had produced a gram of radium or the Hope diamond. "Well, I know you boys got a lot to talk about so I'll say so long."

Left alone with me, Tony spouted some glib, unfelt sentiments about my father's death—what a great scientist and splendid old gentleman he had been. (The two had never met.) He offered me a drink, which I refused, and set about mixing one for himself with such exaggerated care that the finished result should have been, at the very least, a pousse-café or a golden fizz instead of whisky on the rocks.

"Well?" Tony said, plumping himself down on the sofa.

"Tony, it's about Maggie."

"Maggie?" He said it as though it were the name of some vague acquaintance from the distant past.

"Yes, Maggie. Maggie Faye."

"Well, what about her?" His tone was not quite flippant, but it conveyed little concern.

"She very nearly died last night. Pills. She's in the hospital now."

"Gee, that's a shame. You must let me know where so that I can send some flowers."

"She doesn't want flowers, Tony, and you know it. She wants you. God alone knows why, but she wants you."

"And I want to see Maggie—more than anything else in the world. You've got to believe me. But . . . well, I'm in kind of a bind right now. The lawyers."

"Screw the lawyers. We're talking about another human being. She's just a few blocks from here—on Sixty-first Street She's using my name. They don't even know at the hospital who she really is."

"I'd love to. I really would. But trying to get past that jam of reporters downstairs . . ."

"There aren't any reporters there, Tony."

"Oh." He sounded almost disappointed. "Well, thank God for small favors. You can't imagine what it's been like. The way those newshawks hound you! Finally I decided to level with them and . . ."

"I know. I read the newspapers. So did Maggie. That's why she's where she is."

"I was misquoted. Do you think I should demand a retraction or just . . ."

"If you're ready, Tony, we can leave right now."

"Well, I'll have to think up some sort of excuse for Mom. Oh, Mom?" Tony called.

"Here I am, sweetie." Rose swept into the room in a trailing tea gown.

"Mom, we thought we'd run over to the club. Play a little squash. Maybe get some steam."

"Say, that's one peach of an idea, honey. Take your mind off of your troubles. Be back for supper? Will and I are just gonna have something sent up."

"I don't know, Mom. Don't count on me."

"Okey-dokey, but remember, the train'll be down at the siding at ha' past eleven an' we're leaving at midnight—sharp. Will don't like to be kept waiting. He's got a whole railroad to run and . . ."

"Taking a trip?" I asked.

"Just out to the Coast for the holidays."

"We'd better shove off," Tony said, all but propelling me out of the door.

"Toodle-oo, kids. If you wanta phone in, use the private line. I'm not taking no more calls till this mess blows over. Honest to God, what some women will do just to get their names in the paper . . ." The door closed and that was the last of Rose.

Maggie was pathetically glad to see Tony. For just a moment I was reminded of her humble origins. Instead of Maggie Faye, the wit, the celebrity, the constant companion of people at the top, she made me think of a drab little waitress who had been treated to a cheap abortion by the rich country club boy who had got her in trouble. But just for a moment. Then she became light, worldly and casual once more.

"Darling," she said to me, "would you mind terribly waiting down the hall with the ambulatory lushes? I haven't seen Tony since . . ."

"No, Maggie," Tony said. "He's my oldest friend and I know he means a lot to you, too. What I'm going to tell you is something I want to say before a witness."

"Would you like me to call in a notary public?" I asked.

"Please don't kid," Tony said with a dry little sob.

"Whatever you say, dearest," Maggie whispered, falling back exhausted on her pillows.

Nearly sinking to his knees at the side of her bed, Tony took both of Maggie's hands and buried his face in them. "Maggie, you've been through hell. Both of us have, but it's been worse for you—much, much worse . . ."

"Tony, I . . ."

"Please don't say anything, Maggie. Not just now. If you had any idea what it's been like for me, not knowing where you've been. Not being able to reach you . . ."

"She's been at home," I said. "You ought to know where that is. And her telephone number is still . . ."

"But I could never get through. The line was always busy or I'd get that answering service. You don't know how I've felt, Maggie—not being able to see you, talk to you, touch you, hold you. I've done a terrible thing to you, Maggie. I know I have. But I loved you so much I couldn't help myself . . ."

"Oh, Tony . . ."

"I've barged right into the middle of your life and ruined every single thing about it. But, Maggie, if we can just get through this mess, you and I. If we can just hold out until the divorce and I'm free . . . Oh, Maggie, I can't tell you how it's going to be—just the two of us together."

Maggie wept helplessly as Tony began to describe what the future held for them. I felt that I had no business to be in the room with them—my presence seemed almost a sacrilege. What he was saying was too intimate to be shared by anyone else. As he went on, his voice breaking occasionally, I took myself to task as a cold, loveless old cynic incapable of seeing good in anyone else. It was jealousy, I decided, that had made me think so ill of Tony. And again I felt a fresh surge of envy: What had been left out of my makeup that rendered me incapable of loving as deeply, as tenderly, as all-consumingly as Tony?

"Ooops! 'Scuse me, folks," the nurse said, bringing in Maggie's tray. "Here's our din-din and *doesn't* it look yummy! Filet of sole, a nice Jello salad and car'mull pudding. Your wife," she said to me, "didn't hardly touch her lunch and the food's *so good!* Why, our dietician is one of . . ."

"I'll eat everything on my tray tonight," Maggie said. "I promise I will. Even the doilie."

" 'Even the doilie.' Isn't she a scream! Well, I'm glad you're feeling better."

"I feel marvelous," Maggie said. "Simply marvelous." For the first time since my return, she even looked marvelous.

"We'd better be going, baby," Tony said. Baby? Maggie?

"Must you?"

"Yes, baby. You've got to eat and sleep and get all the rest you can. It's for the future. For us."

I caught myself reaching furtively for a handkerchief.

Tony and I went to a miserable Italian restaurant on Lexington Avenue for dinner. "I don't want to be seen," he said. There was little danger of that. It was not yet six o'clock and the food and drink were execrable. Even so, Tony ate heartily, downing three martinis that tasted like an ill-balanced mixture of antifreeze and furniture polish. Even if the food had been decent, I was too moved by the scene that had just taken place to eat very much. "You'll look after Maggie, won't you?" Tony said.

"Yes, of course. But now that everything's out in the open and Muffie and her father have their evidence, I don't think it makes much difference whether you and Maggie are seen together or not."

"Oh, sure," Tony said, mopping up tomato sauce with his bread. "But you see, I won't be here."

I began to have that old feeling about Tony. "Where will you be?" Little by little fragments of conversation came back to me: The Rose ready and waiting far below Park Avenue at the Waldorf-Astoria railroad siding; Mr. Willingham's hatred of being kept waiting . . .

"Out on the Coast with Mom and Will. Just for Christmas, of course. And then there's my business."

"What business?"

"What business did you think? Now that I'm in television . . ."

"From the few words your father-in-law said before going off the air, I got the impression that you were very much out of television."

"Oh, come on now, *High Life* isn't the only program in the world and Murray Manufacturing isn't the only sponsor. But I've got to strike while the iron's hot. Now that I have this thing going for me . . ."

"What thing?"

"Why, this publicity. I couldn't buy press coverage like this for ten million dollars."

"Do you consider being nabbed in bed with Maggie"—I nearly gagged on the words—"some kind of major news break? Something good?"

"Did you ever get your name on the front page for writing a book? It doesn't matter what they say about you as long as they're saying it. Two weeks ago Tony van den Burg was just a name. Maybe I could get past the receptionist's desk; maybe I couldn't. Now they're all curious. They want to know what it is I've got and now's the time to tell 'em. I've got an idea for this program that . . ."

"What about Maggie?"

"Well, what *about* Maggie? She's a big girl."

"Aren't you planning to marry her?"

"I already *am* married," Tony said piously, "with another baby on the way." Bravely as he'd started out, he stammered now and avoided my eye. "B-besides, Maggie's a Catholic and you know how they are about divorces. And, anyway, she's older than I am and . . ."

"Do you mean to tell me that you could fall on your knees like some ham actor at her hospital bed not half an hour ago and . . ."

"Listen, and stop being such a Christer: When somebody's lying there sick and looking like hell, is it such a terrible sin to say something that might cheer 'em up a little? Or do you have to go in there with your hand on the Bible and tell the truth and nothing but the truth so help you God? Mag's a good kid but, let's face it, she's no spring chicken; her publicity breaks have been bad and the stuff she wrote for *High Life* was just plain lousy. She's been on top for damned near twenty years, but just between you and me, chum, I think she's finished."

"So am I. Check!" I called.

"Hey, wait a minute. I'd like some spumoni. Besides, I'm taking you to dinner."

"No, you're not. I'm paying for my own. Not yours. Just mine. For all I care, you can stay here and eat spumoni until it . . ."

"Why didn't you say you were in a hurry? Here, I don't need dessert. I'll grab a cab and drop you."

"No thanks, Tony. I've already dropped you."

Having brought Maggie back to life, Tony now left her without so much as a Christmas card to tell her that he was thinking of her. Very bravely at first, Maggie waited day after day for the ring of the telephone, the splat of a letter through the mail slot. For a time she invented splendid excuses for his neglect: Tony was busy; the postal service, always rotten, was at its worst during the Christmas season; the Willingham lawyers had advised him not to write or telephone. After a couple of weeks of that, not knowing that Tony was in California, Maggie began telling me fantastic lies. While I was at the bank Tony had visited and made passionate love to her; during the night he had telephoned and talked for more than an hour; she even sent herself a fabulous arrangement of brown and green orchids—as ugly as it was costly—with "Tony" badly forged on the florist's card. How galling it must have been for her to be rejected by a lover beneath the constant gaze of the lover she herself had rejected.

With the new year she gradually dropped her pretenses. She went back to the bottle and back to the pills, became sloppy and bloated and ill-tempered. Without her love for Tony, she was sustained only by her hatred of Fred Murray. One can, I suppose, live on hate as well as love, but not as comfortably.

As virulent an emotion as hatred can spread like a brush fire. Within a month Maggie fought furiously with her agent, her publisher, her accountant and her lawyer—the very people who had helped her to reach the top. She dismissed all of them and replaced none of them. With the mass exodus of her advisers I was the only person close enough for constant combat. We had it—daily, nightly, hourly. Finally even I could take no more. After one final name-calling, door-slamming row, I moved out, telling myself—but not actually believing—that Maggie was psychotic. I only came to realize how far gone she actually was when she pled her own slander suit against Fred Murray in court. It was a total rout. The public, by that time, was worse than unsympathetic to Maggie. People were sick of her. Eventually a sister materialized from somewhere in Missouri and led her off to a lifelong series of Catholic nursing homes. For a time Maggie wrote to me—short, incoherent messages scrawled on the backs of terrible-looking religious greeting cards. Then there was nothing. For all practical purposes the fabulous Maggie Faye was dead.

Tony, on the other hand, again entered television—not as an entrepreneur this time, but as a performer. His program, emanating from the West Coast, was called simply *Tony* and it featured Mr. van den Burg, looking incredibly young, as a rather naughty American boy who required mothering as well as bedding down. *Tony* made for a nauseating fifteen minutes five nights a week just before the old movies were run. The format was always the same; Tony entered what was obviously a bachelor's apartment—all very spandy, but requiring a woman's touch —looking lost, lonely and horny. He treated *les girls* to a winsome little smile and removed his jacket and tie. (His shirt, too, on Friday nights to keep their motors running over the weekend.) Then he would wriggle into a tight sweater (pajamas on Fridays), pour himself a glass of milk and talk—just talk—to the millions of women who were presumably watching. His delivery was hesitant and callow, every final G dropped with a thud, but it somehow exuded sex. He was Tom and Huck and Penrod and Holden Caulfield who obviously brushed with Colgate's, gargled with Listerine, showered with Dial and rolled in Mum. At the end of each program he slithered to a grand piano where—hands invisible, as he did not know how to play—with the full cooperation of the studio orchestra and the teleprompter —he recited, over sonorous chords, a few quatrains of mawkish poetry. The sign-off, as he dimpled, twinkled, stretched and yawned, was enough to turn a rat's stomach. "Time to turn in," he would say mellifluously, "but first, a good-night kiss to Mrs. Ada Schultz of Pontiac, Michigan, who will be just eighty years young tomorrow. And a get-well-soon wish for Pearl Grappling in Tulsa, Oklahoma. You be a good girl, Pearl, and do just what that old doctor-man tells you and you'll be up and around real soon. And two good-night kisses to Daddy's twin sweethearts"— he wisely refrained from mentioning that they were called Flopsy and Mopsy—"back home in Connecticut." Naturally, children of that age would have been asleep for hours, but it was the era of the youthful daddy-man sex symbol when film stars of the most equivocal leanings were all being photographed in tight pants at barbecue pits, surrounded by hoards of children who had some-how been acquired. "And a very special kiss for my very special girl—my mom!" The picture of Rose in tears and tourmalines jogging along in her private railway car never failed to come to mind. "And now to you and you and especially to you, g'night!" As the orchestra, throbbing with strings and runs on the harp, played "Let's Turn Out the Lights and Go to Sleep," Tony even assayed a brief burst of song. Cut!

Except as a comic turn, the program was hopeless, but to judge from audience response every lonely woman's bedroom had instantly become Tony's personal seraglio. A docile Elvis Presley and a virile Liberace, Tony was catnip to the ladies. His age was put at twenty-nine—a sensible figure that made him not too elderly for the teen-ager, yet still mature enough to be accessible to the woman past, and 'way past, forty, which age Tony himself had nearly reached. Overnight Tony became a sort of national dildo. Cheap variety stores were heaped with Tony Sweaters,

Tony Pajamas and Tony Dolls. A Tony Hairdo, featuring one curly lock hanging down in front (to disguise his receding brow, Tony was now wearing a small hairpiece and to disguise the hairpiece, one boyish wisp was coaxed forward), was briefly popular.

How successful the program *actually* was will always be a matter of speculation. The usual press handouts about fan clubs, proposals of marriage in the mail, old hags fainting at the sight of Tony in the street and their more athletic granddaughters secreting themselves in Tony's bedroom were released. But then they always are.

Television audiences may be gullible, even stupid. They are also fickle and capricious. But in a strange way they are intuitive. They seem to sense when sincerity is absent, when they are being talked *down* to. Naturally they resent it. And if a performer lacks a solid core of talent or genuineness or originality, they quickly tire of him. Tony had not taken this into consideration. Having been successful at the beginning of his program, he made the mistake of believing his own publicity, counting too strongly on his spurious charm, thinking that he could fool the public forever. He began getting sloppy, even appearing on the air drunk once or twice, taking his audience for granted. It would be pleasant to report that some dramatic event took place to finish off the Tony program—a stabbing, a bastardy charge, something to put Tony off the air with a bang. No such fireworks occurred— even his divorce caused no stir. The program simply died of fatigue. People soon had enough of Tony. Before the year was out his ratings dropped to nothing, his contract had been bought off and he was replaced by a solemn news analyst with no sex appeal whatever. Tony wrote a waspish magazine article deploring the sorry state of American television—quite overlooking the part he had played in bringing it to its present low—and then there was merciful silence.

My own life—existence is probably the word for it—continued. Having neither the need nor the desire for a great deal of money, it naturally rolled in at an alarming rate. The few New York hostesses who could and did read took me up as an extra man to fill in at their dinner parties. Neither miserable nor happy, bored or amused, dead or alive, I simply was.

On the afternoon of my fortieth birthday the telephone rang. It was Tony. "*Surprise, chum!*" he said.

Surprise is right. Such a surprise that, being awakened from my nap, I quite forgot that I had intended never to exchange another word with Tony. "How did you get this number? It isn't listed."

"Don't tell me. I tried every way I knew how. Finally I had to take your publisher's secretary out to lunch, turn on the old charm and get her loaded before she'd tell me. Boy, she sure can put the martinis away. Stingers, too."

"You realize that you could get the poor girl fired; not only for coming back to the office drunk, but also for giving out authors' numbers."

"You wouldn't do a thing like that, would you? Tattle on a cute little dish who . . ."

"No, but I ought to. What is it you want?"

"Oh, come on, pal. It's been a long time since we've seen each other."

"Not long enough, Tony. Besides, today's my birthday and of all the surprises I *don't* want . . ."

"I *know* it is, chum. That's why I called. Have I ever let one of your birthdays go by without calling or writing?"

"Only thirty-nine of them so far. But of course it's the thought that counts. Thank you and goodb . . ."

"Hey, not so fast. You're not getting so rich and famous that you forget your old friends, are you?"

"I'll never be rich and famous enough to forget you, more's the pity. And now if you'll excuse me . . ."

"Well, frankly, there was something else I wanted to talk to you about . . ."

"I was sure of that. What is it?"

"It's about my book."

"Your *what?*"

"My book. My autobiography. I was having lunch with my publisher today and he said that you were the only . . ."

"Which publisher is that?"

"Alfred A. Knopf," he said, mispronouncing the name. "Grand guy. Anyhow, if you want to make a guaranteed one million dollars fast—best-seller list, stage rights, picture rights, television rights, book-club selection, all the rest of it . . ."

"Whose life story did you say this was?"

"Why, mine, natch."

"Sorry, I thought you were speaking of Albert Schweitzer. I'm also not interested." But of course I was. Fascinated. Not in the malarkey about the big money to be made, but in seeing Tony in this new incarnation. In the end I agreed to visit him the following afternoon.

Tony was not stopping in the Willinghams' suite in the Waldorf Towers, but rather at a frightful new hotel that had sprung up so fast and was so wrong for New York that I always felt it had been moved up from Miami while my back was turned. L'Elegance (or The Lelly-gunce as it was called by the mobsters and their doxies who lived there) looked like an upended ice tray from the outside. The inside was Venetian, incorporating whatever bits of rococo grandeur that could be made compatible with a tight budget, automation and eight-foot ceilings. In an attempt at Old World charm, the rooms and apartments in L'Elegance, from Il Piccolo Espresso (coffee shop) in the Piano Basso (basement) to Il Palazzo delle' Doge (duplex penthouse overlooking the Lido Pool and Cabana Club) were given names, not numbers. Mr. van den Burg was lodged in Il Redentore (*salone, camera, terrazzo, due bagni e serving* pantry—*due cento* bucks per *giorno*), or, as the elevator boy told me, employing the purest *lingua romana in bocca tuscana,* 'That's eight-oh-one, Mac."

The Venetian red door of Il Redentore opened a crack and an enormous eye, ringed with artificial lashes, peered out. "Whaddyuh wandt?"

"I'm sorry," I said, "I was looking for a Mr. van den Burg."

"Oh. He's in the john. C'mawn in."

With a rattling of bolts and chains, the door swung open and I was confronted by the girl with no nose. "I was scared you might be somebody eltss," she said, carefully bolting and chaining the door again.

Like the goat with no nose, the girl with no nose smelled fierce. She was saturated with musk and civet and ambergris—all the unattractive secretions of unattractive mammals that are said to make women irresistible to any male. With diligent tubbing, the cloud of perfume that enveloped her might, after several weeks, be dispelled. But what had been done to the girl by surgeon and hairdresser was, I am afraid, irrevocable. Her looks were pure 1960—hair bleached to the color and consistency of spun sugar and, by means of resin, acetone and *Rhus vernicifera*, forced upward into a precarious leaning tower known as a beehive. Where once a nose might have given character to the round, white marshmallow that was her face, rhinoplasty had created a retroussé button, almost indiscernible at a quick glance. Above it, the eyes had seen slit to become the size of eggs; below, the teeth jacketed in blinding blue-white opaque porcelain. By means of plastic sponge inserted beneath the flesh, her breasts jutted out menacingly from her emaciated little body. The whitened lips, the blackened eyes, the opalescent nails, the daubed-on "beauty mark," all of the quick tricks of assembly line sexuality to make her look exactly like any standard strumpet of the sixties were present.

"You muss be Tone's frendt, the orthor?" She had a tendency to dentalize her *T*'s and *D*'s and to sibilate her *S*'s, whether naturally or because of the tremendous load of porcelain that had been clamped onto her front teeth, I could not be sure. In any case, it made her speech sound not only common, but also like a low comedian's broad burlesque of standard pansy dialect. With some effort I dismissed the notion that she was actually a very small man in drag.

"I'm Geni," she said.

"How do you do, Jean?"

"Not Jean. Geni. Gee-Eee-Enn-Eye," she spelled with some effort. "Ssittdown. I'll callum. T-one? Yer frendt's here." Like an apple falling from a tree, she plumped herself down on the long, serpentine sofa. Then, perhaps remembering instructions on "How to Sit," she arranged her bony little frame, limb by limb, into the postures of genteel seduction—"knees together, ankles crossed, insteps arched, back straight, diaphragm in, chest up, chin tilted, head high." I could almost hear the litany of some far-distant charm school flowing through her empty head. Now Geni was at a loss. Had she flunked the lesson in "Social Intercourse"? Failed to meet the tuition? Or simply lost interest? She stared at a vague focal point somewhere above my head with glazed eyes.

"Do you live in New York, Jean—Geni?" I asked finally.

"No. California. Hollywoodt. I'm in pict-turzs."

"Oh. What films have you done?"

She thought the matter over for a while, preparing her reply as though it were to be a sworn statement. Finally she was ready. "Well, I havendtt ackchilly bin—*beeen*—in a pict-ture yedt, budt T-one sezs . . ."

"What does Tone say, baby?" Tony stood in the doorway. He was wearing a white silk kimono and briskly toweling his hair. The picture might have been captioned "Intimate Glimpses of the Stars at Ease." His entrance was, I suspected, carefully staged to give the impression of eternal, buoyant youth. It failed to come off. Tony's hair had become thin; his torso, while not exactly fat, made me think that I could poke my finger into it for quite a long way without touching anything as solid as bone or muscle. "*Boobula!*" he cried, bounding forward to embrace me. As I remained seated in a wing chair, his exuberant gesture had to be abandoned.

"You haven't changed a bit!" Tony said.

"You have."

"Fix us a couple of drinks, Geni. What'll it be?"

"Just ice water, please."

"Scotch for me, baby. Like always. Oy, is this a *leben!*"

"Shouldt I make one fer myszself, too?" Geni asked.

"No, baby. We've got a lot to catch up on. You know, just two old chums sitting around and *hocking a chinik.*" For one who had constantly denied any connection with Jewry, Tony's current speech pattern was heavily larded with Yiddish, correctly used or otherwise. But then it had become the lingua franca of show business and Tony was now very much Mr. Show Biz. Geni disappeared into the serving pantry from where the banging of ice cubes and rushing of water could be heard clearly. "Great little kid, Geni," Tony said. "Sweet. She's my sort of . . . uh . . ."

"*Nafkeh?*" I suggested, dredging up one of my few Yiddish terms.

"Certainly not! Geni's helping me with the book."

"Then I should think you'd want her here to take notes."

"Well, not till we get some sort of working arrangement."

Geni plodded back into the room with two glasses. "Sso whadt should I do?"

"Baby, why don't you go out and get your hair fixed?"

"Idt juszsdt wuzz."

"Well, go buy a dress or something."

"You szstill didn'dt gimme any money."

"Charge it. Use the Diners' Club."

"Oh, all righdt." Geni took her bearings, aimed for the bedroom door, struck a suitably alluring stance and followed the long, pointed toes of her pearlized pumps out of the room.

"Geni's a very intelligent girl. Smart as a whip."

"Radcliffe. I was certain the moment I laid eyes on her."

"Oh, and, *boobula*, I'd appreciate it if you wouldn't mention to anybody that she's . . . uh . . . that she's working here with me. You see, Geni comes from a very old family . . ."

"Of course she does, Tony. Class. Solid class. You can spot it a mile away."

"Well," Tony said, looking away, "if you just wouldn't say anything about seeing her here."

Geni returned, wearing dark glasses and a tremendous mink coat the color of slush. "G'bye, now," she said. She remembered a smile she had once been taught, turned it on, turned it off and clumped out.

"My lips are sealed," I said.

"Now about this book of ours," he said.

"Ours?"

In typical Tony fashion, seeing only the thousands of finished volumes in their highly laminated dust jackets that would presumably fill every shop window in the nation and ignoring the drudgery that must go into any book between the words "Chapter One" and "The End," he plunged into what he considered an ideal "working arrangement." Roughly, I was to do all the work and Tony was to take all of the money. Finally he finished and looked at me with eager, starry-eyed expectancy as though, hypnotized, I was to cross the room and slip page one into the golden electric typewriter that sat anachronistically on the Venetian red lacquered desk. "Well?"

"Well, no," I said.

"So what's the matter?"

"Several things. To begin with, I don't think you've got a story to tell . . ."

"That can always be fixed. That's why I want to hook up with a novelist."

"That's another point. I'm a novelist, not a ghost-writer."

"Now don't get *fancy-schmancy* with old Tony, *boobula;* I happen to know that you've ghosted books before."

"Twice. When I *had* to. Now I don't. And even then the financial arrangements were much more . . ."

231

"Well, what *is* the usual deal for a straight ghost job?"

"Fifty-fifty."

"*Fifty-fifty?*" He paused aghast, tasting the words as though they were hemlock. "Just for an anonymous writing job?"

"Sometime, Tony, you might stop and ask yourself whose name would sell more copies of a book—yours or mine."

"*I* was a star on television."

"So was Lassie. Still *is*, what's more."

Tony reddened. Then he got up, marched to the pantry and mixed another drink for himself. A new character reappeared, one of sweet modesty and true humility. "Talk about *meshuga*, what could I have been thinking of? Why, I'm so used to thinking of you as my oldest pal that I forget you've got a real international reputation. So. You get fifty percent as a ghost. But what'd your cut be if I let you put your name on the book?"

"In that case I'd want *much* more."

"Well, great. We say it's by Tony van den Burg, as told to . . . Huh? Say, listen, I'm trying to throw a good thing to an old friend. All I *really* need is a competent hack . . ."

"Thank you. What about your old friends Faulkner and Hemingway?"

"They're d . . . Hey, are you putting me on? I take the time off to come to New York and offer you something big—really big—on a silver platter. But you've got the *chutzpah* to . . ."

"Speaking of *chutzpah*, what kind of gall do you have to have to think that anybody in his right mind is going to go out and pay money to read the very unimportant little story of your very unimportant little life?"

"Stars' books always sell. Look at Gertie Lawrence, Tallulah Bankhead, Ethel Waters."

"Also look at Ethel Merman, Ethel Barrymore, Lionel Barrymore. People of real accomplishment. Their books died on the vine."

"Well, what about Lillian Roth, Diana Barrymore? A couple

of bottle babies and no hot shakes in show biz. I went to Diana's coming out party and if she was a star then I'm . . ."

"But they both had real stories to tell. They also had Gerold Frank to tell them. And he's no 'competent hack.' "

"D'ya think Frank might be interested in doing my book?"

"No more than I am." The interview at an end, my curiosity more than satisfied, I prepared to get up and go.

"Or what about Maggie Faye?" Tony said desperately.

I felt myself falling back into the chair. "What about Maggie Faye? As far as I know she's in some hospital for . . ."

"Oh, no she's not. Maybe she was a nut, but now she's a nun."

"A nun? Listen, Tony, this is real life, not cheap fiction."

"Well, not exactly a nun, but the next thing to it. Some kind of lay order—you should pardon the expression. I mean they've still got their hair. And, baby, you should see hers! Gray and chopped off at the ears. Talk about ug! No makeup—not even lipstick—and wearing this kind of old long black dress and a hat like a chamber pot. A real meesekite. Fabisseneh! It's some kind of begging order. Probably crooked. There she was out in front of the Alvin Theater the other night, shaking her can for sweet charity. Let me tell you, I grabbed Geni by the arm and ran."

I could feel the pulse in my throat hammering. I tried to say something but it was impossible.

Concerned, as always, with only what he was thinking and saying, Tony continued expansively. "Oh, she saw me, all right. As close as that. And talk about a meesapunum! Now what do you suppose makes a swingin' chick like old Mag do a nutty thing like that?"

With an effort I said, "Did it ever occur to you that perhaps Maggie has found some sort of peace for the first time since . . ."

"Peace my ass! Or piece of ass. And speaking of that, what do you want to bet that with one word from me I could get her out of the monastery, or whatever, and right over to that typewriter?

That is, if I could stand the sight of her. Talk about *ug!*" Tony
repeated. "But the publicity breaks might be sensational. 'Maggie
Faye on Tony van den Burg.' How's that for a switch?"

I got to my feet. "I'm leaving now, Tony."

"Hey, what about our deal?"

"There isn't any deal."

"*Boobula!* Just because we haven't been able to get together on
terms doesn't mean you have to throw cold water on the whole
thing."

"That's the best idea you've had yet, Tony." I picked up my
glass of ice water, emptied it over his head and slammed out of
the room.

For all I cared, Tony could have been in the bottom of hell,
but, as any casual subway reader might have told you, he
remained in the "swank" Il Redentore Suite of the "exclusive"
L'Elegance whenever he and "curvaceous starlet" Geni What-
everhernamewas "(40-20-35)" were not being a "two-riffic two-
some" at some "plush nitery." As a sort of Celebrity Emeritus,
Tony's comings and goings were reported by the Greek chorus of
public relations hacks every hour on the hour, so that his newest
relationship was a secret to no one. Having once pursued and
captured publicity as though it were a royal bride, he could not
now escape it and remained an envied prisoner in its empty
palace.

A few nights after what I had considered to be our final
parting, I was awakened by a desperate pounding on my front
door. I opened it and Geni tumbled into the room. She was
wearing her horrible fur coat over a "baby doll" nightdress.
Makeup was smeared across her stupid, frightened little face and
her hair stood out like a golliwog's.

"Ya gotta help me," she screamed, all studied elegance gone
from her speech, "ya juss gotta!"

"What's the matter?"

"He's gone and shot Tone! He's shot 'um!"

"Who's shot Tony?"

"Nick! He's shot Tone! He's kildum!"

"For God's sake, get hold of yourself. Who's Nick?"

"He's my huszsbind!"

By the time Geni and I got to the scene of the crime, it was bristling with police and reporters. The living room and bedroom were flowing with blood, but no one was dead. Tony had been shot in the shoulder, leaving an interesting mark which he would henceforth display as proudly as a Heidelberg student his dueling scar.

I couldn't help feeling that Tony actually enjoyed the commotion he was creating. Fondling his lucky ermine tail, he was loaded gently onto a stretcher and carried away. As he reached the door, he gazed up into my face and treated me—and the photographers—to a brave sweet smile. "My . . . my old friend. You . . . you came to see poor Tony at last."

Naturally the shooting made all of the morning newspapers, but with this scandal there was a difference. Tony's last foray on the front pages had involved people of wealth and fame and importance. This time he was mixed up with the dregs of humanity—Geni, a former streetwalker, and her husband, an escaped convict. The story was treated accordingly. Rose, once again, was quoted as saying that Tony had always been a good boy. Mr. Willingham was unavailable for comment. The Willingham wealth placed Tony in an expensive hospital for sick stars and two diehard alumnae of one of the long-dissolved Tony Fan Clubs started up what they called a "Prayer-a-thon" for the life that Tony was never in the slightest danger of losing. But the public was gloriously indifferent as to whether Tony lived or died. Like all the people who knew him, the ones who didn't had by now had more than enough of Tony.

From that point on, Tony's fortunes went into a sharp decline. A scurrilous little "dirt" magazine printed a story about him that said absolutely nothing which couldn't have been found in The

New York Times. But, lumped together, the compilation of Tony's lesser vagaries was far from flattering.

His autobiography, *All My Born Days,* which was certainly the work of a "competent hack," if not written by Tony himself, was published by a dim little firm of quasi-pornographers. It was a vulgar, name-dropping little volume, identical in style and content to dozens of other subsidized silver-spoon memoirs. In its pages Tony's relationships with the dead great were warm, deep and succulent. Mention of anyone still living—and capable of bringing suit—was perfunctory at best. More than one critic waggishly wrote of it as *All My Borin' Days* and the book sank as soon as it was launched.

Rose met a rather poetic death. She was struck and killed by a taxicab on West Forty-seventh Street while coming out of Brentano's with an armload of Tony's autobiography. The tragedy did nothing to stimulate further sales. She died without leaving a will, assuming, perhaps, that Mr. Willingham would look after her boy from sheer force of habit, if not out of fatherly affection. Had Tony played his cards right, he might have realized something from his mother's demise. Instead, he waged a losing battle to lay hands on Rose's considerable collection of jewels. They were next seen flashing on the ears, fingers, wrists and throat of a frosty young woman who, after an indecent period of mourning, became the new Mrs. Willingham. After that, Willingham withdrew all further aid.

To do him justice, Tony made a stab at earning a more or less honest living for a time. The Arts appeared to have a magnetic attraction, perhaps because they *looked* so easy. There was a society column called "Bon Ton Tony" notable only for its complete lack of readers. Tony appeared again briefly on television with a dull adaptation of the timeworn sadistic interview formula, asking his victims such piquant questions as "How much money do you have?" "Have you always been a homosexual?" "Tell us what it's like to be a call girl." The program limped along, uninterrupted by the commercial messages of any sponsor, until an Irish playwright of ungovernable temper hauled off and knocked Tony cold in the very eye of the camera.

From his farewell to the performing arts, Tony returned for the last time to his typewriter. *East of Fifth* was suddenly revived and, combining the editorial policies of *Confidential* and *Town Topics*, was reentitled tersely *Lives*. Tony's method of operation was simple. He wrote a story, generally accurate and always embarrassing, had it set in type and then sent galley proofs to the people involved for "editorial corrections."

An article called "The Rise and Fall of Maggie Faye," dealing exclusively with her affair with me arrived with a covering letter requesting my "opinion" and a contribution of one thousand dollars "to help feed, clothe and shelter a poor orphan." (Tony, now in his forties and parentless, qualified, I suppose, as an orphan.) I turned it over to my lawyer and that was the end of the matter.

In the case of Fred Murray's biography, Tony apparently knew some facts and figures about the Murray Manufacturing Company's operations that would have fascinated the Department of Internal Revenue. But unfortunately Tony had underestimated the *opéra bouffe* bravado of his former father-in-law. When he arrived at Murray's office to confer editorially and to collect a fifty-thousand-dollar contribution toward the welfare of the orphan, two policemen stepped out from Murray's private lavatory and Tony wound up in jail. Somehow bail was raised and Tony skipped the country by way of Canada.

He was next heard of in London. My mother had returned at last to her beloved England which she immediately found inferior in every way to the United States. In one of her weekly letters of complaint she enclosed a cutting from the *Express* and added that the name rang a bell with her. It might well have. The name was Tony's—now spelled J. Anthony van den Burgh. Operating from a letter drop more or less fashionably located in Little St. James's Street, Mr. van den Burgh had become a land agent dealing in smart residential properties. Through what he called "an oversight" he had let a splendid townhouse at 50 Belgrave Square to not one, but three American families for the season at one thousand guineas—collected in advance—from each. "As everyone knows," my mother wrote, "there are only forty-eight numbers in Belgrave Square." Everyone apparently did not know it, and I was amused by the mental picture of three cabloads of tenants arriving to occupy a nonexistent house. Tony's victims were far less entertained by the "oversight." Deportation proceedings were instituted. But Tony, ever thoughtful, obliged by leaving England of his own accord. Once again there was silence.

For all practical purposes Tony was dead—dead in the United States and dead in England. Somehow I felt that he was not. Nor was I to be disappointed. Last summer he reappeared for the final time.

x ♥

TONY

at present

For the past six months I have been living here in Tangier, not because I like it, but because prices are low and the weather pleasant. (This seems to be a family failing.) It is conveniently located—twenty minutes to Gibraltar, two hours to Madrid, three to Paris, four to London, as any Tangerino will tell you—so that you can always get away, not that anyone ever does. This is the sort of place where people stick because they are stuck.

Tangier still wallows, a little proudly, in its raffish reputation as a City of Sin, a rumor started by that old gossip Samuel Pepys in 1686. But gossip and memories are almost all that remain. No longer an International Zone, for the last decade Tangier has been only a very minor and rather snubbed part of the Kingdom of Morocco—a tourist port without a single sight to see and a fairly staid, early-to-bed city, at that. Like Rio or Marseilles or Acapulco, Tangier is still known as a sunny place for shady people. But their transgressions are pathetically tinhorn. The town is not large enough to support sin on a grand scale.

Although the big-time smugglers and financial manipulators have fled the city, along with the whores and pornographers of the Quartier Réservé, social Tangier makes a feverish attempt to show a disinterested world that wealth and gaiety still flourish. Barbara Hutton, Merry Farnhey and Norma Clark are in residence from time to time. More constant are the widows—both sod and grass—of minor magnates from England, South Africa and the United States. There are the Proper English who live in moderate splendor on The Mountain and a sprinkling of titles tucked away in houses along the Marshan and in apartments in the town. Chic Bohemia endures the discomforts of the Kasbah. Occasionally a celebrity of the second magnitude will arrive for a fortnight's visit. (It is lunacy to stay longer.) Bridge, gin rummy, Scrabble, luncheon, dinner and cocktail parties are as regular as the tide. And the cast of characters is as unvarying. It is not difficult to be accepted—taken up, in fact. People who would not, *could* not, know one another in London or Paris or New York mingle freely. Although many statements are made, few questions are asked about any new face. After a month of attending the same party every day and drinking in the same bars every night, the new face becomes an old face. He is *in* Tangier Society. All that remains is to try to get out of it.

I have been both in and out. People speak of me as eccentric, antisocial and a good deal more. Although I shall probably never hear the best of the gossip concerning me, it is generally bruited about that I remain holed up with: A) a beautiful Moroccan girl; B) a beautiful Moroccan boy; C) a bottle; D) a pipe of kif. The life here is so deadly dull that I wish any of these stories might be true.

Instead, I am holed up with the not-very-good book which I

am writing in a den of iniquity named "Happy Ours." (The quicker reader will catch the pun immediately.) "Happy Ours" sits on a cliff, just too far above the beach to make bathing a temptation, overlooking the Strait of Gibraltar. (Tangier land agents and tourist agencies would have you believe that this is the Mediterranean when it is only the bottleneck of the Atlantic, but that is a minor matter.) It is a small villa flanked by two even smaller villas called "Bide-a-Wee" and "Dun Rovin." Together, the three houses comprise the life dream, the nest egg, the chefs-d'oeuvre of a retired English civil servant who put them up in the thirties as an income-producing paradise for his declining years. All three houses combine the worst features of Ann Hathaway's cottage and the Taj Mahal. "Midlands Moroccan," I suppose, is the only term that could possibly describe them. They are half-timbered with thatched roofs, but also with keyhole windows, Moorish tilework, Spanish grilles and multifoil doorways. "Happy Ours," the manor house of the lot, is further enhanced by an onion-domed minaret of purely Turkish inspiration. The gardens—for wherever you find an Englishman you will find a garden—are a riot of the most violently colored vegetation; scarlet cannas, fluorescent Marrakech roses, blood-red gladiolas, magenta bougainvillea, brutally blue morning glories and hot orange lilies. Mine also boasts a mushrabia gazebo, seven plaster dwarves, a pink reflecting ball, a Disneyesque faun in cast iron, a stagnant carp pool that breeds mosquitoes larger than the fish, a rustic bench, a wishing well (over the septic tank) and several electrified toadstools. But then "Happy Ours" commands a higher rent than "Bide-a-Wee" or "Dun Rovin."

Within, "Happy Ours" is a monument to English bungalow decoration of the thirties with lavish touches of souvenir shop Islamic art. In the lounge (for, of course, it is called "The Lounge") an impressive suite of Tottenham Court Road over-stuffed furniture has been upholstered with the cut rayon velvet to be found by the bolt in any of the thousands of fabric stores in the Kasbah. The seats of a smart chromium "dinette set" have been covered in Moroccan homespun. The red tile floors are nearly obliterated by six Rif rugs machine-woven in astonishingly divergent patterns and colors. Scattered over them are a brazier, a camel-hide pouf, two camel saddle stools, a large beaten-brass tray on fretwork legs, a couscous container, a copper tea kettle on a trivet, a set of sandalwood and mother-of-pearl chairs and tables and—the only light in the room, save for the harshly brilliant pressed glass chandelier—an incredible standing lamp composed, so far as I have been able to count, of copper, brass, pewter, bronze, lead, stained glass, lump amber, pink silk and bead fringe. On the walls, above a mosaic dado, daggers and scimitars, Berber pistols and rifles, a Moorish bridal mirror, a tarnished gold brocade wedding robe, some camel bells, a large, filigree hand of Fatima and a printed plush tapestry depicting some ladies in a harem vie for attention with framed reproductions of "Beatrice and Dante," "Dignity and Impudence," "The End of the Trail" and "The Last Supper." The original owner of "Happy Ours" died during the first year of his occupancy. His wife followed within a matter of weeks. I can understand why.

Since those melancholy events, the three houses have acquired a sort of local glamour. The Moroccans, with understandable awe, speak of them as the "English palaces," as though Blenheim, Chatsworth and Castle Howard had been set down cheek by jowl on an acre of sandy soil overhanging the strait. With the reverence due a historical shrine, nothing has been changed except ownership. But it does not take each new landlord long to learn that even in the busiest season the "English palaces" are the last three villas to be rented and the first three to be vacated. The rent for "Happy Ours" is now paid out each week to a man called simply Lucky. He is a Moroccan of mixed lineage who bears out everything that Kipling ever had to say against the half-caste.

To mention the very name of Lucky is to summon forth words like stealth, craft, guile, wile and greed. He is a landowner of impressive holdings. In addition to "Happy Ours," "Bide-a-

Wee" and "Dun Rovin," Lucky is the sole proprietor of the Hotel Buckingham Palace (eight rooms and one bath) in the Petit Socco; the Royal Rolls-Daimler Garage; a miserable bakal where a few rotting fruits and vegetables sit untouched for days on end beneath a sign reading "Alimentation aux Gourmets Fortnum & Mason de Tanger, Limited, S.A."; and, in a grim cul-de-sac off the rue Moussa ben Noussai, Lucky's Olde Englyshe Pub—the only bar in Tangier with a jukebox, bead curtains, chromium bar stools (six) and no customers. His orientation, as you can see, is purely British, but it does nothing to entice even the most chauvinistic tourist from off any of the Union Castle cruise ships. Emptiness is almost a trademark of all of Lucky's enterprises. In a more logical community both bailiff and bankruptcy would be imminent. But not in Tangier. For in addition to being landlord, hotelier, mechanic, grocer and barkeep, Lucky is many other things. He deals in money changing, giving half again as much in Moroccan dirhams and francs as any bank in town. He deals more heavily in kif, marked for export via Marseilles or Bordeaux. For the occasional connoisseur, Lucky will even mix up batches of majoun (hashish fudge) on the small Butagaz stove in the rear of the pub. With a cousin from the Rif, he does a brisk business in cut-rate black-market liquor and cigarettes. At interest rates of 10 percent per week, Lucky lends both large and small sums of money. With the aid of some seafaring relatives, Lucky also deals in large quantities of such products as Worcestershire sauce, waxed paper, cold cream and automobile parts—innocent enough, but almost unobtainable in the new Morocco. This is by no means smuggling, you understand. The merchandise has simply entered the country by way of a nearby fishing village, thus avoiding the delays, complications and expenses of import licenses and customs. To assuage his conscience, his god and the law, Lucky also serves full-time as a police informer. He is an important man in the Moroccan community—important and feared. Pimping, the keystone of his considerable empire, is now little more than a hobby since Lucky has become respectable.

Redheaded with a freckled russet skin and an impressive display of gold teeth, Lucky is obviously the bastard of a Moroccan girl and some fair-skinned visitor—English, French, American, German, who can tell? This may account for his being—or at least talking—more Moroccan than King Hassan himself. And talk he does, in his guttural Arabic, his rapid-fire French and Spanish, in his carefully cultivated Cockney English and even in Italian and German, all acquired during his sordid rise to local fame and fortune.

In fact, Lucky is such a talker that, rather than have him come to me to collect the rent each Thursday, I find it more expedient to drop in at the pub on Wednesday evenings with the cash in my hand, buy one drink and then leave.

"Ah, early with the rental payment again. As it says in the Koran, 'Never trust a man who . . .'" It says no such thing in the Koran and I'd hate to think of the scene that would take place if the money were so much as five minutes late.

"Yes," he will say, counting the money showily, "the exact sum. A miserable pittance for one of the true palaces of Tangier, but what can a poor Moroccan expect?"

"This 'miserable pittance' is just what it would cost for a room and bath with full pension in the Rif Hotel."

"The Rif," Lucky says with a shudder. "English!"

"Yes, English like the Olde Englyshe Pub, the Hotel Buckingham Palace, the . . ."

"Foreigners! You come to this country to enslave us. I say, 'Morocco for the Moroccans!'"

"Then why don't you find a nice Moroccan family to rent 'Happy Ours' and let me off my lease? I'll be delighted to move out."

"The day will come soon when the foreign dogs will be driven from our beautiful country. . . ."

"But who will stay in your hotel? Rent your villas? Hire your broken-down cars and your broken-down relatives? You'd even have to close the pub, as good Moslems don't drink."

"*I'm* a good Moslem," Lucky says, pouring a large jolt of Johnnie Walker (to be as English as possible) into a glass and then dousing it with Coca-Cola (to disguise the taste of the whisky as much as possible).

"When's the last time you went to mosque?"

But he does not listen. "Morocco for the Moroccans!" he roars, pounding his fist on the bar so that the limp green and red bunting, the flyblown photograph of the King dance from the vibrations. It is our weekly performance.

I then finish my drink and pay for it. "Good-by, Lucky."

"Wait a minute. You like a girl? Beautiful blonde. German. You like to buy some kif? Very good. Fresh. I prepared it myself. You like to change dollars. I give six dirhams to the dollar. Not five. Not four-ninety-seven. *Six!*"

"I thought all these things were illegal in the new Morocco."

"Ah! Idiots! What do they know about?"

This little morality play, starring Anglo-Saxon Logic against Islamic Passion and running exactly fifteen minutes from prologue to epilogue, has been performed every Thursday evening in the Olde Englyshe Pub since early spring. As I've said, it is quicker and cheaper for me to go to Lucky than to have Lucky come to "Happy Ours." Lucky, while ranting about foreign gangsters ravishing his native land, can never understand my reluctance to join in the pillage. Others are far less straitlaced. During my every brief visit a tiny procession has passed through, one by one, to conduct huskily whispered conversations across the bar in a mélange of languages, to collect small packages, to deliver large packages, to pass plump envelopes back and forth, but never to order so much as a beer.

It was something of a surprise then for me to turn up at Lucky's three weeks ago and find colored lights twinkling in his weedy back garden and to hear the jukebox blasting away with that haunting Moroccan melody, "Is You Is or Is You Ain't My Baby?"

"Festive tonight, aren't you?" I said.

"English scum!" Lucky sneered, jerking his head toward the garden. Then he hissed out a furious stream of orders to the ragbag of a Moroccan woman (his wife) who scuttled out with an enormous platter of couscous.

While Lucky filled some wonderfully dusty old Chateau Lafite-Rothschild 1945 bottles with the local Chaudsoleil red wine, I peered through the bead curtains to see who could be quite so insane as actually to eat at Lucky's Olde Englyshe Pub. There were seven people strung out at a table for eight. They were obviously the leftovers from one of Tangier's perpetual cocktail parties and, to judge from the cast of characters, not one of the best cocktail parties. I was about to turn away when I heard a familiar voice say, "Lady ffynche is ac-tually my aunt. During the war I commanded the ffynche Fund overseas, until I got it in the shoulder."

"No!" I said aloud. "It couldn't be!"

"What did you say?" Lucky began. His speech was halted by the clattering of the bead curtains hanging at the front entrance. And quite understandably. The apparition that appeared was enough to silence the wind itself. From the soles of her jeweled sandals to the top of her jeweled turban, there was a stretch of at least seven feet, almost every inch of which was covered with tight, white jersey and ropes of gold and uncut stones. But her face, my God, her face! Was it the face of an aardvark, an anteater, an armadillo, or just a plain old shark? And instead of doing everything within her power to conceal that face, this woman flaunted it, called attention to it by powdering it an embalmed white, by daubing its lips with what appeared to be ketchup, by outlining its reptilian eyes with malachite green. Perhaps this female—young or old, she was decidedly female— fancied herself as looking like Nefertiti; many such grotesques do, but the end result came a good deal closer to a transvestite young Abe Lincoln.

In a more reasonable century, a girl as large and as ugly would have been clapped into a cloister at the earliest possible moment. In this day and age, girls who look like that, perhaps inspired by the fortunes of Barbra Streisand, instead of skulking anonymously in navy blue or gunmetal gray seem to shout, "Look at me!" With this particular gargoyle, there was no other choice. Once sighted, it was impossible to tear one's eyes away.

"Miss Crystal LaVynne's table?" she said to Lucky. Her voice was English, but not out of the top drawer.

"In the garden, madam," Lucky said, transfixed by the sight before him. "Your name is?"

"*I am* Crystal LaVynne." She was so very much onstage that it seemed a shame for her to be putting on so gala a performance in this dark, dingy saloon with only Lucky and me as an audience. But Miss Crystal LaVynne was no rank amateur. Lizardlike, she squinted through the gloom and spotted me. "No!" she boomed. "No! It can't be! But then it *must* be. Are you . . . are you . . . But of course you are. I heard that you were living in Tangier. My favorite author!" She swept across the room to my table and fell into a deep court curtsy. "Maestro!" she growled in the general direction of the linoleum.

I was embarrassed enough to drop stone, cold dead on the floor beside her.

"My name is Crystal LaVynne. I've only just arrived."

"Yes," I murmured. "If you'd been around here for long I certainly couldn't have avoided noticing."

"I'm staying aboard my yacht, for the moment. You *will* come out for cocktails?" It was put in the form of a question but it was pretty much a command.

"Thank you," I said, "but I'm not much of a swimmer."

"But you *will* come to me? I would like to feel that I have been just the tiniest little part of your beautiful, beautiful new book. Au revoir, cheri, don't forget—Crystal LaVynne."

She shot out into the garden where, playing to a larger audience, her entrance was, if anything, even more spectacular. The Tangier Buss was exchanged all round. It is a kiss delivered slowly, silently, tenderly to each side of the face. The ladies, to avoid lipstick smears, greet one another by bumping cheeks and smacking their lips into the air. I suppose so affectionate a salutation makes them all think that they like one another better than they actually do. Then Crystal's brassy voice shouted out, "Tony, cheri, you will never in one million years guess who is sitting quite by himself just inside."

I did not wait for the guessing game. Tossing a five-dirham note on the table, I shot out of the Olde Englyshe Pub and back to "Happy Ours" by way of back streets and alleys.

Tony, I was certain, could only be visiting Tangier for a few days, holed up in the Rif Hotel with the rich English tourists or in El Minzah with the rich American tourists. Everything worth seeing in Tangier can be covered in the space of a day and few stay longer than a week. There would be no danger of our meeting. But on the following afternoon I heard once again the clarion call of Crystal LaVynne outside my window. Flanked by Tony and an unknown man, Crystal was being led by—or, rather, leading—Lucky about the seedy garden of "Bide-a-Wee." "But, my darlings," she bellowed, "it's the purest camp in the world! I lahve it! It's like one of those frightful semidetached villas on the way out to London airport." It occurred to me suddenly that Crystal had more than likely been born and bred in just such a house. "We'll take it! Emil, write a check this instant! Cheri," she said to Lucky, "is a check on Barclay's Bank all right? The currency in Morocco frightens me so."

Within an hour a small yacht was bobbing a few yards offshore, the windows of "Bide-a-Wee" were open; two of Lucky's unemployable relatives were shuffling about in their babouches trying to behave like experienced servants; the delivery boy (Lucky's youngest son) from Alimentation aux Gourmets

248

Fortnum & Mason de Tanger, Limited, S.A. had deposited a pungent load of groceries and the raddled old Packard touring car, which Lucky's Royal Rolls-Daimler Garage generally rents out for only such state occasions as a parade along the Boulevard Mohammed V, stood at the gate piled high with the considerable luggage of Miss Crystal LaVynne and entourage. I had very near neighbors and, as far as I was concerned, most undesirable ones. As there is barely space to swing a cat between the houses, only three alternatives remained to me: I could leave; I could crank down all the blinds and suffocate; or I could make my presence known. It was not an easy choice. But before reaching any decision, the problem was taken out of my hands. Crystal, looking like a Berber catamite in big, baggy blue bloomers and a jaunty fez, was at my door, flanked by the man called Emil and by Tony.

"*Holá!* The mountain comes to Mohammed!"

There was nothing to do but ask them in for a drink. It was interesting to observe them together. Not that the Crystal creature was, by any standards, an interesting person. Far from it. She was a relentless bore who substituted volume of words and of decibels for rudimentary charm and politeness.

Crystal was not a name-dropper. Far from it. Crystal took a name, tasted it, chewed it up and spat it at you. I could think only of some great shredding machine overfed with copies of Burke's, Debrett, *Who's Who* and the Almanach de Gotha. Happily it was not necessary to concentrate on what she was saying or even to listen very carefully. Her roll call of famous names and addresses gave me ample time to wonder about her. Was there some deep-seated but perfectly obvious psychological reason for the way this animated monolith took center stage and held onto it for grim life? Had she been a large, lumpish child shunted into the background by a cruel family who hated the sight and sound of her? Or was she just a natural-born shit? Yes, I decided, the latter theory must be the true one.

Far more interesting than Crystal's pat stream of self-aggrandizement were her two courtiers. In an earlier age, one or both of them would surely have hit her over the head with a club just to silence her. Today they sat respectfully, listening to her steady flow as though bewitched into thinking that this walking sight gag was either attractive or entertaining. One of the men was introduced to me by Crystal as her half brother, Emil. Half brother he may have been, but there was no resemblance save in a certain commonness of speech which, in Crystal's case, was only intermittent and accidental. Emil spoke rarely. Indeed, he had but slight chance in his half sister's presence. When he did, his voice was gruff, his accent vulgar. The other cavalier was, of course, Tony.

One look at Tony in the harsh, clear sunlight of Tangier made me want to rush to a mirror and take a thorough inventory of myself. Tony was forty-six now, a year older than I, and the fabulous good looks were almost entirely a thing of the past. All too obvious was the baggy-eyed, jowlish bloat of the heavy drinker. The figure, too, had gone—not to out-and-out roly-poly obesity, but to unhealthy paunch and blubber. From the dead, metallic sheen of the hair, I was sure that it was dyed—and not professionally. It had been badly cut, or not cut, and it gave every appearance of having been fluffed out inexpertly to appear more plentiful than it actually was. His clothes, too, were rather the worse for wear. Tired, I guess you'd call them. Serious attempt had obviously been made at achieving a sportive look by tossing together a number of unsympathetic elements—some rather formal-looking trousers, supported, quite needlessly, at the waist by a frayed club tie; bath clogs for sandals; a not entirely clean shirt, damp beneath the arms; and a limp hank of material tied hopefully at the throat as an ascot. These flaws, however, were more pathetic than fatal. A month of rest, diet and exercise, a trip to a good tailor and a better barber could almost banish them. I discovered the real trouble only when Tony, commanded to do so by Crystal, spoke. His lights had gone out. Try as he would for the bantering, casual tone of before, Tony was running scared.

Crystal and—it seemed to me—Emil, too, asked questions, listened carefully to the answers and then sat back watchfully to make sure that Tony and I actually knew one another as intimately as Tony must have claimed we did. Satisfied, Crystal once again took over the conversation. After an interminable hour had passed, I excused myself with a hastily made-up story of a business appointment and hid out in the American Library.

"Happy Ours," uncomfortable enough in total isolation, became unbearable with "Bide-a-Wee" occupied. Having tried my best to retire from the social life of Tangier, it was suddenly thrust under my nose most of each day and all of each night. Useless to make excuses, to say that I would be out. Every word, every footfall, every flush of every toilet—when they worked—in each house could be overheard in the next. Crystal took to entertaining with a vengeance.

After six months in Tangier, it seemed to me that I knew almost everyone in every social clique, but from the people who appeared at "Bide-a-Wee" for luncheon, for tea, for cocktails, for dinner, for the raucous all-night parties, it was obvious that I did not. Crystal's "set"—if such it could be called—embodied none of the obvious choices. Absent were the few honourables and baronets and knights available. Likewise the two or three well-known English writers and the Proper English residing on The Mountain stayed away to a man. It struck me as odd that Crystal would shun or be so shunned by her own countrymen. The Nice Americans did not come, either; were not even invited. What did show up was the scum of the expatriate world: the nonpainting painters and nonwriting writers; the remittance men, the con men, the moochers and freeloaders; the mobile alcoholics; the most flagrant of the perverts; and, of course, the bores. They were the people who were not received anywhere else in Tangier —and not for reasons of snobbery. To their unsavory ranks were added a sprinkling of transients, but not the typical jolly hols tourists who pour off cruise ships, off planes from Madrid or the Gibraltar ferry to rush through the Kasbah, ogle the belly dancers at the Koutoubia Palace, devour whole sheep at an "authentic" mechoui, fling themselves onto the beaches and depart again, sunburned and diarrhetic, lugging beaten brass trays behind them. These people were rather slick and silent visitors, uninterested in local color and with no need of asking directions. A Sicilian known as Al Italia was a constant guest. Also appearing at each of Crystal's parties was Lucky. Few Moroccans attend foreign colony functions and those who do are friendly, charming and cultured. Being none of these things, Lucky's exact function, beyond supplying food, liquor and servants, mystified me.

Crystal, secure as reigning queen of the nobodies, was not satisfied to stay at home forever, dispensing her royal favors. Tired, perhaps, of talking about herself, she wished to be seen and to be talked *about*. Dressed in various adaptations of native costume, she set out to frequent the handful of more-or-less fashionable places: Dean's for elevenses; El Djenina for lunch; Porte's for tea; the Nautilus for dinner; Scott's or the Parade for late-night drinking. In a miserable little hole like Tangier where gossip replaces work, recreation and sex, there was plenty to be said—none of it complimentary. People had it "on good authority" that Crystal was the daughter of a Lambeth butcher—Kosher, some added—who had been evacuated during the war and learned her affected ways in the home of a saintly marchioness, who was invariably a friend of a friend; Crystal had been a Piccadilly streetwalker, others said, which struck me as a most unprofitable calling, if looks had anything to do with volume of trade; Crystal worked hand in glove with the London underworld; Crystal was the key figure of an international vice ring. Like all gossip, it might or might not have contained a germ of truth. About the only rumor with any staying power was that Crystal had recently been asked to leave Capri, which amounts almost to being kicked out of hell. None of the stories made any difference to me. I simply wanted Crystal and her household to move on and leave me alone. They did no such thing.

The clatter of my typewriter on the morning after their first visit had the effect of a dinner gong on Tony. The sun, the sea air, the constant supply of liquor and the security of being settled in even so comfortless a place as "Bide-a-Wee" brought a certain calm to him. Trembling less and seeming not as frightened as before, he paid another call, glass in hand.

I made no secret of withdrawing the welcome mat. "Don't sit down, Tony. I'm busy. Even if I weren't, you wouldn't be welcome here. We're not friends."

"Well, if we're not friends, I'd like to know what we are."

"Enemies, Tony. I hate your guts."

"But, chum, we've known each other ever since . . ."

"I know about a thousand people, Tony. None for as long as you, but I like nine-hundred-and-ninety-nine of them better. Now get back to your pals Crystal and Emil LaVynne."

"Emil's name isn't LaVynne," Tony said, grasping for any sort of conversational straw. "It's Emil Lime. It's a palindrome. You know, the same thing spelled backward or forward."

"What do you suppose he changed it from?"

"Shhhh. They'll hear you."

"Good. Now go."

"They like you a lot. They both told me so."

"Well, I don't like them or you. And I'm telling you so."

"Crystal and I are engaged."

"That's just perfect. Good-by."

"She's a fabulous girl—and a great beauty, I think."

"So's Medusa, I think."

"All sorts of famous artists want to paint her—Henry Koerner, Sidney Nolan, Feliks Topolski . . ."

"I seem to see her blasted into the side of Mount Rushmore, where I heartily wish I could be at the moment—or someplace equally far from here."

"Don't you like Tangier?"

"I loathe it. It's Canarsie with minarets—a town that never made it filled with people who never made it. So it's ideal for someone like you. Now get the hell out of my house."

253

"Please," he almost sobbed. "I've had a rotten time of it these past few years."

"And you've deserved it. Why you're not in jail is a mystery. And believe me, Tony, if I can ever do anything toward putting you there, I'll move heaven and earth to do it." I turned back to my typewriter. Mechanically Tony made one last stab at turning on the famous old charm, then thought better of it and left.

If only that could have been the end of him. It was not. Wherever I went, Tony and Crystal and Emil Lime were certain to appear. The acoustics between the two houses being what they were, I could hear them, too.

When the three of them were at home together, the noise was unbelievably loud. Crystal was very much onstage—shrill, affected and campy—while Tony and Emil were a lot louder in their audience response than any performance, no matter how brilliant, warranted. When Emil was out of the house—which occurred oftener than seemed possible in a place as sleepy as Tangier—the source of sound shifted. Crystal was a most demanding fiancée. She had to be made love to, at least verbally, every moment when she was not talking herself. It was almost pitiful to hear Tony at these times. What he had to say to her was practically the same old line he had delivered to the daughters of America's *haute bourgeoisie* at boarding school dances thirty years before. But how strained and weary and unfelt the delivery had become after all this time. The glories of Lochby Court; the glister of the Vandenberg cars; the chicté of our school, of the coming-out parties of tender buds who were by now multiple divorcées, lardy matrons or even grandmothers—all of this ancient history and even fresher material sliced from the tenderloin of Tony's long career came over with about as much freshness and vivacity as might be expected from some exhausted provincial touring company still performing *Charley's Aunt*. And then, after an almost desperate reading of his triumphs as war hero, tycoon, television star, journalist and author, silence would set in and Crystal could be heard, giggling like a dulcet hyena.

"Oh, don't! Oh, Tony, it's much too hot. Oh, Tony, these trousers—they cost a packet at Courrèges. Here, ducks, let me do it. There. Dar-ling, you're getting the most frightful spots on your back." From that point onward I tried not to hear.

Tony got away from "Bide-a-Wee," too, but not as frequently as Emil. I noticed, however, that any excuse involving the supplies for Crystal's yacht gave him his liberty.

Alone in the house without their American guest, Crystal and Emil underwent a sea change, too. Emil talked a great deal more, his terrible accent, which I cannot to this day exactly place, becoming coarser than ever. Crystal, dropping the oh-but-darling shrieks and coos of Knightsbridge for a series of singsong phrases, grunts and groans quite like his, was practical and businesslike.

"Eh, Crys, 'as 'e gone?"

"Yes, gone. You heard him. And good riddance. Oh, but he's fat and mucky. Suet!"

"'Ear 'im talk an' anyone would think 'e was a regular Lawrence 'Arvey. W'ere's 'e gone to?"

"To the boat. You heard."

"S'pose 'e really knows 'ow to maintain a Diesel en-gine, Crys?"

"How should I know, Manny. That's your end of the arrangement. He talks a very big yachtsman. His family's boats. Pal of old Sir Thomas Lipton's and all that rot. He rowed at that fancy school, too."

"Rowing an' Diesel is two different things, Crys."

"All right. I know it. You were the one that found 'im. You were the one said he'd do and to sack the crew. What does Al think?"

"Al isn't so sure. Lucky's not so sure, Crys."

"Not so sure of what?"

"Not so sure 'e trusts this Tony pal of yours."

"Well, I'm not so sure I trust Lucky. Christ, but I wish we'd never come to this fucking place!"

"It won't be long now, Crys. Getting bored with your Yank playboy?"

"Bored? Jesus! Just one more . . . 'Ere now, stop that, Manny. It's too bloody hot for . . . Oh, Manny . . ."

"Let's go upstairs, Crys."

I was stunned but not really surprised, if that makes any sense. As stagey and shallow as she was, I had felt from the moment I first saw Crystal LaVynne—or whatever her name really happened to be—that there was nothing really weak or silly beneath her carefully contrived exterior. What she and Emil/Manny—whatever their relationship—were up to was beside the point. I knew it wasn't good. For the first time in years I felt almost sorry for Tony. A terse little speech of warning—"Tony, I don't like you, but I like your friend Crystal even less and . . ."—was even forming in the back of my brain when the European edition of the *Herald Tribune* arrived. In it was a short obituary for Maggie Faye. It was hardly a panegyric. Brief mention was made of her early success, her style and beauty. A good deal more was said about the Van den Burg scandal and its ensuing disasters. The major part of the article was devoted to her decline and her hopeless attempts at reclamation. She had been discovered, dead for some days, in a tenement room. Death was attributed to a combination of malnutrition, drugs and alcohol. I clipped the article, in case there was the slightest danger of my forgetting any word of it, and resolved to do everything in my power to get Tony.

The following day I received a telephoned invitation to cocktails with the United States Consul-General. As a rule only the most pressing official business can lure me to any far-flung outpost of our government. Wild horses couldn't have kept me from this. It was "a small get-together of American residents to meet Mr. and Mrs. Greer Perry." The Perrys—"a charming couple"—had arrived to fill some very minor post. The hierarchy of our Foreign Service has always mystified me, but it took no expert to guess

256

that Greer was a long way from being Secretary of State if third or fourth assistant-something in a backwater like Tangier was all he had been able to achieve by now. On my way to the Chemin des Amoureux, dressed in my best blue suit, it also occurred to me that but for the Perry millions, no one would bother to open so much as a box of Crackerjack in honor of quite so minor an underling as Greer.

The party was indeed small. Of the few Americans invited, even fewer had seen fit to attend. Greer and his wife had drawn so small a gathering of compatriots that there was no trouble spotting him. There he stood, large, pale and pompous, a hundred hairs, perhaps, plastered over the top of his head. I went to him immediately. "Greetings, Greer. Welcome to Tangier. And I hope you'll be lucky enough to get out of it quickly."

"I read that you were here in the alumni bulletin. Elspeth and I find Tangier charming. Most picturesque."

"Elspeth?"

"My wife." His nostrils quivered. "What is that you're drinking?"

"Bourbon. This is about the only place in Tangier where you can . . ."

"I hope you realize what it's doing to your system—and your soul."

"Vaguely. Say, what is this, Greer? Have you finally seen the light and been saved by AA?"

"Not AA, Moral Rearmament and Elspeth."

Elspeth herself materialized from nowhere. She was a large English woman in her late thirties, wearing a blue print dress and a large corsage of the local pink lilies. She laughed a lot, albeit mirthlessly, displaying enormous gums and tiny corn teeth. I recalled from somewhere that after Maria Luisa, Greer had contracted a brief, disastrous marriage to a French girl. This, the third foreign entanglement, looked no more promising.

Elspeth had presumably devoured, but not digested, all the available literature on what a diplomat's wife should be. She was suddenly all over me saying how nice it was for Greer to meet an old school chum so many miles from home and wasn't it a small world? Next she tried for mutual acquaintances. "My uncle, Sir Rupert Beddoes, has a place on the Old Mountain and my brother Derek Fairways"—by whom she meant Lord Fairways—"keeps a little garçonnière in the Medina. He's so interested in Morocco and the Moroccans." (His interest, in fact, amounted to a morbid fascination.) "Djew knaow them by any chance?" Everyone did. Having established her wealth and aristocracy, she moved on to patronize a nice old American widow so poor that she attended official parties only to load up on canapés. I could see that Elspeth was going to be a great addition.

The new, godly Greer was more taciturn than the drunk of so many years before. I felt that he was probably bursting to say something unkind about someone, but that religion was holding him back.

"How's Posy?" I asked, not caring very much, but doing my best to fill a long lull.

"Not very well, I'm afraid. She married Morgan Wyckoff, you know. Fine chap. But they live in Oyster Bay and the drinking element there is . . . Well, enough said. If I could only get her interested in Moral Rearmament."

"I don't believe there's a branch here in Tangier. A real pity."

"Never fear," Greer said with a hollow chuckle. "Elspeth will get one going. She's a great organizer."

"I'm sure of it."

Again a lull. I wanted another bourbon, but thought better of it. Finally Greer spoke or, rather, pontificated. "There's so much work to be done here in Tangier. So many of my countrymen *lost!*"

I couldn't resist. "Speaking of that, Greer, there *is* someone here who will surely be needing your help. Someone you know."

"Oh, really?" Greer said with a beatific smile. "Who?"

"Another old school chum." Pause. "Tony Vandenberg."

Greer leaped as though a million volts of electricity had gone through him. Then he regained some of his composure. "Really? Well, I'd be only too glad to do whatever I can."

"I knew you would. Tell me, why don't you and . . . and Elspeth come round to my place for . . . for tea tomorrow? Tony lives quite close by. I'll ask him, too. He's just about hit bottom."

"I'm sorry to hear that."

"I was certain you would be."

My tea party, dainty with ecru lace and cakes from Porte's, was by no means the most successful social function of the season, but I enjoyed it thoroughly. Crystal came on strong, wrapped insecurely in a great, white haik that made her look more like the week's wash on its way to the laundromat than Mysterious Morocco. The sight of Elspeth Perry quite undid her. Elspeth, who was related to the saintly marchioness who had sheltered Crystal during the war, as she seemed to be related to everyone in England with any pretensions of grandeur, remembered Crystal vividly. Smelling of piety and elastic underpinnings, Elspeth was able to make her adversary's dim origins glaringly obvious. ("How frightfully nice to see you once agayne, Miss Levine. I've wondered about you so many, many times since Auntie Ursula took you in with the rest of those darling children from Ealing. And your father? I've prayed so often that the law would look more kindly on his little weaknesses. If only we could all love and understand one another, there'd be no wars and then there wouldn't be any black market to tempt a poor butcher who was only trying to look after his little family. But that was all so long ago. You're looking well, de-ah. Found a good position, I expect, and able to send your poor mother a little something from time to time, I hope.") When it came to recalling a half brother, Elspeth was remarkably obtuse and insisted on a full explanation, interrupting often with embarrassingly pointed questions.

During our blessedly brief acquaintance, I noticed that Elspeth was able to say perfectly outrageous things to and about people, but swaddled so lovingly in the clothing of Christian fellowship that only the blackest sinner would have dared to risk the wrath of God by telling her where to head in. Tony's weary face was a study during the whole encounter with Crystal, but it was as nothing compared to how he looked when Greer charged in, late because of having had to solve a knotty problem in international affairs concerning the renewal of a lapsed passport. Not having been as one with the Deity for as long as Elspeth, Greer showed marked signs of inner conflict. I felt that he would have liked to have snubbed me, insulted Crystal, struck Tony and polished off the entire bottle of rum with which Crystal kept lacing her tea. But whatever Greer felt, he was brought sharply to attention with the introduction of Al Italia, who had been brought along, quite uninvited, by Crystal. Mr. Italia was a swarthy, compact, silent man who, from his two-tone shoes to the carefully waved tar of his hair, looked like nothing quite so much as a heavy from an old gangster movie. Greer positively sputtered when they were introduced, placed his right hand behind his back and bowed just perceptibly when Mr. Italia stretched out a hairy paw, the nails glossy with liquid polish.

Well, as I said, nobody enjoyed the short afternoon except me. Crystal, who despised silence, was curiously quiet. Tony looked sick. Emil Lime and Al Italia were sullen. Only Elspeth kept the conversational ball rolling, all but calling a group prayer before Crystal stood up and took her band of friends away. "How interesting to see that Levine girl again," Elspeth mused, popping the last of the marzipan into her mouth. "I'm so pleased that things have worked out for her. Auntie Ursula always feared that a girl from such a dreadful background would come to a bad end. But she . . ."

"Elspeth! Will you be still!" Greer hissed.

"Of course I forgive you, Greer," Elspeth said. "But that was a most unchristian . . ."

"Shut up, Elspeth. This is important. Do you realize that that common Jewish whore with Tony is . . ."

"Greer! Remember, we're all God's children and . . ."

". . . is in the company of a *public enemy!*"

"You mean Al Italia, if that's really his name?"

"Of course it isn't. He's just some greasy wop—Sicilian actually —who entered the States illegally and has been mixed up in narcotics ever since . . ."

"At an M.R. house party in Palermo . . ."

"As for Tony (this is strictly off the record, you understand), he's rather *non grata* in the States, himself. Something about jumping bail on a very serious charge. Blackmail."

"You don't say?" I said innocently.

"Greer! He happens to be a friend of my cousins, the . . ."

"Elspeth, I am severely torn between my love for my fellow-man and my duty as a representative of the United States."

I wondered exactly how torn Greer really was. If God had entered Greer, the penetration had not been sufficient to change him too much. Signs of the *real* Greer Perry were popping up all over.

"I'm so sorry you've been upset," I said, easing them into their car. "I just felt that Tony was at such a low ebb that someone like you might be able to help him. Just a leg up along the Twelve Steps. That sort of thing."

"Yes. Of course."

"Peace!" Elspeth cried with a winning show of gums.

The only motive behind my mischief of bringing Tony and Greer Perry together was to make Tony even more miserable— miserable enough, perhaps, to abandon his current meal ticket and move on. The coup had come off better than I had hoped. All of "Bide-a-Wee" was in a state of flux. Al Italia took to visiting oftener than ever, but the perpetual parties and Crystal's public appearances were suddenly canceled. Ended now were Crystal's voluble endearments and anecdotes. Conversation was rare, terse and mostly whispered. Signs of a move were obvious, and I congratulated myself on my cleverness.

But I was too smug too soon. Before forty-eight hours had passed, Greer Perry was involving me in something I couldn't quite understand and didn't want to. "I'm so sorry, Greer," I said over the telephone, extricating myself like an eel from his dinner invitation. "And do explain to Elspeth, but I'm finishing this book and . . ."

"Elspeth won't be dining with us, and I'm afraid it's something you *can't* get out of. Matter of our country's security. Let's say Guitta's at nine."

"Guitta's at nine," I said with a sinking feeling.

"And so you see, that's what kind of people you have living next door to you," Greer said, pushing his Coca-Cola aside and eyeing my wineglass at once disdainfully and longingly.

"No. I had no idea. And I have no idea how you got your idea."

"A few calls to Rabat. Can't go into the details. Classified," he said importantly. "But it's no secret that Tony jumped bail on a very serious charge in the States. He's also wanted in England. I knew all about him the moment I saw him at school. Thoroughly rotten."

"But one of God's children," I reminded him.

"True," he said. "But a just God punishes as well as rewards. And so if you'll do as I ask . . ."

"Are these orders from you or from higher up, Greer? I'm not cut out to be a spy."

"I ask you only to see and to hear."

"That can hardly be avoided. But tattling to you can. I thought you said you wanted to *help* Tony. And I'm not interested in doing that either. You're not just sore at Tony because of . . . . of what happened in Southampton, are you? Things would have been a lot worse if he'd actually married your sister. As for Maria Luisa . . ."

"I have forgiven everyone everything. But when it comes to smuggling narcotics . . ."

"Smuggling? People all over Tangier smoke kif. You can buy all you want not fifty yards from here. It's cheaper than chewing gum and far more plentiful."

"As a member nation of Interpol, it's still illegal and any traffic . . . Well, I can say no more." In the Arabic learned at a six-week cram course, Greer summoned the waiter, who speaks fluent English, and tried to explain that he wanted the bill.

Except for a welcome silence, there was nothing unusual to report about the goings-on at "Bide-a-Wee," and I was happy to be completely unhelpful whenever Greer Perry telephoned. Once I watched Crystal pointing out to Emil, Tony and Al Italia such boring landmarks as the coast of Spain and the Rock of Gibraltar less than twenty miles across the strait. But my curiosity was not piqued. "On a clear day you can see Gibraltar," is one of the platitudes of Tangier. I nodded to them and went on with my writing.

Greer never gave up. "Where do you get your money changed?" he asked over the telephone.

"At the British Bank of the Middle East or Cook's. Why?"

"Do you know that there are people who give—illegally, mind you—much more than the official rate of exchange?"

"Everybody knows that."

"And do you also realize that it's a very serious offense to take Moroccan money out of the country?"

"Who else would want any? Toilet paper's more valuable."

"Even so, there's a considerable traffic in smuggling money out of the country, and I want to track it down."

"Isn't that a matter for the Moroccan police, or is our country taking over petty crime in Tangier, too?"

"I can't reveal my sources."

"Please don't."

"Do you know a place called—uh—Lucy's London Pub?"

"Do you by any chance mean Lucky's Olde Englyshe Pub?"

"Perhaps I do."

"Well, I don't recommend it. He waters the Scotch. As for the gin . . ."

"I am *not* interested in liquor."

"Excuse me. I forgot. But what about Lucky's?"

"Oh, nothing," he said elaborately. "But if you should ever happen to stop in there . . ."

"I do once a week. Lucky's my landlord."

"Well, just keep your eyes and ears open there, too. I do wish Elspeth and I could have you in, but her brother, Lord Fairways, is in a spot of trouble just now . . ."

"He just about always is. Well, good-by, Greer."

I was so intrigued by whatever might be going on at Lucky's that I went in twenty-four hours ahead of schedule to pay my week's rent. My timing couldn't have been better. Lucky was behind the bar, carrying on a heated argument with Emil Lime and Al Italia. Tony stood a little apart, looking ashen and belting down drinks as fast as he could. The conversation—if that is what the shouts and bellows in a mélange of accents and languages can be called—stopped abruptly with my entrance. Lucky, Emil and the sinister Mr. Italia took no pains to conceal their annoyance at my visit. Tony seemed positively delighted to see me. I ordered a bottle of Moroccan beer and perched on a barstool.

"Something you wanted?" Lucky asked.

"Just to pay my rent. And of course to enjoy your company."

"The rent, as usual, will be . . ."

"Oh, I'm in no great rush, Lucky. The night is young and it's not due until tomorrow, anyhow. Your first visit to Tangier, Mr. Italia?"

"Yes," Al Italia said.

"No," Tony said.

"W'at 'e means," Emil said nervously, "is that Al's been through Tangierz before but 'e's never 'ad the chance to see it proper. Right?"

Lucky took away my empty beer bottle and said, "That will be two dirhams."

"Not so fast, I think I'll have another." I drank very slowly. All around me there was stealthy, impatient movement. Tony put a fifty-franc piece into the jukebox. The voice of Louis Armstrong —very big in Tangier—burst into the room like a tornado.

Be my life's companion and you'll never grow old, never grow . . .

"Turn that racket off!" Emil shouted. Lucky pulled the plug on the music and the place was silent again except for the shuffling of feet.

"*Tout le bar est en mouvement ce soir,* Lucky," I said.

"Talk English!" Emil snapped.

"I simply said to my old friend, Lucky . . ." My eye was caught by a thick manila envelope lying on the bar. "What's this, a manuscript?" I said, picking it up by the corner. Having intended only to annoy, the action surpassed my wildest hopes. A blizzard of hundred-dirham notes—thousands of dollars' worth —fluttered out.

"*Hey!*" Emil shouted, falling to his knees to gather up the money.

Had I gone too far? Perhaps. The next sensation, far from pleasant, was the feeling of something hard and cold against my ribs and Al Italia's breath in my ear.

"Don't!" Tony shouted.

"'Ere, 'ere, Al," Emil said in a hopeless attempt to sound casual. "Mustn't be so nervous." The pressure was removed from my side. Forcing a hollow little laugh, Emil said to me, "Mr. Italia, 'ere, is quite naturally nervous about carrying so much money. You can never tell with all these shifty natives."

"My," I said, "it *is* a lot of money. However do you manage to spend it all in a place like this? Try as I will, I can hardly go through . . ."

"Get out of here," Al muttered.

"H-here, *I'll* see him home. I—I was about to go anyhow," Tony said.

"Do that, Tony," Emil said.

I felt Tony's hand tremble as he took my arm and almost dragged me through the bead curtains.

We did not go home. Instead we went to the Parade Bar and sat in the garden empty of all life save a parrot that specializes in sneezing and a caged owl that merely blinks. "Rather a rough bunch you're running with recently," I said.

"Believe me, I didn't know," Tony said. His hands shook so violently that he needed both of them to lift his glass. "What did I ever do to deserve this?"

"Let me count the ways."

"But when I met Crys on Mykonos . . . that yacht . . ."

"You've always been something of a pushover for things nautical, Tony. I recall so well your father's yacht—several of them, if memory serves."

Ignoring me, he charged on. "But Crystal's not what I thought she was."

"Just another pretty face, I suppose."

"You heard what Lady Elspeth said. Lady Elspeth comes from one of the oldest families in England. As for Crystal, she's . . . why, she's not even *honest!*"

"Are you?"

"It's not the same. Now she's trying to drag *me* down with her!"

"Just say no and walk away from it."

"But I can't."

"Why not?"

"I've asked her to marry me."

"Such commitments haven't stopped you before."

"But you don't understand. . . . She's very wealthy and . . ."

"I'm afraid I do, Tony. You're no damned good and you're weak. You've got to where you've gone—wherever that may be—by latching onto people who are even weaker than you. Even me. Once. Now you've found someone who's stronger, for a change. Stronger and even rottener than you, if that's possible. Somehow I can't work up much sympathy."

"If you only knew what she was up to."

"I'd love to have you tell me."

"I . . . I can't."

"Have it your own way, Tony."

"That . . . that damned boat of hers. She . . . she expects me to be able to run it."

"Whoever gave her the notion that you could?"

"Stop being funny. This is serious. You don't happen to have a couple of hundred dollars, do you?"

"Certainly."

"Could you . . . would you loan me . . ."

"Never use 'loan' as a verb. Don't you remember the English usage I tried to help you through at school? The answer, by the way, is no."

"It's only a lend . . . a *loan*. Just so I can get out of here and . . ."

"And what? Spin your way around the world, lying and cheating and getting kicked out of new places? No thanks. I've got better things to do with my money. Check, please," I called to the waiter.

"Hey, wait a minute! I just saved your life."

"Thank you, Tony. Now try to save your own."

Tony was still spluttering helplessly, drunkenly as I darted out into the Rue des Vignes, got into my car and started. The wheels had barely begun to turn when I saw Elspeth and Greer Perry marching purposefully into the garden of the Parade.

The following day was odd in every sense of the word. The sun rose, a big red ball, as always. But instead of turning into a brilliant white, which it generally does between six and seven, it stayed red. Most unusual. As for the sky, it was dappled with little fluffy clouds that, in a more northerly clime, would presage snow. By eight o'clock the sky darkened and a few tentative drops of moisture fell into the garish gardens of the English palaces. A few moments later rain was teeming down. From the first of June through the end of September rain is almost unknown in Tangier. Like Acapulco winters, the summers in Tangier are world famous for their sunny monotony. Like everyone else in Tangier, I went to the garden to marvel at the phenomenon, marveled, and then hurried back to the shelter of the house. Scampering in from the rain, my attention was attracted, as always, by the sticky pink of the oleander hedge that separates—but not very effectively—"Happy Ours" from "Bide-a-Wee." I shuddered involuntarily at the gaudy juxtaposition of the oleander, the roses, the bougainvillea and tiger lilies, when something even more arresting caught my eye. The garden of "Bide-a-Wee" was seething not only with rain but with activity. For a household that lay abed until noon each day, this was odd indeed. Even odder was what they were doing out in the pouring rain. Under Crystal's tense supervision, I could see Emil, Al Italia and Tony loading the dinghy until its gunwales were nearly underwater and then rowing out to the yacht, unloading and returning for more. What had been brought into "Bide-a-Wee" —Crystal's matched white luggage, Tony's rather seedy pigskin bag, Emil's anonymous bits and pieces, a portable television set, an elaborate radio, an all-out picnic hamper, a traveling bar and other essentials of ostentatious tourism—was not what was being taken out. These were made up of enormous bales, wrapped in burlap and sealed. I stole into the house, went up to my bedroom for the binoculars to get a better look. The rain was too dense for perfect vision. However, I could hear.

"That does it, Crys," Emil said. "And good job it's finished. Can't 'ardly see your 'and in front of your face in this downpour."

"That's what I've been telling him, Crystal," Tony said. "Emil and Al, too. It's raining so hard we can never get that tub out of here. Now, if we could only wait until better weather . . ."

"*Better weather?*" Crystal screamed. "You idiot, don't you

realize this is the best weather we could possibly have? It's a gift from heaven, that's what it is. Nobody but a bloody fool would venture out on a day like this."

"Nobody *is* venturing out, Crys," Tony said, his voice quaking. "The strait is dangerous."

"Pooh! You can see Spain any other day. Twenty miles to Algeciras. Less even—eighteen."

"The ferry to Algeciras didn't even leave this morning. I tell you, Crystal, it's dangerous."

" 'E's right, Crys," Emil said.

"And as for my getting the boat out into the Atlantic and up to Cadiz . . ."

"So this is the famous yachtsman who's piloted the *Queen Elizabeth* through the Hebrides, or whatever you said."

"It's true, Crys. I've sailed with—well, with all sort of people. But today . . ."

"But today you're sailing with me. With us. And no mistake about it. *Unless* you'd prefer to stay right 'ere in this sinkhole and face the music—alone."

"Crystal, you were never entirely clear about what sort of sailing you wanted me to do. If I'd had any idea of . . ."

"Well, I'm being clear now. We're getting out of here and you're running the boat. Your things packed, Manny?"

"Right you are, Crys."

"Al?"

An animal grunt seemed to indicate that Al Italia was ready to leave.

"Well, what's keeping us? Get the luggage on and we can go. And Tony, for Christ's sake stop sniveling!"

"I . . . I'm going to have to bail out the dinghy first, Crys. It's nearly swamped, what with this rain."

"Well, get to it!"

The telephone at my side rang with a clangor that nearly sent me out of my skin. "Hello?" I said.

"Greer Perry here. There's something I've got to tell you, but I can hardly do it over the telephone. And it's raining."

"Yes. I know."

"Elspeth and I were promised that it never rains during the summers here."

"Well, why don't you ring through to Rabat and complain to King Hassan? Better yet, Elspeth might take it up directly with God."

"What's that? Hello? What I had to tell you about concerns this mutual American acquaintance of ours. You know the one I mean? I'm trying not to use names. Never know who might be . . ."

I glanced quickly out of the window and dropped the telephone. Tony wasn't bailing out the dinghy. He was *in* it! In it and rowing like hell for the cove.

"Hello? Hello? Are you there? Can you *hear* me?"

"Jesus!" Crystal screamed from the garden below. "Manny! Al! Look! He's leaving us!"

"Bastard," Emil yelled. A shot rang out.

"Hello? Hello?"

"Greer, what *do* you want?"

"Well, I called to tell you, strictly *entre nous*, of course, that I've been able to arrange extradition papers, so that all one has to do is pick up the person in question and he goes right back Stateside and into hot water where he . . ."

Al and Emil were both firing now, but still Tony kept rowing. He had almost reached the yacht. "He's in enough water right now. Not hot, but if you can extradite him from it I'm sure he'll be your slave for life."

"Who? What are you talking about?"

"Tony, you horse's ass. Who have you been talking about? By God, he's made it to the boat! He's aboard!"

"I'll *have* to ask you not to mention names over the telephone. When I took you into my confidence on a classified matter . . ."

"Oh, shut up, Greer. Tony's gone anyhow—if he doesn't get

killed first." Having reloaded, Crystal's business associates sent forth another volley of shots. "My God, I wonder if he even knows how to start that thing."

"Who? What thing?"

"Tony. He's taking off with Crystal's yacht—and a load of kif that would . . ."

"But that's piracy! Or is it barratry?"

"You were in the Navy, Greer. I wasn't. But it's a hell of a show from here." It was. Al Italia had waded out waist-deep into the sea and was firing away at the yacht. Crystal and Emil were screaming from the shore. There was a great blast from the whistle of Crystal's boat. Tony had obviously pushed the wrong thing.

"You've got to stop him!" Greer shouted.

"Afraid I can't. It's raining."

"The Navy. I'll call the Moroccan Navy."

"Is there a Moroccan Navy, Greer?"

"Well, well, I don't really know. But running narcotics—that's an international offense. How do you get in touch with the British Navy?"

"Search me. Why don't you ask Elspeth's brother. He'll know. Oh, my God, he's got the thing going! I can't look! He's headed straight for shore! With any luck he'll mow down Al Italia."

"Is this some sort of practical joke? Remember, you're dealing with the Government of the United . . ."

"It's no joke and it's not very practical, but Tony's on his way."

"I'm calling the police!"

"Bully for you. The British Navy and the Moroccan police!"

"And the Coast Guard, if they have one. He'll never get out of this alive. He'll go to prison and . . ."

"The police are down below at this very moment, Greer. Is there some message I could give them?" Indeed they were, Tangier's fabled police force—"efficient, courteous and fast"—

swarming all over the garden of "Bide-a-Wee." With them was the omnipresent Lucky, pointing dramatically at Crystal, Emil and Al Italia. There was a great deal of aimless—in the truest sense of the word—shooting. Tony by then was out to sea. "He's gone, Greer! Gone! He got away!"

"He did no such thing, goddamn it!"

"Greer!"

"This is what I've been waiting for. Extradition to the States for blackmail. Hijacking a ship, smuggling narcotics. He'll hang for this."

"But first you'll have to catch him, won't you, Greer?"

"Damn your insolence! He'll never make it alive, anyhow. He knows *nothing* about yachting. I suspected as much. Just a pose. And last night he came right out and told Elspeth and me that . . ."

"Oh, go soak your head, Greer."

"What?"

"I said, Peace."

There is always gossip in Tangier with at least six versions of every story. But nothing, not even the deportation of a very naughty London star in 1962, has ever equaled the saga of John Anthony van den Burgh. Even the Proper English up on The Mountain are claiming to have known Crystal intimately to give their versions of the story a greater ring of authenticity. Lucky, our local entrepreneur and police spy, has become almost a national hero. His battle cry, "Morocco for the Moroccans" has been daubed (in Arabic) on the wall of every foreign consulate. Privately, he is rather miffed at the loss of several bales of kif. It was the same kif he has been selling to dope runners and then reclaiming, by means of a police tip-off, since the Independence. Nine or ten years fresher, it would have been worth a fortune. Now it is gone. No one knows where.

Greer Perry is in terrible odor with the State Department—A) for bothering them with the extradition of anyone quite so trivial as Tony in the first place; B) for bungling what should have been the simplest of routine procedures; and C) for getting roaring, cursing, window-smashing drunk to celebrate his total defeat. After the briefest of careers in Tangier, he is being recalled "for reasons of health." Only diplomatic immunity kept him out of the Kasbah jail, where he could have joined such illustrious guests as Crystal LaVynne, Emil Lime and Al Italia. Hardly a penologist's ideal, even to mention the Kasbah jail is to chill the blood of anyone who lives in Tangier.

Whether Tony would be better off there or wherever he may happen to be is a moot point. The eyewitness accounts of his fate multiply in the bars, the drawing rooms, the patios every day. Of the many versions I have heard, one has him in irons aboard a British man-o-war; another has him held prisoner by smugglers in Spain; another has him safe and sound on Sicily (which, considering Al Italia's widespread acquaintance on that interesting island, should not make it the healthiest place in the world); another has him adrift, foodless and fuel-less, in mid-Atlantic, just in time for the September hurricanes; still another has him dashed to bits on the rocks off Mogador. But there has been no official report of his capture, no body washed ashore, no wreckage sighted. I sometimes have fantasies of Tony, like Philip Nolan, wanted in and by three countries, drifting, drifting, drifting, with no place to land and—to make matters even more dramatic— with no knowledge of how to run the ship. Well, learn by doing, as John Dewey used to say.

A much-forwarded copy of our school's alumni bulletin has just arrived. In the rather razzmatazz style considered so breezy thirty years ago, our class secretary has conscientiously shared all the news he has been able to gather. There are the usual reports of marriages, divorces, births and deaths; the chroniclings of new jobs and promotions; the breathless firsthand reports of the achievements of our far-flung classmates ("Hung on the feed bag with Greer Perry in N.Y.C. Old 'Gig' is going great guns with the State Dept."). The news of our class ends on a rather wistful note: "Can anyone tell me whatever became of Tony Vandenberg?"

Tangier
August, 1965